GW00992362

Beryl

Butterworths Gem Books
Edited by Peter G. Read

Beryl
John Sinkankas

Garnet
John D. Rouse

Pearls
Alexander E. Farn

Quartz
Michael O'Donoghue

In preparation

Jet and amber
H. Muller and H. Franquet

Opals
P. J. Darragh

Topaz
D. B. Hoover

Butterworths Gem Books

Beryl

John Sinkankas,
Captain US Navy (Ret), PhD(Hon), CG
Fellow, Mineralogical Society of America

Edited by

Peter G. Read
CEng, MIEE, MIERE, FGA

Butterworths
London Boston Durban Singapore Sydney Toronto Wellington

First published 1986

© **Butterworth & Co (Publishers) Ltd. 1986**

British Library Cataloguing in Publication Data

Sinkankas, John
   Beryl.-(Butterworths gem books)
   1. Beryl
   I. Title   II. Read, Peter G.
   553.8   QE391.B6
   ISBN 0-408-01543-8

Library of Congress Cataloging in Publication Data

Sinkankas, John
   Beryl

   Bibliography: p.
   Includes index
   1. Beryl.   I. Read, Peter G.   II. Title.
   QE391.B6S57   1985   553.8'7   85-16637
   ISBN 0-408-01543-8

Photoset by Butterworths Litho Preparation Department
Printed in Great Britain by the Garden City Press Ltd., Letchworth, Herts

Preface

When it was originally suggested that I should write a book on beryl to fit within the *Butterworths Gem Books*, edited by Peter G. Read, circumstances prevented my doing so at the time. It was decided instead that Peter Read would undertake the task of abridging my much larger book, *Emerald and Other Beryls* (Chilton Book Co, 1981) to provide a condensed version emphasizing the gemological aspects of my text and thus conforming to the scheme laid down for other books in the series. This has now been done and the present work respresents selections from my original book, in places reworded, rearranged, and augmented by Mr Read with new information and a number of references to recently published papers. All of the illustrations, including my watercolours and my drawings have been selected from the original work.

As may be expected in any abridgement of a text complicated by numerous in situ references to the literature, Mr Read's task was far from simple and I am most grateful for his discriminating selection of text portions that would most likely serve the needs of readers of *Beryl* and the skill with which he put it all together.

John Sinkankas
San Diego, California
September, 1985

Acknowledgements

The author and publishers would like to acknowledge the help of the many colleagues and friends who contributed to the completion of this book. All the water-colour drawings are the original work of John Sinkankas, who has also provided many of the drawings. The author and publishers are also deeply indebted to the Chilton Book Company of Radnor, Pennsylvania without whose help and co-operation this book could not have been published. The publishers also acknowledge the assistance of the Chilton Book Company in providing the colour plate section in this book.

Contents

PROFILE: SUMMARY OF CONSTANTS AND CHARACTERISTICS

RI (mean)	DR	Dispersion	SG (mean)	Hardness
Aquamarine (blue/green)				
1.570–1.575	−0.006	0.01	2.68	7.5
Bixbite (red – same constants as morganite)				
Emerald				
1.579–1.585	−0.0065	0.01	2.72	7.5
Goshenite (colourless)				
1.570–1.575	−0.005	0.01	2.66	7.5
Heliodor (yellow)				
1.568–1.573	−0.005	0.01	2.68	7.5
Maxixe (blue – subject to fading in strong sunlight)				
1.584–1.592	−0.008	0.01	2.80	7.5
Morganite (pink)				
1.586–1.594	−0.0075	0.01	2.85	7.5

Chemical composition	Crystal system	Optical clarity
$Be_3Al_2(SiO_3)_6$	Hexagonal	Transparent to transluscent

Habit	Prismatic hexagonal crystals (morganite–tabular)
Dichroism	Aquamarine, medium (blue, very pale blue)
	Emerald, medium (yellow-green, blue-green)
	Heliodor, weak (yellow, very pale yellow)
	Maxixe, strong (blue, colourless)
	Morganite, medium (pink, blue-pink)
Fluorescence	Emerald, LW/SW U-V, X-ray); red
	Morganite, LW/SW U-V; weak lilac; X-rays; red
	Bixbite, bands at 425, 510, 545 and 780 nm
Absorption spectrum	Emerald, strong doublet at 680, 683 nm, line at 637 nm, weak band at 580–625 nm, line at 477.5 nm in chrome-rich stones
Principal occurrences	Aquamarine; Brazil, India, Malagasy Republic, Namibia, USA, USSR.
	Bixbite; USA (rare)
	Emerald; Brazil, Colombia, India, Pakistan, South Africa, Tanzania, USSR, Zambia, Zimbabwe
	Goshenite; Malagasy Republic, Brazil, USA (rare)
	Heliodor; Brazil, Malagasy Republic, Namibia
	Maxixe; Brazil (rare)
	Morganite; Brazil, Malagasy Republic, Namibia, USA

Chapter 1

Emerald and beryl in antiquity

Although ordinary beryl is the principal ore of the element beryllium, the mineral is far better known as the source of beautiful coloured gems produced from clear specimens of emerald, aquamarine, and other coloured varieties. Colours range from the rich green of emerald, through many tints of green, blue, and yellow, and include rich red and even a completely colourless gem known as goshenite.

Emerald and other gem beryls have been known to mankind far beyond the bounds of recorded history, and it is impossible to say where or when the species was first recognized as a distinct mineral and its coloured varieties put to decorative use. If the mica deposits of India were known tens of centuries ago, which seems reasonable since they form distinctive outcrops which can scarcely fail to attract attention, then it is also possible that the paler varieties of beryl that accompany the mica could have been discovered as well. If, as suggested by some ethnologists, the original home of mankind is India, the first use of beryl may have been very early indeed. The deposits which produce mica in India also produce some beryl even today, including crystals containing clear gem areas.

Assuming prehistoric men and women made their way across the narrow straits separating the island of Sri Lanka from the Indian mainland, the gravels of that island, known since antiquity for producing gemstone pebbles, must also have yielded up to them pebbles of aquamarine, a gemstone still found there today. Because beryl is also known in Mongolia, the Asiatic portions of the USSR, Japan, and elsewhere in Asia, it is likely that crystals of beryl have long been picked up as attractive curiosities, if not cut and polished into gems.

However, while it is possible that beryl was recognized early in various parts of Asia, it is not until the settlement of the Mediterranean regions and the development of advanced cultures along its shores that written records preserved for us definite knowledge of the beryl, more especially the emerald.

Emerald in ancient Egypt

The first reliable accounts of emerald are found in Egyptian records, but exactly when Egypt's emerald deposits were first exploited is still a subject of controversy. The deposits are located in a bleak desert, far to the southeast of Cairo, and the earliest date ventured for their exploitation is given by H. P. Little[1] as about 3500 BC. Little had studied a translation of the oldest extant Egyptian manuscript, entitled 'The Instruction of Ptah-Hotep', and concluded from one of its sentences that the emerald was known at least by Ptah-Hotep's time. However, Little hastened to add that the term for emerald used in the manuscript may not have been applied to the mineral we now know as beryl.

Nearly the same date for the earliest knowledge of beryl in Egypt (i.e. 3400 BC) was given by S. H. Ball in two papers on the history of gemstone mining and commerce in antiquity[2,3]. According to Ball, the emerald mines were already being worked by the 12th Dynasty, or in the period 2000–1788 BC. The love of wealthy Egyptians for jewels and the many decorative uses to which gemstones were put on large and small objects alike resulted in a thriving industry devoted to the recovery and trading of precious metals and gemstones. Ball noted that 'from approximately 3500 BC to about 200 BC, Egypt, drawing on its turquoise, emerald, olivine [peridot], and semi-precious stone mines, was the world's most important gem producer'[3].

In a later work, Ball[4] also noted that 'emerald and beryl appear first commonly in the jewellery of rich Egyptians in the 12th Dynasty . . . but C. M. Firth found at Dakka on the Nile beryl beads in several predynastic graves'. He further remarked that tools discovered in the emerald mines, to which a date can be fixed with certainty, were from the reign of Sesortis II in the 12th Dynasty.

On the other hand, Oskar Schneider[5], the German archaeologist and Egyptologist, searched the literature for references to early knowledge of this gemstone and concluded that 'the Egyptian emerald was already being mined and used in personal ornament and amulets by at least the 18th Dynasty', or about 1500 C, a date much later than that proposed by Ball.

The problem of dating is complicated by uncertainties attending the use of ancient terms for emerald. Apparently the Egyptian *mafek* and the Greek *smaragdus* (the latter believed to be derived from a similar term in Sanskrit) were both applied indiscriminately to any greenish stone that either was emerald or looked like emerald. It is this ambiguity which is the crux of the problem. Furthermore, as A. Lucas[6], an authority on the nature and uses of ancient Egyptian materials, was careful to point out, many archeologists made the same mistake, as evidenced by collections in which many greenish stones were labelled 'emerald' when they were not, or described by the even vaguer appellation 'mother-of-emerald'.

Lucas also noted that extensive workings in the Egyptian mines are 'probably of Graeco-Roman date age, and there is no evidence that the mines were worked in the reign of Amenophis III as stated by Wilkinson',[7] and 'so far as can be ascertained, beryl was never used in ancient Egypt before Ptolemaic times (i.e., prior to 332 BC) and all the stones of earlier date called beryl that have been examined by the author have been found not to be beryl'. Several misidentifications were noted by Lucas, showing that some jewellery stones and scarabs labelled as emerald were made from green feldspar or some other greenish mineral.

The opinion of Lucas, whose qualifications as a chemist in the employ of the Department of Antiquities at Cairo seem beyond question, casts justifiable doubt upon the extremely early dates assigned by Ball, Schneider, and others. It is far more certain that the mines were vigorously worked during the Graeco-Roman periods of Mediterranean domination, or roughly from 330 BC onward, and more or less continuously thereafter up to about the year 1237 AD, during the reign of Sultan al-Kaamel. Desultory exploration continued until apporoximately 1740 AD, after which the mines were totally abandoned and lapsed into an obscurity so profound that they were considered 'lost'. Indeed some people believed them never to have existed at all.

It was not until the French explorer Fréderic Cailliaud rediscovered the so called 'Cleopatra's Mines' in 1816 that their existence was reconfirmed[8]. An excellent chronology of events concerning these mines appears in Schneider[5]. The latest scientific-geological investigation of these deposits and associated workings in the Wadi Sikait region was made in 1961 by Basta and Zaki, who provided detailed geological and mineralogical information but also commented discouragingly on the feasibility of working the mines for profit[9].

Until the 16th century, when the remarkable gems from Colombia gained widespread notice, the Egyptian deposits were the only known source of emeralds. The Egyptian mines were worked to satisfy a vigorous demand despite great natural hardships, poor working conditions, problems in logistic support, and the difficulty of recovering emeralds from hard rock without fracturing the crystals. Compared to Colombian stones, those of Egypt were murky, filled with disfiguring inclusions and flaws, generally quite small, and frequently of inferior colour. Possibly it was the unique grass-green colour of emeralds in general, coupled with a considerable fund of magical and curative powers these gems were deemed to possess, that encouraged mining despite meagre yields and the appalling conditions under which they were recovered. The mines must have been profitable, however, because the stones found their way via trade channels throughout the civilized world of the Mediterranean, Near East, and India.

As reported by modern visitors, the Egyptian mines consist of an astounding network of inclines, tunnels, and chambers, accompanied by ruins of elaborate housekeeping structures on the surface, suggesting that substantial quantities of stones must have been produced. There are no early production statistics, but the lure of profits led to several modern attempts to reopen the mines, the most ambitious being that of Streeter & Company, the firm of London Jewellers. In 1899 they recovered only extremely small quantities of gem material and were soon forced to abandon mining. The progress of this campaign was described by D. A. MacAlister, the geologist member of the expedition[10]. Later attempts by other parties were equally unsuccessful, which suggests that the richest portions of the deposits had been mined out or that the deposits were never very productive but could be made to pay in ancient times through use of slave labour.

All evidence strongly suggests that the ancient Egyptian emeralds were small and suited only for shaping into beads or rudely polished geometric shapes to be inset into precious metal jewellery and ornamental or symbolic objects. It is unlikely that many reasonably flawless and richly coloured gems were ever produced in weights beyond several carats. It is the small gemstones that tend to disappear with the passage of time, or at least become indistinguishable from more modern emeralds,

4

Figure 1.1 Top: F. Cailliaud's rendering of the view across Wadi Sikait looking north, showing numerous buildings of the emerald miners, with the principal and lesser temples to the right. Plate 3 of *Travels in the Oasis of Thebes* (London, 1822). *Bottom:* A modern photograph, looking northwest from near the principal temple, taken in March 1980 by Dr. Peter Bancroft.

and the larger, finer stones that are preserved. Towards the end of their working life, the mines are said to have supplied emeralds to Cleopatra who, it is reported, gave many 'fine specimens' bearing an engraving of her likeness to her favourite ambassadors[10a].

But if so many stones were mined, where have they gone? In today's collections of antiquities, there seems to be a paucity of emeralds of *any* description that can with certainty be of an Egyptian origin. For example, in a catalogue of Greek, Etruscan, and Roman jewellery of the British Museum[11], F. H. Marshall noted that 'in spite of the popularity of this stone in ancient times, it is not often found in antique jewellery'. He mentions only two pieces in the collection set with undoubted Egyptian emerald, and 'it seems certain, that the term *smaragdus,* which occurs often in descriptions of ancient jewellery, must have also included the plasma [a dark green quartz] which is so common in Roman times'.

Careless application of the term *emerald* to any green gem without the benefit of a mineralogical identification led to over-estimates of quantity, G. Maspero being among those guilty of this mistake. In a work on Egyptian archeology[12], he enthusiastically describes a 'profusion' of small figurines in precious stones, including emerald, that were found during his explorations among the tombs of Egypt, as well as large scarabs of emerald that could be dated to the First Theban Empire (about 2160 BC). All of these, however, turned out to be some other green stones. Other evidence for the scarcity of Egyptian emeralds even in authentic ancient jewellery is noted by Gregorietti[13], who stated that this gemstone 'is rarely found in Egyptian jewellery from tombs, although a small number has been found on mummies'. Vilimkova's study of ancient Egyptian jewellery[14] makes no mention at all of emerald, and its numerous colour plates show the pieces to be devoid of emeralds. As will be shown later, emerald was not an important stone in engraved gems during Graeco-Roman times.

The conclusions to be reached from this discussion are several. First, one must conclude that large quantities of stones were not produced from the Egyptian mines, and that most of those that were produced were small and mediocre in quality, with very few specimens of importance. Secondly, such small stones probably disappeared into less valuable forms of jewellery that have been lost in the passage of time. It is also possible that much of the poor grade of emerald was absorbed in amulets and in medicines. Amulets usually vanish into the same graves as their owners, and gems used in crushed form as medicines are utterly wasted. Because the belief in the magical and medicinal virtues of precious stones has always been most firm in India, possibly much of the Egyptian emerald found its way to that country, to which we will now turn.

Emerald and beryl in ancient India

Knowledge and use of beryl and emerald in India may be even older than in ancient Egypt, but it lacks convincing documentation. According to S. M. Tagore, who prepared a monumental study of gemstones with special reference to their position in Indian culture[15], 'the emerald had been used amongst the Hindus from time immemorial', being held so high in esteem that 'even any other flawless gem assuming the form of an emerald is highly prized'. Tagore devoted a number of pages to discussions of emerald and beryl, quoting from ancient Sanskrit sources and attesting to the rich fund of gemmological knowledge possessed by the ancient inhabitants.

G. C. M. Birdwood, in a monograph on Indian industrial arts[16], mentions references to the emerald in ancient writings, noting especially the amulet or talisman composed of nine gems known as the *nava-ratna* or *nao-ratan,* of which one stone was the emerald. Tagore and Birdwood also mention the *vedas,* the most ancient of Hindu sacred writings, in which legends, deities, rituals, and other matters important to the ordered conduct of life, religion, and profession were set forth for guidance. The vedas contain frequent references to precious stones, including the beryl and emerald. The most important of these with respect to the lore of gems (matters still of grave interest to modern Indians) is the *Rig-Veda,* which, like other vedas is dated to the so-called Vedic Period of about 1500 to 1000 BC.

Although the vedas speak of precious stones as if they were well known at the time of writing, it seems that knowledge of the emerald must antedate the Vedic Period, or must have originated some time before 1500 BC. This provides a fair correspondence to the period in Egypt when the mines were flourishing. On the other hand, it cannot be unequivocally stated that all early Indian emerald came from Egypt, as witness the discovery in 1944 in Rajasthan of important emerald deposits of the same type as the Egyptian. This discovery suggests the possibility that this region could have supplied these gems in an earlier time. Furthermore, aquamarines have been found in several widely scattered areas in India in mica deposits and elsewhere. Aquamarine is regularly found in the gem gravels of Sri Lanka, and its transport to India many centuries ago would have posed no problem. In fact, Ball's chronology of gem mining[3] gives beryls as being produced in India by 400 BC.

Regardless of where the inhabitants of India obtained their first beryls, it now appears that a brisk trade in emeralds developed at the same time that the ancient mines in Egypt were in operation. H. C. Beck described a hoard of beads found in the ruins of the city of Taxila in the Punjab, among which were beads of beryl[17]. He suggested an age for the hoard of between 700 BC and AD, which is even earlier than the age given by Ball. Strabo, the celebrated Greek geographer who lived between 63 BC and 19 AD, and to whom we owe much of our knowledge of the ancient world, visited India and remarked on the extensive use of beryls and other gemstones in the ornamentation of drinking vessels and other small objects belonging to the wealthy. Indian interest in gemstones continued unabated from this early period onwards, as evidenced by the prominent display of precious stones in personal ornaments and small implements, vessels, and costume accessories. Birdwood[16] provided a number of illustrations of such objects from relatively recent periods, as did B. J. Bhushan[18] in a richly illustrated monograph on Indian jewellery. However, the fullest and best treatment of native jewellery and ornament is that by T. H. Hendley[19] in which colour plates of considerable beauty, many depicting emeralds, are a prominent feature.

Beryl in the ancient East

Aquamarine and other pale-coloured varieties of beryl, but not emerald, occur in Japan, Mongolia, and a few other places in the Far East, but their use in antiquity appears to have been very limited. There is no evidence that the emerald was used in the Orient prior to the Christian Era, and only infrequent mentions of it, largely speculative, are to be found in works by students of Chinese or Japanese cultural history. In the past century, the Chinese have used aquamerine and other pale beryls for small carvings as snuff bottles and figurines, but the sources of the mineral are rarely mentioned. However, the use of elongated sculptured prisms of stone for personal documentary seals suggests the use of the prismatic crystals of aquamarine that are known to occur in Mongolia.

In his study of numerous materials used in ancient Persia and China, B. Laufer[20] states that 'the emerald appears to be first mentioned in the *Co ken lu*, written in 1366', while in his work on jade[21] he noted that emeralds 'were unknown to the

Figure 1.2 Fine example of the Mogul jeweller's art in the form of a gold aigrette, set with cabochon emeralds and rubies, and meant to be fastened to the turban by means of the ties shown. After an illustration in E. Jannettaz *et al. Diamants et Pierres Precieuses* (Paris, 1881).

Chinese in the Han period' (206 BC–221 AD). Furthermore, he states that 'the Chinese made its acquaintance only in recent times from India and in the 'Imperial Dictionary of Four Languages' it is called *tsie-mu-lu* (Manchu *niowarimbu wehe* 'greenish stone') corresponding to Tibetan *mar-gad* and Mongol *markat,* both the latter derived from Sanskrit *marakata,* which itself is a loan word from Greek *smaragdos;* to the same group belongs the Persian *zumurrud,* to which the Chinese word seems to be directly traceable'.

In their compendium of minerals and stones used in Chinese medicine, taken from a Chinese work of 1597 entitled *Pen Ts' ao Kang Mu,* Read and Pak[22] mention only the 'oriental topaz' or 'gold beryl' in a single definition, suggesting that no clear distinction was then drawn between these two minerals. In another place, Laufer[21] mentions that the Emir Suleiman of the Kingdom of the Caliphs sent a 'flask of jade ornamented with jewels' to an ambassador of China in 716 AD. If this is true, it suggests that the jewelled jades of the Moguls of Iran-India – and the small polished gems used to decorate them, namely diamonds, rubies and emeralds – were known at a very early time to the Chinese, thus pushing back even farther the date by which the Chinese became acquainted with the emerald.

While beryl has been found in Japan, Hong Kong, Malaya, and in one place in Burma, none of the deposits are important, so it is not surprising that beryl is a mineral only lately known to the Far East. The absence of beryls is specifically mentioned by the French gem dealer and traveller Jean-Baptiste Tavernier (1605–1689), who travelled to India and brought back gems of great value. The latest edition of his travels, edited by Crooke[23], states that:

> 'As for the emerald, it is an ancient error of many people to suppose that it was originally found in the East, and the majority of jewellers and artisans, when they see an emerald of high colour inclining to black, are still accustomed to call it an oriental emerald, in which they are mistaken. I confess I have not been able to find the places in our Continent from whence these kinds of stones are obtained. But I am assured that the East has never produced them, either on the mainland or on the islands; and having made a strict inquiry during all my journeys, no one has been able to indicate any place in Asia where they are found'.

As given in a footnote by Crooke, 'Tavernier appears to have been wholly unaware of the true source of the emerald in early times. Although common beryl is abundant in India, the emerald, though highly-esteemed, and well known at a very remote epoch, does not appear to have been found there'. Ignorant of the fact that emeralds came from Egypt, Tavernier went on to suggest that some Colombian emeralds were shipped from South America to Spanish colonies in the Philippines and then shipped westward to the Far East and ultimately to Europe, wherein they were mislabelled 'oriental emeralds'.

Beryl in Graeco-Roman times

One of the earliest mentions of emerald by someone who could claim expertise in mineralogy appears in the *Peri Lithon* ('Of Stones'), written by Theophrastus (ca. 372–287 BC), a disciple of Aristotle, and preserved for us only in a fragment of a larger work. Theophrastus described emerald and its curious powers, and it is he who is responsible for the oft-repeated claim that gazing upon an emerald strengthens the eyesight.

The first English translation of *Peri Lithon* by John Hill[24] is now superseded by two modern translations which clarify obscure points and introduce new information. The first of these, by E. R. Caley and J. F. C. Richards[25], returns to the fundamental question which must always be asked in taking the words of ancient authorities at face value, that is, is the emerald (or beryl) of antiquity the same mineral that we know today? Caley and Richards suggest that 'the statements of Theophrastus make it doubtful whether true emerald was even known to him, and there appears no certain evidence on other grounds of its use among the Greeks'. This view is supported by D. E. Eichholz[26] in the second modern translation of Theophrastus. Both translations comment on the obvious impossibility of certain large monuments of the ancients being made of *smaragdoi* (emeralds), as claimed by Theophrastus, and thus cast doubt on his real knowledge of the true emerald.

To some degree this doubt is confirmed by R. A. Higgins, who wrote authoritatively on ancient Greek and Roman jewellery[27], noting that in the earliest periods gemstones and enamels were very sparingly used, the preference in ornaments being for gold alone. However, during the Hellenistic period 'inlaying [with gems] was lavishly practised' while 'in the second and first centuries we also find emeralds, amethysts, plasma and pearls'. Despite these doubts about Theophrastus's testimony, well-authenticated pieces employing engraved gems and dating from well before his time confirm the fact that emeralds and beryls were known during that period.

During the past several centuries, Graeco-Roman engraved gems have received much careful study, primarily as archaeological artifacts, but careful and accurate mineralogical identification of the stones and minerals used in them is a relatively recent development. In regard to the emerald, for example, C. W. King, the noted English expert on engraved gems, stated that in his experience gems made from beryl antedated those made from emerald, usually being fine works of the Greek school[28]. In a catalogue of the engraved gems in the Fitzwilliam Museum, Cambridge, J. H. Middleton[29] declared:

'Though the emerald was rarely employed for the engraved gems of the Greeks, yet it was often used, chiefly for pendants, to decorate gold jewellery. Small emeralds frequently occur in the form of necklace beads, mixed with beads of amethyst and rock crystal, in many cases these emeralds are not cut; the natural hexagonal form of the crystal is preserved, and nothing is done to the gem except that a hole is drilled through its axis for the insertion of the gold wire which holds it'.

In his monumental work on engraved gems, A. Furtwängler discussed the use of emerald and beryl and cited several examples of famous intaglios cut from them, but he also noted that while the emerald was much used for jewellery gems it was seldom engraved, and that the beryl did not come into common use for engraved gems until the time of the Romans. These opinions are repeated by G. M. A. Richter in her work on Greek and Etruscan engraved gems[31]. She furnishes a colour photograph of the more precious gems in which appears a small greenish-blue intaglio of aquamarine and a light green intaglio of emerald.

The scarcity of beryls among the Greeks is emphasized by the total lack of mention of either emerald or aquamarine as gem materials in the large work on Greek engraved gems by J. Boardman[32]. Nevertheless, it is clear from the statements of others that beryls were known to the Greeks and one cannot claim that Theophrastus was totally ignorant of the true emerald.

Another ancient source of emerald is located high up in the Habachtal in the Austrian Alps near Salzburg. The deposit was discovered by the Romans while prospecting for metallic ores in the region, and it is reputed that several centuries later the Archbishop of Salzburg was one of the first to make a serious attempt to mine the Habachtal emerald deposit. It is reported that some of the old Salzburg families still own specimens mined during that period[10a].

Pliny's *Natural History*

Nearly at the height of its domination of the civilized world, Rome produced one of its most famous citizens, Caius Plinius Secundus, or Pliny the Elder (23–79 AD), a highly disciplined and learned individual. He conceived the idea of compiling in

Figure 1.3 Antique intaglio gems. *Left:* Neptune in aquamarine; *right:* the head of an unidentified woman in emerald. The actual gems are only a fraction of the size shown here. From P. S. Bartoli's engravings in *Museum Odescalcum* (Rome, 1747), the catalogue of the collection of antiquitites then owned by Livio, Duke of Bracciano and nephew of Pope Innocent XI.

one book everything that was known about nature and its productions, and the final result was his famous *Natural History*. It contains information from more than 2000 sources, many of them ancient and now lost, so that our knowledge of them is preserved only in this encyclopaedia. Since the original Latin version, over 250 editions have appeared in many languages, but only three complete editions in English exist, the first by Philemon Holland[33], first published in 1601, the second by J. Bostock and H. T. Riley[34], published in 1855–57, and the third the Loeb Classical Library edition[35] of ten volumes, published from 1938 to 1962, of which the last volume, comprising books 36–37 and translated by D. F. Eichholz, is of interest here. The most detailed study of Pliny's gemstone references, including emerald and beryl, is that of S. H. Ball[4].

The emerald is treated by Pliny in chapter 16 of book 37. However, because he depended on information garnered from secondhand sources, it raises more questions than it answers regarding the identification and sources of the minerals. He indiscriminately lumps them all together under the term *smaragdus* ('emerald'), of which he describes no less than twelve kinds. Obviously all of them cannot be beryl because he includes among them the enormous columns and other architectural monuments previously mentioned by Theophrastus, from whose *Peri Lithon* he drew information.

Of the twelve kinds, the best, according to Pliny, is the Scythian emerald, from a supposed source in an ancient land that once extended an indefinite distance north and northeast of the Black Sea and east of the Aral Sea. The entire region is now in the USSR, and the discovery of true emeralds in 1830 in the Ural Mountains, spurred speculation about these deposits being the source of Pliny's Scythian emeralds. Eichholz[35] clings to this view, but it is not shared by others. Despite intensive exploration of the deposits, no trace has ever been found of prehistoric workings or the presence of artifacts that would confirm ancient mining activity.

The same lack of archaelogical evidence haunts the second most favoured emeralds of Pliny, those from Bactria. Eichholz suggests the Bactrian emerald was a garbled paraphrase of Theophrastus's, 'alluding to one of the blue stones used by the Persians in inlay-work, probably the blue turquoise', and for this reason 'the Bactrian *smaragdus* is therefore a fiction'. However, it is interesting to note that splendid aquamarines, among other gemstones, have recently been found in northeast Afghanistan, whose territory coincides more or less with that encompassed by ancient Bactria.

Pliny's third-ranking emerald is identified as found around Coptos, or the city now known as Qift on the Nile River north of Thebes. No emeralds exist here, but ancient Coptos was the terminal of a caravan route to the Red Sea which passed through the emerald mine district, and it could have been a trading centre for these stones. Probably these mines, in the Wadi and Gebel Sikait district, correspond to those labelled 'Ethiopian' by Pliny. In chapter 18, Pliny cites a King Juba who gave the location of the mines as 'three days journey from Coptos', according to Holland's translation, or 'twenty-five days' according to Bostock and Riley as well as Eichholz. The latter time is far more reasonable considering it is approximately 180 miles (285 km) from Coptos to the mines.

All other *smaragdi* described by Pliny are clearly materials other than emerald.

In some instances they seem to be greenish copper minerals, massive quartz varieties, or even green monumental stones. Only one other mineral, called *limoniatis* by Pliny, is classed as a possible emerald by Ball[4].

Following his discussion of emerald and emerald-like stones, Pliny describes the *beryllus* and its varieties. Ball interprets these kinds of beryl as aquamarine, golden beryl (called 'chrysoberyl' by Pliny), the chrysoprase (of Pliny), the *hyacintho-zontes* (a deep blue beryl), the *aeroides* (a pale blue beryl) and the common beryl. Pliny observed that many persons considered the *berylli* to be of the same nature as *smaragdi,* or at least very similar, and remarked that beryls came from India, rarely from elsewhere, and that they are cut with six angles or 'cut by skilled craftsmen to a smooth hexagonal shape'. This suggests that Pliny was aware of the usual hexagonal prismatic shapes assumed by beryl crystals[4].

In regard to lapidary treatment of beryls, Pliny contradicts himself by stating that 'in the case . . . of the stones of Scythia and Egypt, their hardness is such, that it would be quite impossible to penetrate them'. (Despite Pliny's statement, Egyptian emerald was cut with little more difficulty than the many varieties of quartz that were used to make engraved gems). In the same passage he says, 'It was universally agreed upon among mankind in respect to these stones, and to forbid their surface to be engraved', the reason given that when left unengraved they benefit the eyesight[34]. If there is any truth in this remark, it could possibly account for the general scarcity of engraved emerald gems as noted above. Pliny also noted that Alexander the Great allowed only the celebrated gem engraver, Pyrgoteles, the privilege of copying his visage on gems and then only when made of emerald.

In her treatise on Roman engraved gems, G. M. A. Richter[36] described 783 specimens, of which only ten could be identified as beryl and only two of those as emerald. The absence of this mineral in engraved gems in the Roman period is puzzling because it was known that supplies of emerald were forthcoming from the Egyptian mines, and one would imagine that so precious a material would seem eminently suited for the highly prized engraved gems which were in demand by the wealthy. As previously suggested, however, it may be that extremely few of the crystals were suitable for such purpose, and any gem engraver would be sure to look askance at a raw material filled with dark inclusions and fissures which could be exposed during engraving, resulting in the loss of detail as well as unsightly areas.

The availability of Egyptian emeralds in the Roman period is shown by examples of emerald-set jewellery in R. Siviero's catalogue[37] of the collection of jewellery in the National Museum in Naples. A number of pieces contain crudely shaped and polished hexagonal crystal sections, some drilled parallel with the prism faces as a means of fastening them in their mounts. Most of the museum pieces were recovered from the ruins of Pompeii and Herculaneum, cities not far from Naples that were buried in the ashes of the great eruption of Mount Vesuvius in 79 AD. Pliny himself, impelled by scientific curiosity rather than regard for personal safety, insisted on viewing the eruption close at hand and thereby lost his life. Siviero's catalogue clearly shows the poor quality of the emeralds, by present-day standards, and supports the view previously maintained that extremely few good-quality emeralds ever came from the Egyptian mines.

Large European emerald objects

A monstrous 'emerald' weighing 28.75 pounds (12.9 kg) was given to the Benedictine Abbey at Reichenau, near Constance, Switzerland, by Charlemagne (742–814 AD), according to abbey records[42]. However, on a visit to the abbey, William Coxe, Rector of Bemerton, saw the stone and conjectured that it was 'nothing more than a transparent green spathfluor', that is, green fluorite.

Robert de Berquen in his *Merveilles des Indes*[43] told of an emerald as large as 'half a melon' which 'glittered extraordinarily', and was hung from the top of the nave in the Cathedral of Mainz some 600 years before his time, or about 1060. The existence of this remarkable object has never been confirmed.

Another equally famous emerald is the Sacra Catina, or Holy Grail, a shallow circular vessel or dish preserved in the sacristy of the Cathedral of San Giovanni in Genoa. Its history as a religious relic begins during Biblical times when it was presented, so the story goes, by the Queen of Sheba to King Solomon, remaining for centuries thereafter in Jerusalem. In King Herod's reign, it was part of the royal table service, and just before the crucifixion, it was used by the celebrants of the Last Supper[44]. One account went so far to say that Christ himself drank from the vessel at the supper[45]. Succeeding in their siege of Caesarea Palastina in 1102, the Crusaders discovered the vessel and gave it over to the Genoans to fulfill a promise of loot-sharing in return for Genoan help. It was sent to Genoa for safe-keeping in the cathedral where twelve nobles, called the Clavigeri, were appointed its guard. Once a year, it was exhibited to the public, but only from a distance, and only the most privileged were permitted to closely examine it.

Because of its diameter, reported as '16–17 inches broad', or more commonly as about 14 inches (36 cm) in diameter and 5 inches (12.5 cm) deep, the sacred vessel was recognized as glass as early as the 16th century[44]. Later visitors, when shown the vessel, confirmed this identification and even remarked on the presence of bubbles typical of glass. In 1880, Genoa fell to Napoleon and the Sacra Catina was sent to Paris for examination by experts of the Cabinet of Antiquities who pronounced it a fine example of antique glass work. An edict of the Congress of Vienna of 1815, called to settle European affairs after Napoleon's fall, directed that the vessel be returned to Genoa. It was broken along the way but was skillfully repaired and fitted with a rim of gold filigree and a tripod stand. Even today, some Genoese claim that the present object is merely a glass model that was tested at Paris and that the geniune object, made of emerald, always remained in Genoa and is still in safekeeping.

Among the largest and most remarkable emeralds that Georg Agricola had heard of, in addition to the Sacra Catina, was a giant specimen shaped into a dish or shallow cup, also claimed to be the holy grail, preserved in a monastery near Lyons[46]. Both this object and the Sacra Catina are mentioned by Conrad Gesner in his mineralogical work of 1565[47]. Another colossal emerald mentioned by Agricola, said to be kept in a small shrine dedicated to King Wenceslaus at Prague, 'is not small since it is over nine inches long'. Kunz[45] (p. 259) offers the view that it was probably made from Silesian chrysoprase, a green variety of chalcedonic quartz which occurred in masses large enough for the purpose. Lastly, Agricola mentioned an even larger specimen at Magdeburg, 'which forms the base for the small tower-shaped golden chest in which the sacrament is carried'.

The Emerald Buddha

In the East, the most famous 'emerald' object is the statue of Buddha in Bangkok, Thailand, which presumably because of its colour has been named the 'Emerald Buddha', although it is now admitted by the government that the stone is not emerald. The statue reposes high atop an elaborately ornamental pedestal in the Chapel of the Emerald Buddha in the Grand Palace grounds in Bangkok. It is available for viewing by the public, but no one may approach closer than about 30 feet (10 m).

The history of the Emerald Buddha is told in the *Chronicle of the Emerald Buddha,* as translated from a palm-leaf manuscript in Pali language by C. Notton[48]. Notton described the many vicissitudes of the statue, through all of which it had emerged unscathed. A pretty legend is attached to the origin of the carving. Nagasena, a pupil of Maha Dhamma Rakitta, determined to make the religion of Lord Buddha 'very prosperous' and conceived the idea of creating a statue of him out of precious stone. The an-el Indra, hearing of this, came to Nagasena and instructed him to go to Mount Vipulla where large precious stones were known to exist. However, at the mountain, the guardian genies would not surrender a suitable stone, but they suggested an alternative material, Keo Amarakata, or 'crystal-smaragd', which is 'a magnificent gem measuring about four times the size of the fist and three fingers in width, and about one cubit one hand in length'. A heavenly sculptor by the name of Visukamma was given the stone to carve, and in about seven days and seven nights had completed the statue, about one cubit (ca. 18 in or 45 cm) in height.

According to an offical government guidebook to the Grand Palace obtained during my visit in 1977, 'the effigy was first discovered in Chiengrai in 1464, brought down to Lampang where it remained till King Tilok of Lannatai brought it to Chienmai, the capital, where it was fitly enshrined'. At some later time it was taken by King Jayajettha to Luang Prabang, thence to the town of Wiengchand where it remained for a long period. A punitive expedition lauched against Luang Prabang by the King of Dhonburi returned the statue to what now is the site of Bangkok. The temple in which the statue now rests was built in 1785 by King Rama I.

During my visit to the temple, I observed the statuette of Buddha in the seated position in good light but from the considerable distance mentioned above. The colour is dull greyish-green, resembling the colour of celadon ceramic glazes, and the surfaces glisten with polish that is almost glassy in appearance. Both the uniformity and brilliance of polish, plus the considerable size, suggest that the material is some fine-grained igneous rock or possibly a siliceous material akin to jasper. The official guidebook, however, says that it is 'one-piece jade'.

The Buddha's Tooth emerald

Ball[42] briefly described a stone, purporting to be an emerald, which supports the sacred relic known as 'Buddah's tooth', preserved in the Dalada Malagawa temple at Kandy, Sir Lanka. The carving, said to be about 4 inches (10 cm) long and 2 inches (5 cm) deep, shows Buddha holding the sacred tooth in one hand. It is enclosed in seven cases, each successively more ornate than the last, and once a year the shrine is paraded through the streets of Kandy on an elephant. Ball noted that 'as the original shrine and the tooth were utterly destroyed by the Portuguese in 1560 the carving is evidently a relatively recent one'. There appears to be no offical identification of the stone itself, and it cannot be said at this time whether it is indeed an emerald.

Hernando Cortez emeralds

In his Third Letter of May 1522, Hernando Cortez reported to the Spanish Court the accomplishments of his expedition into Mexico and described an enormous emerald, shaped like a pyramid, that rested on a skull in the Hall of Justice in Texcoco. Surrounded by feathers and costly gems, it was known as the Tribunal of God and was used by the Aztec judges as an aide in deciding the guilt or innocence of accused parties brought before them. The size of the stone was such that its base was as broad as the palm of the hand.

This object, along with Cortez's letter, was sent to Spain in the care of two compatriots, one of whom died in a drunken brawl in the Azores, and the other, presumably with the emerald still in his possession, was captured by a French privateer. According to Ball[42], much of the loot obtained by the privateer passed into the hands of Francis I, King of France, but to this day no one has been able to account for the emerald itself.

After the Roman Empire crumbled in the 4th century AD, much of the knowledge of gemstones that was passed along during the Middle Ages continued to lean heavily on Pliny, and little new information was added. Excellent discussions of writings that appeared in this era are to be found in the monumental works of L. Thorndike[38] and in the discussion of the development of the geological sciences by F. D. Adams[39].

Early use of beryl in the Americas

At the time of the Spanish Conquest of the New World in the 16th century, emeralds were already well known there and employed in ornamental and objects of ceremony. According to Ball[4], Colombian emerald was so common in Peru that for at least two centuries after the Conquest it was known as Peruvian emerald. In the same reference, Ball gives the date of 1000 AD as that by which emerald was in the hands of the natives and 'hence Muzo or other Colombian mines were probably already opened up'. He also recorded the use of beryl by North American Indians and by the aborigines of Brazil.

G. F. Kunz[40] describes a labret made from an oval beryl 3.5 inches (89 mm) long and 1 inch (25 mm) thick that was found among artifacts of the Botocundo Indians of Brazil. Other pre-Colombian finds of emerald and beryl confirm that these minerals were known to the Indians well before the discovery of America. Furthermore, Colombian emeralds were not only traded to other South American countries but also into Panama and as far north as Mexico. Important finds of emeralds in grave sites of Coclé, Panama, are described by S. K. Lothrop[41].

In the pre-Colombian era, only the emerald deposits of Colombia were systematically worked, no other deposits being known in the entire Western Hemisphere despite the presence of enormous resources of alluvial beryls in the interior of Brazil. These were apparently not known to its natives or, if known, ignored. As remarked by Ball[4], a few beryls were put to ornamental use by Indians in Idaho and in North Carolina, but nowhere was this mineral specifically sought out except in Colombia. More on Colombian emeralds appears in Chapter 2.

References

1 LITTLE, H. P. An ancient reference to the emerald. *Science* 45, no. 1160, pp. 291–2 (1917)

2 BALL, S. H. Egyptian gem stones of the pre-Ptolemaic days. *Jewelers' Circular* 96 (Feb. 23): 147–57 (1928)

3 BALL, S. H. Historical notes on gem mining. *Economic Geology* 26:681–738 (1931)

4 BALL, S. H. *A Roman Book on Precious Stones* Los Angeles: Gemological Institute of America. 338 pp. (1950)

5 SCHNEIDER, O. Der aegyptische Smaragd . . . nebst einer vergleichenden mineralogischen Untersuchung der Smaragde von Alexandrien, vom Gebel Sabara und vom Ural. *Zeitschrift für Ethnologie* 24:41–100 (1892)

6 LUCAS, A. *Ancient Egyptian Materials and Industries.* 2nd ed. London: Edward Arnold & Co. 447 pp. (1934)

7 WILKINSON, J. G. *The Ancient Egyptians.* Vol. 2, p. 237; cited in Lucas, above (1890)

8 CAILLIAUD, F. *Voyage à l'Oasis de Thèbes . . . fait pendant les années 1815–1816, 1817–1818.* 2 vol. Paris: Imprimerie Royale. English summary: *Travels in the Oasis of Thebes . . .,* edited by E. F. Jomard. London: Sir Richard Phillips & Co., 1822. 66 pp. (1821)

9 BASTA, E. Z. and ZAKI, M. Geology and mineralisation of Wadi Sikait area, South-eastern Desert. *Journal of Geology of the United Arab Republic* 5:1–38 (1966)

10 MacALISTER, D. A. The emerald mines of northern Etbai. *Geographical Journal* (London) 16:537–49. (1900)

10a MUMME, I. A. *The Emerald.* Mumme Publications, 135 pp. (1982)

11 MARSHALL, F. H. *Catalogue of the Jewellery, Greek, Etruscan, and Roman, in the Departments of Antiquities, British Museum.* London: The Trustees of the British Museum. 400 pp. (1969)

12 MASPERO, G. *L'Archeologie Egyptienne.* Paris. pp. 161, 234–6. (1887)

13 GREGORIETTI, G. *Jewellery Through the Ages.* New York: American Heritage. 319 pp. (1969)

14 VILIMKOVA, M. *Egyptian Jewellery.* London: Paul Hamlyn. 142 pp. (1969)

15 TAGORE, S. M. *Mani Málá, or a Treatise on Gems.* 2 vols. Calcutta. Stanhope Press. 1046 pp. (1879)

16 BIRDWOOD, G. C. M. *The Industrial Arts of India.* London: Chapman and Hall. 344 pp. (1880)

17 BECK, H. C. The beads from Taxila. *Memoirs of the Archaeological Survey of India,* no. 65. 66 pp. (1941)

18 BHUSHAN, B. J. *Indian Jewellery.* Bombay: D. B. Taraporevala Sons. 168 pp. (1955)

19 HENDLEY, T. H. *Indian Jewellery.* London: Journal of Indian Art. 189 pp., 167 pls. (1906–09)

20 LAUFER, B. *Sino-Iranica: Chinese Contributions to the History of Civilization in Ancient Iran.* Field Museum of Natural History Publication 201, Anthropoligical Series, vol. 15, no. 3. Chicago: Field Museum of Natural History. pp. 185–630 (1919)

21 LAUFER, B. *Jade: A Study in Chinese Archaeology and Religion.* Field Museum of Natural History Publication 154, Anthropological Series, vol. 10. Chicago: Field Museum of Natural History. 370 pp. (1921)

22 READ, B. E. and PAK, C. A compendium of minerals and stones used in Chinese medicine from the Pen Ts'ao Kang Mu . . . 2nd ed. *Peking Society of Natural History Bulletin* 3, part 2, 98 pp. (1928)

23 TAVERNIER, J.-B. *Travels in India by Jean-Baptiste Tavernier, Baron of Aubonne.* Translated by V. Ball from the original French edition of 1676. 2nd ed. Edited by W. Crooke. 2 vols. London: Oxford University Press (1925)

24 HILL, J. *Theophrastus's History of Stones.* 2nd ed. London. 342 pp. (1774)

25 CALEY, E. R. and RICHARDS, J. F. C. *Theophrastus on Stones.* Ohio State University Graduate School Monographs, Contributions in Physical Science, no. 1. Columbus: Ohio State University Press. 238 pp. (1956)

26 EICHHOLZ, D. E., ed. and trans. *Theophrastus De Lapidibus.* Oxford: Clarendon Press. 141 pp.

27 HIGGINS, R. A. 1961. *Greek and Roman Jewellery.* London: Methuen and Co. 236 pp. (1965)

28 KING, C. W. *Antique Gems, Their Origin, Uses and Value.* 2nd ed. London: J. Murray. 498 pp. (1866)

29 MIDDLETON, J. H. *The Engraved Gems of Classical Times, with a Catalogue of the Gems in the Fitzwillian Museum.* Cambridge: University Press. 157 pp. (1891)

30 FURTWÄNGLER, A. *Die antiken Gemmen: Geschichte der Steinschneidekunst im klassischen Altertum.* 3 vols. Leipzig: Giesecke & Devrient. Vol. 3, 464 pp. (1900)

31 RICHTER, G. M. A. *The Engraved Gems of the Greeks, Etruscans and Romans.* Part I. Engraved Gems of the Greeks and Etruscans. London: Phaidon Press. 339 pp. (1968)

32 BOARDMAN, J. *Greek Gems and Finger Rings, Early Bronze Age to Late Classical.* London: Thames & Hudson. 458 pp. (1970)

33 HOLLAND, P., trans. *The Historie of the World, commonly called, the Natural Historie of C. Plinius Secundus.* 2 vols. London: Adam Islip (1601)

34 BOSTOCK, J. and RILEY, H. T., trans. *The Natural History of Pliny.* Vol. 6. London: Henry G. Bohn. 529 pp. (1855–57)

35 PLINY. *Natural History. With an English Translation in Ten Volumes.* Vol. 10, Books 36–37. Translated by D. E. Eichholz. Loeb Classical Library. Edited by T. E. Page *et al.* London: William Heinemann. 343 pp. (1962)

36 RICHTER, G. M. A. *The Engraved Gems of the Greeks, Etruscans and Romans.* Part II. Engraved Gems of the Romans. London: Phaidon Press. 307 pp. (1971)

37 SIVIERO, R. *Jewelry and Amber of Italy: A Collection in the National Museum of Naples.* New York: McGraw-Hill Book Co. 153 pp. (1959)

38 THORNDIKE, L. *A History of Magic and Experimental Science.* 8 vols. New York: Columbia University Press. See especially vols. 1, 2, 6, and 7 (1923–58)

39 ADAMS, F. D. *The Birth and Development of the Geological Sciences.* Baltimore: Williams & Wilkins. 506 pp. (1938)

40 KUNZ, G. F. Report on jewelry. *Universal Exposition of 1889 at Paris.* pp. 381–7 (1889)

41 LOTHROP, S. K., *et al. Coclé, an Archaeological Study of Central Panama. Part I: Historical Background, Excavations at the Sitio Conte, Artifacts and Ornaments.* Memoirs of the Peabody Museum of Archaeology and Ethnology, Harvard University, vol. 7. Cambridge: The Museum. 327 pp. (1937)

42 BALL, S. H. Some facts about famous emeralds. *Jewelers' Circular* 88, no. 10, pp. 63–65. (1924)

43 BERQUEN, R. de. *Les Merveilles des Indes Orientales et Occidentales* . . . Paris: C. Lambin. 112 pp. (1661)

44 STELLA, E. *De Gemmis Libellus Unicus.* Strasburg. 128 pp. (1530)

45 KUNZ, G. F. *The Curious Lore of Precious Stones.* Philadelphia and London: J. B. Lippincott. 406 pp. (1913)

46 BANDY, M. C. and BANDY, J. A., trans. *De Natura Fossilium (Textbook of Mineralogy),* by G. Agricola. Geological Society of America Special Paper 63. New York: Geological Society of America. 240 pp. (1955)

47 GESNER, C. *De Rerum Fossilium, Lapidum et Gemmarum* . . . Zurich. ca. 340 pp. (1565).

48 NOTTON, C. *The Chronicle of the Emerald Buddha.* Bangkok Times Press. 52 pp. (1932)

Chapter 2

Emerald and beryl in medieval and modern Europe

The painfully slow progress of science in Europe during the first thirteen centuries AD is thoroughly documented by Thorndike[1], who found only rudimentary mineralogical information on emerald and beryl among European writings and some tidbits of curious lore on the emerald. In the same vein, Adams[2] noted that 'nothing was known in these ancient times concerning either the chemical composition or crystallographic form of minerals, although these are now considered to be the most important factors in the distinction of mineral species'.

The fact that the post-Plinian era developed little new scientific knowledge on beryl is not surprising in view of the hardness of this mineral and its complete resistance to any kind of chemical attack that the ancients could devise. For all practical purposes, beryl was unassailable, its constituents unknown, and only its reaction to the ministrations of the lapidary provided any clue to its affinities to other similar-appearing minerals. It was not until the 18th century that beryl could be broken down and its components examined chemically.

Some attempts were made in the post-Plinian era to classify gemstones according to colour and other obvious external features, but on the whole Pliny's information was relied upon and uncritically repeated in book after book, often embellished with ingenious speculations and unwarranted conclusions. Such books, or 'lapidaries', dealt not only with gemstones but many other products of the earth as well, including fossils, stone-like animal calculi or bezoars, and organic substances such as amber, coral, jet, and pearl.

Biblical lapidaries

The first of many lapidaries to concern itself with gemstones mentioned in the Bible made its appearance as a brief treatise by Epiphanius (310?–02 AD), Bishop of Constantia in Cyprus. Although written in the 4th century, it was first placed in print as part of Conrad Gesner's compilation of mineralogical and gemmological works entitled *De Omne Rerum Fossilium*[3], published in Zurich in 1565. Emerald and beryl are both included, and C. W. King[4] has especially noted Epiphanius's descriptions of 'Neronian' and 'Domitian' emeralds, which are 'particularly austere and green in tint', supposedly due to immersion in an oil pigmented with verdigris to turn them darker green.

In her excellent summary of early lapidaries, incidental to her analysis of Albertus Magnus's work on stones, Wyckoff[5] noted the 'unease' manifested by Church authorities concerning magical virtues attributed to gemstones. Despite the attitude of the Church toward heathen superstitions, she remarks,

> 'Even devout Christians could not entirely shake off the old belief that precious stones possess some sort of supernatural powers or significance . . . this interest was to some extent legitimized by focusing attention on the stones mentioned in the Bible, especially the two (different) lists of 'twelve stones' – those in the breastplate . . . and those in the foundations of the New Jerusalem'.

Thorndike[1] also noted that Epiphanius's treatment of the breastplate stones 'perhaps gives an excuse and sets the fashion for the Christian medieval *Lapidaries*'. Thus a model was established not only for medieval lapidaries but also for all books treating gemstones, for there is scarcely one of importance that does not include a substantial treatment of Biblical gems.

An extended scholarly study of Epiphanius's Biblical lapidary is to be found in Blake and De Vis[6], who examined an Old Georgian version and fragments of the same treatise written in other languages. The subject of Christian lapidaries in general, including Epiphanius, is discussed in detail by Evans[7], but much more information on emerald and beryl is given in Blake and De Vis, even more than can be found in the version incorporated in Gesner.

Other early lapidaries

Another important early work is an encyclopaedic compilation prepared in manuscript for Isidore of Seville and called *Etymologiae*. Isidore became Bishop of Seville about 599 AD, and presumably the manuscript was written near the close of the 6th century. It is mentioned by Adams[2] and discussed more fully by Thorndike[1], who, however, does not refer to the mineralogical portions of the work.

As early as the 9th century, the prophylactic and curative powers of gemstones were formally recognized, and in a work by Costa ben Luca (or Qusta ibn Luqa) of Baalbeck, issued in 862–866 ad for Caliph al-Musta, the 'marvellous powers of gems worn suspended from the neck or set in a ring upon the finger' were affirmed, as was the 'fact' that 'emerald wards off epilepsy'.

The most important and influential lapidary of the medieval era was that written by Marbod or Marbodus, Bishop of Rennes, who lived during the 11th century. According to Thorndike, it was 'very likely completed . . . before the close of the eleventh century'. Both Thorndike[1] and Adams[2] devote much space to it, Thorndike going so far as to say it is 'the classic on the subject of the marvellous properties of stones', while Adams states that it is 'the earliest lapidary of the Middle Ages, and also the one which is quoted most widely'.

In his analysis of Marbod, Adams divided the stones described in five categories, the first containing twenty-six stones that are mythical and for which the descriptions are 'so trivial that it is impossible to connect the name to any particular mineral'. The second category contains six stones of animal origin, while the third includes four stones that, with some confidence, can be recognized as minerals. The fourth contains fourteen varieties of quartz, and the fifth and last group, of special interest here, contains fifteen minerals, including emerald and beryl. As usual, very little physical description but much curious lore is given.

Marbod's work appears in an English translation by C. W. King in his *Antique Gems*[8]. Wyckoff[5] noted that Marbod's information was largely obtained from Solinus, Isidore, and other early writers, but rarely from Pliny, although it must be said that the writers mentioned depended heavily on Pliny for *their* information.

Chronologically, Albertus Magnus' work on minerals is next after Marbod. It is characterized by Wyckoff as 'an impressive attempt to organise the science of mineralogy', and while it includes much that is superstitious and speculative, it does introduce new data. The first printed version appeared in Padua in 1476 and, as the work proved very popular, it was quickly followed by other editions. Adams called it 'one of the best and most comprehensive of the western medieval lapidaries' and remarked that while Albertus attempted to explain the formation of minerals and gemstones, causes of colour, and other properties, he also 'enlarges at length on their mystical and wonder-working powers and virtues, . . . there [being] scarcely an ill that flesh is heir to, for which he does not indicate some stone that will act as a protector'.

In connection with beryl, Albertus remarked on its high degree of transparency, comparing it to rock crystal, its generally pale colours, the fact that it is produced mainly in India, and recited its magical and medicinal properties. An unidentified stone, called *diadocos* (by others *diadochos*), is said to be pale in colour and to resemble the beryl. Wyckoff comments that 'the mysterious powers attributed to it by later lapidaries come from Damigeron (an ancient writer) . . . and seem to have to do with its use in some ritual of hydromancy or crystal-gazing', for which last purpose some authorities claim that clear beryl, shaped into spherical form, has been used. Emerald also is mentioned by Albertus, but he repeats the unclear distinctions among the numerous varieties originally listed and described by Pliny, indicating that Albertus was not only unfamiliar with them but had to repeat old information in lieu of anything better.

Almost at the same time that Albertus was preparing his manuscript, another lapidary was being composed for Alfonso X, King of Spain, ca. 1278 AD. In this splendidly illuminated and illustrated work, the original of which is preserved in the Escurial Library in Madrid, the principal object was to demonstrate the connections of gemstones and other minerals to celestial bodies. It thus forms the first major work on the astrological significance of gemstones. A facsimile edition[9] in colour, published in 1881, is discussed by Adams[2] and extensively treated by Evans[7]. In it appear several hundred stones, whose treatment reflects the views of Arabic science.

The manuscript was originally, according to Adams, 'a Chaldean lapidary of unknown date, which was translated into Arabic by Abolays and from Arabic into

Spanish by Garci-Perez'. The stones are classed by colour and placed under the twelve zodiacal signs with brief remarks on properties, uses, and medicinal virtues, but with careful attention paid to how the powers and virtues are influenced by planets and stars. In commencing on this work, G. F. Kunz[10] reports that the emerald is said to be 'controlled by Jupiter, and also by Mercury and Venus', while the planet Venus 'also lent virtue to the beryl'.

The *Speculum Lapidum*

Of much greater importance than the works described so far is a treatise on stones by Leonardus Camillus, a physician of Pesaro, Italy, first put in book form in 1502 under the title *Speculum Lapidum*[11], or 'mirror of stones'. The latter title was adopted for the anonymous English translation printed in London in 1750[12]. As can be seen from the span of 250 years between these editions, the book long retained popularity and importance. Adams has noted that it marked the passage of the Middle Ages into the Renaissance and 'bridged over the transitional period between the old and new mineralogy, since the first edition appeared . . . forty-four years before the publication of Agricola's *De Natura Fossilium* [first ed., 1546]'.

As customary, Leonardus gathered his information from previous writers but with the important difference of adopting the first glimmerings of scientific method. He treated more thoroughly than ever the physical properties of minerals and gemstones, such as diaphaneity, hardness, specific gravity (but without numerical values), compactness, colour, form, and geographic origins. The second part describes a large number of minerals and gemstones previously recorded by other writers and still others that were fabulous and remain unidentifiable. A third part, omitted in the English translation of 1750, dealt with virtues and properties of gems as enhanced by having their surfaces engraved with suitable signs and symbols.

Concerning the beryl, Leonardus noted that its colour is 'olive' or 'like sea water', and nine varieties are known but 'all of a pale green', and that India and Babylon produce beryls, but those from India are finest. He recounts virtues assigned to beryl and its uses in medicine. The *crissopassus* mentioned by Solinus is taken to be 'a species of Beryl, having the gold Colour mixed with purple'. It is one of the gemstones now unidentifiable. The *crisopilon* and *crisoberillus* are also given as beryl varieties, while *diadocus* is 'like Beryl in Colour, with a Paleness'. Under the term *smaragdus* for emerald, Leonardus describes its many varieties and sources, quality of colour, and reflectivity when polished. He also recorded several anecdotes of enormously large emeralds which he properly calls 'false emeralds'. Finally, in a surprising departure from custom, he affimed that emerald affords 'grateful Refreshment to the Eyes' when gazed upon, but dismissed other magical or medicinal properties with the remark that 'many virtues are fabled of it'.

New World emeralds

Until the early decades of the 16th century, emerald came almost exclusively from Egypt, but the discovery of America and the subsequent colonization of South

America resulted in enormous quantities of far larger and finer emeralds being suddenly cast upon the market. A new era in the history of this gemstone had begun.

Although the sources of New World emeralds were variously given by early writers of the 16th and 17th centuries as Mexico, Ecuador, Peru, and New Granada

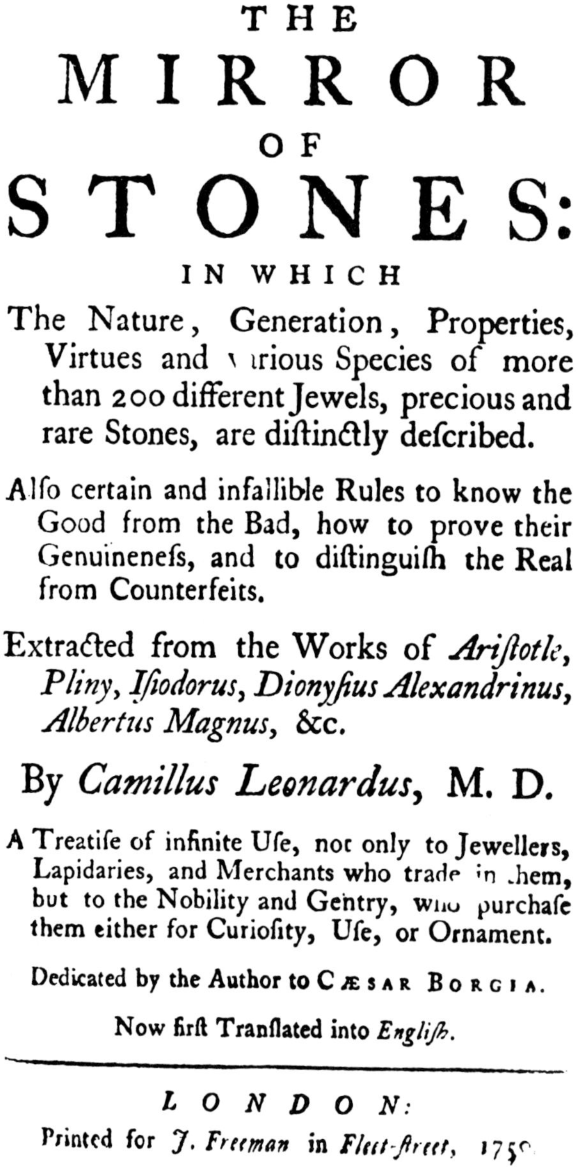

T H E
M I R R O R
O F
S T O N E S:
I N   W H I C H

The Nature, Generation, Properties, Virtues and various Species of more than 200 different Jewels, precious and rare Stones, are diſtinctly deſcribed.

Alſo certain and infallible Rules to know the Good from the Bad, how to prove their Genuineneſs, and to diſtinguiſh the Real from Counterfeits.

Extracted from the Works of *Ariſtotle*, *Pliny, Iſiodorus, Dionyſius Alexandrinus, Albertus Magnus*, &c.

By *Camillus Leonardus*, M. D.

A Treatiſe of infinite Uſe, not only to Jewellers, Lapidaries, and Merchants who trade in them, but to the Nobility and Gentry, who purchaſe them either for Curioſity, Uſe, or Ornament.

Dedicated by the Author to C Æ s a r B o r g i a.

Now firſt Tranſlated into *Engliſh*.

L O N D O N:
Printed for *J. Freeman* in *Fleet-ſtreet*, 175º

Figure 2.1 Title page of the English translation of Camillus Leonardus's *Speculum Lapidum*. First published in Latin in 1502, it exercised an enormous influence on succeeding treatises on gemstones.

(Colombia), it was later established that deposits in Colombia were the sole source and that those stones found in other regions as far north as Mexico were obtained through trade. Ball[13] gives 1000 AD or earlier as the time by which the Indians of Colombia had discovered emeralds, but the lack of records makes it impossible to fix a firmer date. Widespread trade in emeralds suggests that they had been found considerably earlier.

According to Lothrop[14], the first stones to fall into the hands of Europeans were obtained by the Spanish explorer Pedrarias when he touched at a place now called Santa Marta on the north coast of Colombia while en route to Darien in Panama. In 1519, Hernando Cortes received gifts, including splendid emeralds, from Montezuma in Mexico, and later obtained other fine specimens looted from Tenochtitlan. The great quantity of emeralds in his possession is well documented. Upon his return to Spain in 1528 he reportedly presented costly carved emeralds to his bride Doña Juan de Zuniga, and in his history of Spain, Juan de Mariana mentions vases cut from emeralds owned by Cortes that were valued at 300 000 ducats.

These early emeralds were obtained through looting, and it was not until 1537, when Jiménez de Quesada conquered Colombia territory (then bearing the name New Granada), that the first rumours were heard of emerald mines at a place called Somondoco. Following up these stories, de Quesada located the deposits in an area now called Chivor. However, according to Schumacher[15] and Canova[16], the first Spaniard to actually view the mines was Captain Pedro Fernandez Valenzuela.

In August 1537, de Quesada conquered the town of Tunja, seized 1815 emeralds from the residence of the fleeing tribal chief, and ultimately obtained about 7000 stones during his campaign of conquest[14]. Sometime before 1555, Valenzuela began working Chivor with great energy and presumably at great profit inasmuch as the natives were enslaved as miners. However, the other great emerald deposits of Muzo, which were in the same general region and were capable of producing even larger and finer crystals, defied Spanish efforts to locate them until about 1560, when, according to Codazzi[17] and Otero Muñoz, the first Spanish mayor of the newly founded town of Muzo discovered them.

By mid-16th century, a flood of emeralds and gold inundated Spain and swelled the coffers of the Spanish royal treasury. One would assume from the size of the hoard that numerous large and fine emeralds would still be found among the crown jewels of Spain, but curiously this is not the case. Despite holding a complete monopoly on the production and distribution of New World emeralds, it seems that Spanish authorities and nobility were not given to storing up treasures of precious stones, as was the practice in many other European kingdoms, and instead regarded emeralds as merely another commodity to be exchanged for the far more expendable gold, of which they seemed never able to get enough. How else can one account for the enormous quality of stones that, up until modern times, found their way into the hands of the rulers of Egypt, the Ottoman Empire, Persia and India? By the 17th century, emeralds were so abundant in Persia and India that Tavernier[19] was moved to remark that no true emeralds occurred in the East at all and those in the hands of the potentates must surely have come from the New World, possibly via the Spanish colonies in the Philippines. The depressing effect of flooding the market with New World emeralds will be returned to later in this chapter.

Agricola's *De Natura Fossilium*

One of the most important mineralogical-gemmological works of all time appeared in 1546 under the title *De Natura Fossilium,* written by Georgius Agricola, now known as 'The Father of Mineralogy'. An excellent translation of the first edition was prepared by Bandy and Bandy[20], from which the following remarks are derived. Agricola devoted an entire 'book' or large chapter to the subject of gemstones, and, unlike his predecessors, provided many illuminating comments of considerable accuracy on the nature, properties, and treatment of gemstones, indicating a firsthand knowledge of many of the species and varieties mentioned.

As is to be expected, Agricola was forced to depend on Pliny, among other authorities, for descriptions of stones with which he was not personally familiar. For example, he mentioned the 'Bactrian' emeralds as being collected by horsemen because they lie scattered on the surface of the ground. He repeated the error that Egyptian emerald is too hard to be engraved but almost in the same breath stated that lapidaries customarily cut and polish emeralds without apparent difficulty. The use of metal reflective foils set behind gems to increase brilliance is also explained, a green foil being used for emerald and the 'chrysoberyllus'. He also explains that this practice makes it impossible to determine the true colour of the gem unless it is removed from its mounting.

By Agricola's time, the use of green glass to imitate emerald was a long-established practice, but such falsifications, said Agricola, can be detected by the scratch test, glass being softer than emerald, and by the touch test, emerald feeling colder than glass, and also by the fact that 'glass is usually rough on the surface'. perhaps referring to the tendency for glass to abrade readily when worn in a ring. Agricola must have had considerable experience with cut gems. For example, his descriptions of flaws in emerald and beryl, though brief, are precise. (For extended remarks on Agricola's treatise, see Adams[2]).

Gesner's *De Omme Rerum Fossilium*

Gesner's *De Omme Rerum Fossiium*[3], published in 1565, contains other works of importance besides Epiphanius's treatise on the twelve Biblical stones. Among the eight short works it contains is Franciscus Rueus's *De Gemmis Aliquot,* a general treatise on gemstones first published in 1547 but appearing in its second edition in Gesner's work. The emerald and beryl are briefly described without incorporating any new material. Rueus's work is discussed by Thorndike[1] as part of a much longer commentary on the compilation as a whole. Gesner included an essay written by himself entitled *De Rerum Fossilium, Lapidum et Gemmarum.* Thorndike calls this treatise 'purely descriptive and classificatory', meaning that Gesner attempted to organize minerals, gemstones, and fossils in some scheme based on external features, placing them into fifteen categories (which are discussed at some length by Adams).

For the first time in a purely mineralogical work, Gesner introduced woodcut text illustrations of minerals, crystals, fossils, and even cut gems. One of these depicts a striated, prismatic, terminated crystal of tourmaline, which Gesner calls a 'Brazilian emerald'. The tourmaline obviously bears little resemblance to the true emerald crystals of Egypt, and its inclusion in Gesner's book indicates the inability even of experts of that period to clearly distinguish similarly coloured minerals from each other or to see anything remarkable in decided differences in crystal form. By use of the term 'Brazilian emerald', Gesner perpetuated a misnomer which lasted into our present century. Thus green tourmalines from Brazil were called 'emeralds' on the basis of colour, and green sapphires from Ceylon became 'oriental emeralds', while the true emerald was labelled 'occidental' in allusion to its source in the Western Hemisphere. It is possible that Gesner did not recognize the differences in crystal forms between the true emerald and the Brazilian tourmaline; nevertheless, in another place in his text he accurately describes the six-sided crystals of beryl, which he classes in the same group as similar six-sided quartz crystals.

Value of emerald and other gemstones

In 1572, not long after Gesner's book was published, the first book to give a systematic means for evaluating precious metals and gems appeared in Valladolid. Entitled *Quilatador de la Plata, Oro y Piedras,* it was written by a goldsmith, Juan Arphe de Villafañe or Juan de Arfe y Villafañe[21]. The third book of this treatise establishes rules for appraising gems; it includes emeralds but entirely ignores other varieties of beryl. A woodcut diagram of the recommended style of cut for the emerald is apparently the first illustration of an accepted facet cut for emerald to appear in print. It shows a simple square-cut gem, cut unacceptably shallow by today's standards, but satisfactory in those days when almost all gems were backed with foil to assure a reflective brilliance. Today this brilliance is achieved solely by cutting to proper proportions. The emerald is ranked third in importance, after diamond and ruby, and *esmeraldas viejas* ('old emeralds') are valued more highly than *esmeraldas nuevas* ('new emeralds'). The 'old emeralds' were actually green sapphires, called 'oriental emeralds' by some because of their origin in the East, and the 'new emeralds' or 'occidental emeralds' were the gems that originated in Colombia.

Arphe included tables of values in ducats for increasing weights of cut gems for diamonds, ruby, oriental or old emerald, the *meridional* or 'southern' emerald (another name for the Colombian stones), and the spinel. Each table is accompanied by a small woodcut showing the actual size of the gem for each weight. As is to be expected, the values increase with increasing weight, but in every instance the green sapphire is valued at exactly twice that of the emerald, which seems to confirm the fact that flooding the Spanish market with Colombian emeralds did indeed depress their value. This may also have encouraged gem dealers to divest themselves of surplus stock by selling stones to dealers in other countries of Europe as well as in Arabic and Indian states, the rulers of the latter, one may be sure, recognizing bargains and snapping them up.

Another Spanish book on precious metal and gem valuation appeared in 1721 in Madrid as *Litho-Statica, Theorica, y Practica de Medir Piedras Preciosas*[22]. Also written by a jeweller, one Dionisio de Mosquera, it provides a businesslike summary of all the factors that must be considered in evaluating cut gems.

QVILATADOR
DELA PLATA, ORO, Y PIEDRAS,

COMPVESTO POR IOAN ARPHE de Villafañe: natural de Leõ: vezino de Valladolid.

q Impreſſo en Valladolid,por Alonſo y Diego Fernãdez de Cordoua,Impreſſores de ſu Mageſtad. Año M. D. LXXII.

CON PRIVILLEGIO.

Figure 2.2 Title page of *Quilatador de la Plata, Oro y Piedras* by Arphe de Villafañe, published in Valladolid in 1572. This work for jewellers gave rules for the valuation of precious metals and gems.

Mosquera mentioned the *aguacate* or 'avocado' shape of pendant emeralds, apparently an accepted form of drop-cut, even though polished without facets. He also described defects in emerald which diminish their value and provided tables of prices for cut gems of specified weights. Like his predecessor Arphe de Villafañe, he also valued 'without exception' the 'oriental emerald' above the 'occidental emerald'.

Some early 17th-century lapidaries

Andrea Bacci published his *Le XII Pietre Pretiose*[23] in Rome in 1587, another treatise on the twelve Biblical gems containing no new information and only mentioning the emerald and beryl. Considerably more information, as well as additional remarks on curious lore, was provided by Gabelchover in his Latin translation of this work, published in Frankfurt in 1603 as *De Gemmis et Lapidibus Pretiosis*[24]. It may be the first gemmological treatise to specifically draw attention to the Colombian emeralds, which are labelled 'Peruvian' after their supposed country of origin.

In 1605 a substantial work on gemstones, entitled *Libro de las Virtudes y Propriedades Maravillosas de las Piedras Preciosas*[25], appeared in Madrid, written by the apothecary Gaspar de Morales. As Thorndike remarks, the title suggests that the work is entirely on curious lore, but in fact the first book contains a number of chapters which treat origin of gemstones, Biblical stones, physical properties, distinction of genuine from false gems, how gemstones acquired their virtues, an alphabetical list of gem colours, medicines made from gemstones, and other information. The second and third books describe a large number of gemstones, including the emerald and beryl, with remarks on varieties, sources, qualities, and properties. Curiously, Morales did not mention the emerald of the New World, although they were already known in Spain.

Also in 1605, J. B. Silvaticus of Milan published an odd treatise combining discussions of the medicinal virtues of such unrelated substances as unicorn horn (narwhal tusk), bezoar, emerald, and pearl in a single work entitled *De Unicornu Lapide Bezaar Smaragdo et Margaritis Eorumque in Feribus Pestilentialibus Usu*. Thorndike briefly discusses this book, noting that Silvaticus dismissed emerald as being ineffective in medicines.

De Boodt's landmark lapidary

In 1609 appeared a true landmark in lapidaries, and the most important work of all those so far described. It was written by Anselm Boetius de Boodt (ca. 1550–1632) and entitled *Gemmarum et Lapidum Historia*[26]. Published in Hanover, it received prompt acclaim and wide distribution, and it exerted an enormous influence on succeeding works. It was republished in 1636 with a commentary by Adrian Toll, a French translation appeared in 1644, and a third and last edition appeared in 1647. Adams called it 'in many respects the most important lapidary of the seventeenth century', while Thorndike found that 'it shows a marked advance in several respects . . . it completely omits all matter concerning marvel-working images carved on gems (and) profits by the discovery of the new world and knowledge of distant lands'. In regard to the value of emeralds, Thorndike noted 'de Boodt says that the Peruvian emeralds have brought down the price of that stone and are preferred by most dealers to those from the orient'.

Evans[7] remarked that this work 'is an attempt . . . to arrive at a rational classification of precious stones according to . . . opposites', that is, whether they are large or small, soft or hard, rare or common, etc. This scheme received harsh criticism from Adams, who, largely concerned with scientific advancement, found de Boodt's scheme of little value. On the other hand, Thorndike, ever concerned with curious lore, pointed out that de Boodt's writing combined scepticism with credulity in regard to the powers and virtues of minerals and gemstones.

Regardless of Adam's criticism, de Boodt's treatise is a fund of information accurately reflecting contemporary knowledge. De Boodt cited his authorities but augmented borrowings with firsthand information of his own which he must have garnered in his capacity as adviser on gemmological matters to the court of Emperor Rudolf II in Prague. (His primary duty was court physician). It is apparent from reading his material on lapidary work in particular that he brought to his writing a far greater expertise than had been possessed by previous authors of gemmological treatises.

In regard to emerald, de Boodt repeated the most important contributions of previous writers and emphasized that the prevailing custom among jewellers was to classify gems according to 'oriental' and 'occidental' origins. This unfortunately perpetuated confusion when such terms were applied to beryls. In describing localities of origin, he mentioned emerald from Brittany and other places in Europe but gave no specifics, and he noted that Peruvian emeralds are a 'very pleasing green' and obtainable in such large specimens that 'some exceed in size the palm of the hand'. He also evaluated emeralds against values of cut diamond gems. Beryl, he noted, is found in Germany and Bohemia.

Often appended to and bound up with the third (1647) edition of de Boodt is Joannes de Laet's work of the same date, *De Gemmis et Lapidibus*[27]. It was also issued separately and was meant to serve both as a supplement to de Boodt and as an independent work. De Laet, or Jan Van Laet (died ca. 1650), amplified de Boodt's remarks on emerald and used for the first time in a gemmological book the word 'America' when speaking of Colombian emeralds. He described the locality somewhat more accurately, but still inadequately, as 'the Promontory of Helen in the Province of Manta, Peru'. He also notes the 'Brazilian emerald' of Gesner and the latter's illustration of it, but de Laet did not question the identification. Some information is provided on beryl but none of it is new.

Mineralogia, Sive Naturalis Philosophiae Thesauri[28] was an encyclopaedic mineralogical treatise in which gemstones receive due attention. Written by Bernardo Cesi (ca. 1581–1630), it was published in Lyon, in 1636. Both Thorndike and Adams comment unfavourably upon it. When the entries for emerald and beryl are examined, it will be found that each is described twice, once as stones in the High Priest's breastplate and again in the Apocalypse. Cesi added nothing new to the then current knowledge of gems.

Nicol's *History of Pretious Stones*

Not too long after the publication of Cesi's work, a vastly superior work appeared in England when Thomas Nicols published his *A Lapidary: Or, The History of Pretious Stones*[29] at Cambridge in 1652. It holds the distinction of being the first

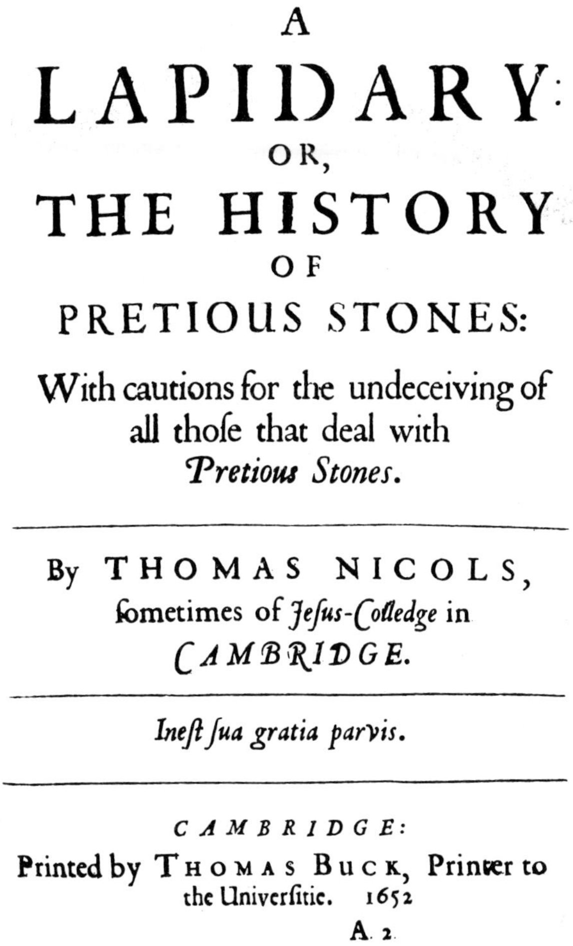

A
LAPIDARY:
OR,
THE HISTORY
OF
PRETIOUS STONES:

With cautions for the undeceiving of
all thofe that deal with
Pretious Stones.

By THOMAS NICOLS,
fometimes of *Jefus-Colledge* in
CAMBRIDGE.

Ineft fua gratia parvis.

CAMBRIDGE:
Printed by THOMAS BUCK, Printer to
the Univerfitie. 1652
A 2

Figure 2.3 Title page of the first English work on gemmology, published by Thomas Nicols in Cambridge, 1652.

worthy gemmological monograph published in the English language and is remarkable for its terse, sometimes dry recitals of information rendered in the quaint diction of the time. The material was gathered from traditional as well as recent sources and included much new information as well. While the dedication freely acknowledges use of de Boodt, Nicols states that his aim was 'to take away that confusion about the *species* of gemms, which doth cause them to be hardly and difficultly known of what *species* and kinds they are'. He goes on to say that he not only studied de Boodt 'but also divers other Lapidists, to shew the true way of discerning factitious and artificiall stones or gemms, from those that are really and truly the works of nature'. The folding table of classification which he includes is very similar to that found in de Boodt.

The first part of Nicol's work, the 'Generall Treatise', discusses such topics as origin of gemstones, colour, properties, adulterations and 'improvements', artificial gems, and lapidary treatments, with several interesting essays on the supernatural characteristics of gemstones, their causes, and rules on how to discover them. The second part is descriptive, emerald and beryl receiving fair treatment. Here we find recommendations on use of reflective foils for transparent beryl gems, specific recipes for making imitative glasses, and remarks on nomenclature, varieties, localities, properties, and curious lore.

Nicols also prepetuated the terms 'oriental' and 'occidental' as applied to emeralds, noting that the 'best [are] brought from the East-Indies' (he was probably referring to green sapphires), but that 'excellent ones [are also] found in the Occidentall or Western parts, and in the parts of Europe'. The emeralds of Colombia are described as having a 'pleasant green colour, but send forth no rayes, these are softer than the Orientall ones, and often full of green clouds'. On the whole, this is a good description of typically included emeralds which, because of the abundance of inclusions, reflect light poorly from their back facets.

In another place, Nicols described the 'Smaragdo-Prassius' as 'a transparent green gemme . . . betwixt a *Prasius* and an *Emerauld* . . . which Boetius [de Boodt] taketh for a kind of *Emerauld*, or a bastard *Smaragde*'. There are two kinds, one from Bohemia 'which are transparent through a fine cloud' and another, '*American* ones, which are half-transparent, like unto *Vitriol*'. Both are possibly beryls, perhaps yellow-green beryls or aquamarines known to occur in Bohemia and in Brazil. (Nicols's term 'America' might be a reference to Brazil).

Concerning clear beryl, Nicols noted its use in spheres whose 'form hath the same power of begetting fire from the Sunne by its beams, that a Crystall glass hath' and that 'the price of *Beryll* is augmented or diminisht according to the elegancie of its colour', going on to add wisely that 'this rule is to be observed in the price of all jewells'.

Mineralogy in the mid-17th century

In Bologna in 1648 a large and impressively illustrated work on the products of the mineral kingdom entitled *Musaeum Metallicum in Libros III Distributum*[30] was published posthumously for its author, Ulyssis Aldrovandi (1522–1605), the celebrated Italian naturalist. It is typical of the encyclopaedic natural history works of that period because it attempted to gather everything known about minerals, stones, ores, fossils, and gemstones under one cover. One of its distinctions, according to Adams[2], is the fact that 'this is the first instance in which the word *Geologia* or *Geology* appears in literature when used approximately in its present sense'. In regard to beryl, Aldrovandi repeated material in Marbod and de Boodt, among other authorities, and treated beryl and emerald in terms of synonomy, descriptions, properties, localities, varieties, imitations, curious lore, and medicinal uses.

Among its woodcut illustrations are several purporting to be beryl specimens, but they are so poorly done that, as Adams pointed out, 'since specimens of rocks and those of many minerals do not lend themselves easily to pictorial representation, some of these cut can scarcely be said to illustrate the text, they rather require the text to explain them'. None of the beryl illustrations are recognizable as such; indeed, several are obviously druses of quartz.

Adams closed his chapter on medieval mineralogy with a discussion of Aldrovandi's work, and his remarks are fitting:

> 'Medieval mineralogy in fact was not a science . . . not a solid tower of learning . . . but a fairy castle, the insubstantial fabric of a dream, often quaint and even beautiful, but destined to crumble away because it had no foundation in reality . . . it was now to be succeeded by a true science of mineralogy built upon the basis of close observation and diligent study of the materials of the earth's crust'.

It is at this point in time – the mid-17th century – that gemmology began to divide into two branches, the first becoming part of the developing science of mineralogy, and the seond retaining the romantic aspects of gemmology still so dear to many today and treasured by many more in the past. The commercial aspects of the gemstone trade tended to resist the injection of too much science into gemmology, and consequently books written on gems tended to emphasize lore and romance over the unglamorous mineralogical facts. The names of gemstones, long established to the satisfaction of gem merchants and customers, proved particularly resistant to change, as evidenced by the extremely long time that the names 'oriental' and 'occidental' remained appended to emeralds and other gems. If an 'oriental emerald' could always be sold under that name, even if it happened to be a misnomer, or if a 'balas ruby' lent the impression that a variety of true ruby was being offered, what harm was done? Thus gemmological knowledge tended towards stasis and continued to embody much that was romantic and little that was scientific, a state of affairs that lasted for a very long time.

Boyle and his contemporaries

In the latter part of the 17th century, several important works mentioning emerald and beryl appeared, the first being *Le Mercure Indien, ou le Tresor des Indes*[31], written by a Pierre de Rosnel and published in Paris in 1667. Despite claiming familiarity with the West Indies and their products, the exact source of Colombian emeralds is not given, possibly because the Spanish were not anxious to reveal this information. Rosnel merely said 'the common opinion is that they occur in the mountains called Manta or Porto Viejo', both places in Ecuador. Rosnel, like others of his day, had examined colour-zoned crystals of emerald from Colombia and repeated the widely held view that such crystals, part white, part green, were 'unripe', and, had they grown under the blazing sun of the East, would have eventually darkened to a uniform green. In another place, he spoke of the quality of 'Mexican emeralds' and others from 'several parts of the Indies', again repeating a common belief that emeralds occurred in many places in South America.

The second work published in this period (in London in 1672) is as close to being completely scientific as was possible in those days. It was written by Robert Boyle (1627–1691), the celebrated English physicist. Its somewhat misleading title, *An Essay About the Origine and Virtues of Gems*[32], suggests a tract largely on curious lore, but in fact it is primarily on the formation of minerals and their crystals through the agency of mineralizing solutions, with relatively minor remarks on the general impossibility of gemstone medicines being effective because of their insolubility. In a rambling discourse typical of his writings, he introduced material on crystallography and physical properties and showed that he habitually used hydrostatic weighings to ascertain stone densities and thus aid in their identification.

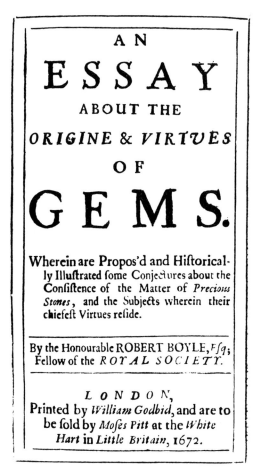

Figure 2.4 Title page of Robert Boyle's famous dissertation on the formation of minerals and gemstones.

Boyle not only mentioned emerald in connection with its colour and how that varies from specimen to specimen, or even within a single crystal, but also cited José de Acosta's famous account of the Spanish in the New World, *Historia Natural y Moral de las Indies* (1590), to the effect that '*Emeralds* grow in Stones like unto Christels, and that he had seen them in the same Stone fashioned like a Vein; *And they seem,* adds he, *by little and little* to thicken and refine. And in the same place this Learned Author has a memorable observation that may confirm what I have just now related, and what we mentioned a little below, about *colourless Gems I have seen,* says he, *some that were half White and half Green; others all White, and some Green and very perfect'.*

In regard to medicinal properties of gemstones, Boyle adopted a somewhat ambiguous view of their effectiveness, inclining mostly to doubt the efficacy of gemstones in pharmaceutical preparations but still admitting that some soluble minerals, or at least soluble constituents in them, might have some effect. (This subject was of special interest to Thorndike[1], who devotes an entire chapter to Boyle).

Not long after Boyle's essay appeared, two works were published in Europe which held up to ridicule the magical and medicinal properties of gemstones. In 1687 at Leipzig University, Johann Jakob Spener published a short academic dissertation entitled *De Gemmis Errores Vulgares*[33] in which he reviewed some of the more glaring examples of erroneous belief quoted by earlier writers, including the fascinating if unsupportable conviction that an emerald worn during intercourse would shatter, particularly if the coupling were illicit. Also dismissed was the belief that emeralds were good for warding off demons.

The second work on this theme, first published in 1703, came from the pen of a famous London physician, Dr. Robert Pitt, and was entitled *The Craft and Frauds of Physick Expos'd*[34]. As the *Dictionary of National Biography* puts it, 'it was written to show the small cost of the really useful drugs, the worthlessness of some expensive ones, and the folly of taking too much physic. The book gives a clear exposition of the therapeutics of that day, and is full of shrewd observations'. Pitt pointed out that the essential insolubility of gemstones made it impossible for them to chemically affect the body and noted that stones ingested by birds 'were found to have past through, without any change of Colour or Figure', and in the case of the 'Confection of Hyacinth', the precious hard stones 'can only make the pretence of its being sold at a dearer rate'. Lastly, he remarks, only 'the smallest and vilest' of such stones as hyacinth, sapphire, smaragd, and topaz are used in such preparations.

Advances of the 18th century

By the commencement of the 18th century, much was being done to systematize mineralogy and chemically analyze minerals, salts, and other substances, but little could be accomplished with the means then at hand in respect to chemical analysis of the many hard, resistant oxide and silicate minerals, among which gemstones figure prominently. In 1730, Magnus von Bromell (1678–1731) published results of fusion experiments on many minerals and established a fusibility scale which still finds use today in determinative mineralogy. The more heat-resistant species, including beryl, remain unmelted in the blowpipe flame and thus were put in the 'infusible' category.

The first, albeit indirect, steps taken to solve the puzzle of chemical composition of gemstones were those of Johann Heinrich Pott (1692–1777) of Germany, who, encouraged by the King of Prussia, began a series of fusion experiments aimed at the discovery of the ingredients of porcelain. His results, published during 1751–57 as his *Lithogéognosie*[35], were called by Thomson[36] 'one of the most extraordinary productions of the age'. Pott fused a variety of 'earthy' substances, alone or mixed with other substances, including fusions of the topaz of Saxony and several crystalline and cryptocrystalline varieties of quartz. These experiments led to the recognition of silica and alumina as constituents of some of the harder and hitherto most resistant gemstones and minerals, and they demonstrated the usefulness of certain alkalis in facilitating fusion. The resulting melts could now be chemically attacked and their components determined. While beryl eventually succumbed to analysis via the fusion method, the presence of its unique element, beryllium, was not detected until the end of the century. At this time beryl was thought to contain only silica and alumina as principal constituents.

In 1747, a mineralogical work that is generally conceded to be the first to introduce a modern scheme for classification of minerals was published by Johann Gottschalk Wallerius (1709–1785) in Stockholm as *Mineralogia, Eller Mineral-Riket*[37]. Disappointingly meagre in its discussions of emerald and beryl, it nevertheless provides a few valuable bits of information, primarily on current sale values of gems. Unlike the diamond, the prices demanded for emerald are quite variable because of differences among stones in colour and clarity. For pure-coloured and clean small emeralds, the base price was fixed at 4 riksdalers per carat, but for one-carat gems the price ranged between 30 to as much as 80 riksdalers, depending upon vividness and purity of colour. However, the price did not escalate with increased weight, as does the price of diamonds, because larger emeralds were rarely pure and without flaw. Wallerius gives a table comparing the prices for rose-cut diamonds and emeralds, which shows that the base price for the diamonds was 64 riksdalers per carat in Hamburg and 70 riksdalers in Amsterdam, or somewhat over twice the price demanded for emeralds of comparable size.

The Brückmann treatises

The state of mid-18th century gemmological knowledge is nowhere better recounted than in the compilations of fragmenta assembled by U. F. B. Brückmann in his *Abhandlung von Edelsteinen*[38], first published in 1757 and appearing subsequently in a second edition and supplements. Brückmann maintained a wide correspondence with European scientists, collectors, and connoisseurs and acted as a clearing house for all new developments in gemmology, thus making his treatises exceptionally useful storehouses of extant knowledge.

In the first edition of 1757, emerald is treated in terms of nomenclature, physical properties, and other salient data, with Brückmann noting that while emerald loses colour during heating, the colour returns upon cooling. Emerald crystals are erroneously described as 'five-sided', but only a fragment of a crystal was available for his examination. Localities included Cyprus, Britanny, Bohemia, Switzerland, and America. Concerning value, he says, 'Before the emerald appeared so abundantly from America, it was valued close to the diamond, but now for those which are very good and clean the value is not far from one-fourth that of diamond, so that if a diamond is reckoned at 800 thaler, the emerald of the same weight can only bring 200, or less, in our day'. In another place he mentioned a popular conviction that emerald colour was due to copper.

Brückmann also described beryl and golden beryl, but the physical properties given are largely incorrect. Brückmann claimed that when beryl was heated, it lost colour and melted into a glass, and that such colour as was present owed its origin to a 'mixture of iron and copper'. The value of beryls was equated to that of topaz. The golden beryl or 'chrysoberillus' was classed by Brückmann as a kind of chrysolite, perhaps a peridot, which indicates the confusion that still reigned as to the true identities of the various beryls and minerals which superficially resembled them.

Brückmann's second edition of 1773, much larger and more elaborate than the first, provided more information on beryl. Here the hardness of emerald was stated to be the same as that of beryl and aquamarine. Brückmann disagreed with one authority who claimed that the 'oriental emerald' was supremely hard, Brückmann apparently having examined true emerald while the other authority had examined green sapphire. In regard to melting, Brückmann found that emerald could be fused into a glass providing its crushed powder was first mixed with borax. At the time of writing, the value of 'beautiful emeralds, of 3 to 4 carats' was about 50 to 60 thalers. Emeralds worn in rings 'readily loses its polish and acquired fissures', said Brückmann, but such can be easily corrected by recutting the gem on a lead lap charged with emery followed by polishing on a tin lap with tripoli. Thus he gave for the first time accurate information on lapidary techniques used for emerald and other beryls.

Brückmann noted that beryl occurred in fairly large specimens but was seldom found without inclusions or flaws, and it was not related to topaz because the latter gemstone was unaffected by fire whereas the beryl melted into a glass when fluxed with borax. An earlier statement on beryl colour was also modified to claim that it was owing to lead and copper instead of iron and copper. 'A beautiful aquamarine glass' could be made from lead-glass plus copper and cobalt. Little value was placed in those days on beryl gems, ordinary kinds selling for from 4 to 5 thalers per carat in 2-carat size.

Ceylon and Pegu (Burma) are mentioned as localities for emerald, as are Italy, Germany, and Hungary. Localities for American emeralds were still not known and were given in this edition as the valleys of the Tunka and Tomana rivers and formerly from the Manta Valley. Beryl is said to occur in Saxony, Bohemia, and Hungary, and other places in Europe.

The recently discovered pyroelectric properties of 'Brazilian emerald', or tourmaline, were taken by Brückmann as evidence that some gems bearing this name must now by classed as tourmalines instead of beryls, for 'when warmed, they draw to themsleves ashes and other light materials'. The discovery of this property of tourmaline was due to the work of John Canton in 1754 and Franz Ulrich Aepinus in 1757, and when publicized it did much to discourage the use of the misnomer 'Brazilian emerald'.

After his second edition, Brückmann published two supplements, one in 1778 and the other in 1783. In the first supplement he cited Romé de Lisle's recently published *Essai de Cristallographie*[39] on emerald and commented on an emerald matrix specimen in the Davila collection catalogue[40], which was particularly rich in beryl specimens. Pyrite inclusions in emerald of 'Peru' were noted for the first time, and the 'Peruvian emerald mine' is described as being 'in the Tunia Valley, or Tomana Valley, not far from Cartagena, between the mountains of Granada and Popoyan, from whence they are brought to Cartagena'. However, confusion as to exact source still existed, for on the same page is the claim that 'emeralds are also found on the entire Peruvian coast, from Cape St. Helena in the Province of Manta to the Bay of Bonaventura', and further, 'various streams in this region are named the Ry de Esmeraldas, Ry pueblo de Esmeraldas, because they provide emeralds'.

The second supplement of 1783 contained a further miscellany of information, including for the first time several chemical analyses by Achard and Bergmann, whose work is discussed in the next section. The supplement also contains remarks on the new and very important Siberian aquamarines, which Brückmann had obtained for his collection in 1780. The largest of these crystals was a six-sided prism with flat termination, measuring 1½ inches (38 mm) long and ½ inch (13 mm) thick, of a 'beautiful sea-green colour'. Although Brückmann does not supply a definite locality, they probably came from the same sources in the Altay Mountains of Asiatic Russia that Peter Simon Pallas, the distinguished Prussian traveller and naturalist, had described in a letter to Brückmann of 15 December 1780 as being in 'high snowy mountains' along the Chinese border.

Advances in chemical and physical analysis

Despite advances in chemical and crystallographic mineralogy, the distinction between 'oriental emerald' (or sapphire) and 'occidental emerald' (or beryl) remained unclear. For example, in his *Essai de Cristallographie*[39], published in 1772, Romé de Lisle, also de L'Isle (1736–1770) discussed both gemstones in the same breath and seemed not to appreciate the significance of their different crystal forms, even though these differences were plain to see in the drawing which accompanied his text. Furthermore, he included the 'emerald or Peridot of Brazil' with other varieties of emerald, although his drawing showed it clearly to be a crystal of tourmaline. However, in a greatly enlarged edition of this work[41], published in 1783, these errors were corrected, the beryls were put together, the sapphire placed with other corundums, and the tourmaline placed by itself as distinct species. Thus long-standing confusions were cleared up. In this edition, Romé de Lisle included values for specific gravity as determined by Brisson, which was a further valuable identification tool.

By the late 18th century, much progress had been made in the chemical analysis of the harder, hitherto intractable minerals, including beryl, through fusion of the powdered mineral with alkalis and the production of water-soluble residues which could be analyzed by wet methods. Some authorities credit the celebrated Swedish chemist, Torbern Bergman (1735–1784), with this innovation in 1780[42], but the German chemist Franz Carl Achard (1753–1821) published in 1779 the results of his somewhat earlier experiments, showing that he had accomplished essentially the same kind of analysis[43]. Achard analyzed ruby, sapphire, emerald, zircon, pyrope, and chrysoprase, and discovered in emerald a proportional composition of 6.5 for silica, 2.5 for lime, 18 for alumina, and 1.5 for iron. He reaffirmed the fact

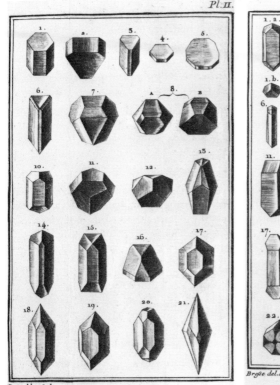
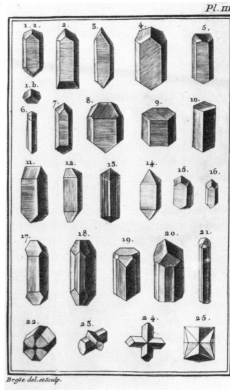

Figure 2.5 Romé de Lisle's representations of crystals of the 'emerald of Peru', figure 1 of Plate II and figure 23 of Plate III. From his *Essai de Cristallographie* (Paris, 1772), which provided one of the earliest systematic descriptions of the crystal forms of many minerals.

that heating did not destroy the colour of emerald, but that very high heat resulted in fusion to a glassy mass that resembled milky chrysoprase in hue.

Specific gravity of minerals and other substances was determined with considerable accuracy by Mathurin Brisson (1723–1806), who published his results in 1787 in *Pesanteur Spécifique des Corps*[44]. This treatise also contained an engraved plate of crystal forms, leaving no doubt that beryl was the mineral he actually measured. *Table 2.1* compares Brisson's values to modern values of specific gravity of beryls and other minerals often confused with beryl.

TABLE 2.1 Brisson's specific gravities

Name	Mineral	Brisson's Specific Gravity	Modern Value*
Emerald of Peru	Beryl	27755 (2.7755)	2.71
Chrysolite of Brazil	Beryl	26923 (2.6923)	2.7
Occidental aquamarine	Beryl	27227 (2.7227)	2.69
Oriental aquamarine	Topaz	35489 (3.5489)	3.53
Emerald of Brazil	Tourmaline	31555 (3.1555)	3.06

*Mean values, from B. W. Anderson. *Gem Testing*, 9th ed. London: Butterworth's, 1980, page 86.

Brisson's values are reasonably close to presently accepted figures, and for many years they were the standard. The accuracy of his figures did much to remove confusion between true beryls and similarly coloured species such as corundum, tourmaline, olivine (peridot), and chrysoberyl.

Near the close of the 18th century, the discovery of beryllium oxide finally permitted the first accurate analysis of beryl. This noteworthy chemical achievement was made by French chemist Nicolas Louis Vauquelin (1763–1829), acting upon the suggestion of Abbe René Just Haüy (1743–1822), the great French mineralogist and crystallographer who had noted similarities between emerald and other varieties of beryl and suspected they were one and the same species. In 1798 Vauquelin analyzed beryls and discovered the presence of the unique oxide, which he called *glucina* (beryllia)[45]. A new element was obviously present, but it was not isolated until 1828 when Friedrich Wöhler and Antoine A. B. Bussy independently produced small quantities of beryllium, or glucinum, as the French called it[46].

In the same year that he found beryllium oxide, Vauquelin published the first reasonably accurate chemical analysis of beryl[47] (see *Table 2.2*).

TABLE 2.2 Vauquelin's 1798 analysis of emerald

Component	Composition %
Silica	64.60
Alumina	14.00
Glucina	13.00
Lime	2.56
Chromium oxide	3.50
Water and volatiles	2.00
	Total 99.66%

This was the first analysis of show the element chromium in emerald, it previously having been mistaken for iron, and Vauquelin was the first to suggest that chromium was the element responsible for the typical colour. Later analyses of beryl by Vauquelin and others corrected the error of including lime (calcium oxide) as an essential component of beryl.

Haüy and his successors

Within a few years at the end of the 18th century, more scientific knowledge of the beryl was accumulated than had been garnered in all the previous centuries. There were now reasonably accurate analyses, good values for specific gravity, and a clear understanding of the fundamental crystal forms of beryl. Such information was duly incorporated in what may be called the first modern textbook of mineralogy, Abbe René Just Haüy's *Traité de Minéralogie*[48], published in Paris in 1801. Following the custom of French mineralogists, he called beryl 'émeraude', but he modified the basic term with adjectives to designate other varieties. His text included information on nomenclature, physical properties, crystallography, chemistry, special features of beryl, and descriptions of other minerals that looked like beryl and could be mistaken for it. Classic sources of specimens were also mentioned, such as the small but fine crystals from Elba, the beautiful prisms of aquamarine and golden beryl from Adun Chilon in Transbaikalia, and a new source in the Forèz of Burgundy. Haüy also mentioned that beryls from Colombia were as large as 16 cm (6 in) long and 54 mm (2 in) in diameter but that most were much smaller. Much larger crystals were noted from Siberian sources.

Haüy acknowledged the chemical work of Vauquelin, and he noted the electrical properties in beryl claimed to have been observed by Kirwan, the optical property of double refraction, and the presence of typical inclusions in emerald which caused gems of 'beautiful green, transparent and free of flaws' to command high prices because of their rarity. Importantly, Haüy believed that iron was the colouring agent in aquamarine but that chromium was responsible for the colour of emerald.

From the gemmological standpoint, an even greater milestone was reached in 1817 when Haüy published his *Traité des Caractères Physiques des Pierres Précieuses*[49]. This is the first scientific scheme for systematic gemstone identification, setting forth how gemstones, especially those that were in cut form, could be tested without damage according to colour (as the opening argument), specific gravity, hardness, presence or absence of double refraction, frictional electricity, and pyroelectricity. A large table listed stones by colour and gave their distinctive properties. For the first time, an optical property, namely double refraction, was recognized as a valuable clue to identity. Haüy admitted the danger of testing for hardness but urged that scratch tests be applied below the girdle of a cut gem where a mark would not be conspicuous.

As an outgrowth of Haüy's work, a small pocketbook of gemmology was published in 1832 by Johann Reinhard Blum[50]. Despite its small size, it contains a remarkable fund of accurate information as well as very specific gem identification methods. The author, later to become an eminent mineralogist of Germany, brought to his writing a scientific background in mineralogy coupled with several years practical experience in a jewellery manufacturing centre of Germany. Blum provided a good account of beryl, including crystallography, inclusions, properties, streak and blowpipe reactions, fusion, chemical analysis, and locality information. The emerald deposit in the Habachtal near Salzburg in Austria is mentioned for the first time in a gemmological treatise, as are the recently discovered (1830) emerald deposits of the Urals.

Blum stated that emerald was sawn with emery grit, the facets cut with emery on a copper lap, and then polished on a tin lap using tripoli, pumice, or 'tin ash' (tin oxide). Cutting styles and the use of reflective foils were also discussed. Cut emeralds of 'medium quality, clear and beautiful, but somewhat light colour' were valued at 18 to 24 gulden. Dark stones of the 'first water', that is, virtually free of inclusions were much more expensive, fetching from 50 gulden for a 4-grain (ca. 1 carat) gem to as much as 1600 gulden for a 48-grain (12 carat) stone. Defects of emerald were unevenness or murkiness of colour, white flecks or clouds, fissures, and feathers.

Blum provided similar information on beryls, with a note on the relatively recent discoveries of spendid crystals in Russia at Mursinka, Miask, and near Nerchinsk on the mountain Adun Chilon in Siberia, in Transbaikalia. Beryls from Brazil and Scotland were also noted, as was the 1811 discovery in Brazil of an aquamarine crystal weighing 15 pounds and the 1825 discovery of a rolled pebble of 'noble beryl of very beautiful colour', weighing 4 pounds, which was offered for sale in England at a price of £600.

In 1860, the first truly modern book on gemmology, *Handbuch der Edelsteinkunde*[51], by Karl Emil Kluge (1830–1864), appeared in Leipzig and at once established the pattern for later works on the same subject because the author had discarded curious and romantic lore and enlarged the text sections devoted to the scientific aspects of gemstones. The first or 'general' part took up crystallography, physical, optical, and chemical properties, type deposits, uses of gemstones in antiquity, lapidary treatment, chemical and heat treatments aimed at improving colour, and gemstones as objects of commerce. The second, or 'special' part systematically provided descriptions and sources for all classes of gemstones, including pearls and corals, and tables of properties to be used in identification. Emerald and beryl were accorded much space, and recent scientific data, refinements of older data, and some new locality information on them were incorporated.

Other works along the same lines quickly followed, but the most complete was the now-famous *Edelsteinkunde*[52] of German mineralogist Max Herman Bauer (1844–1917), first published in 1896, and passing into a third edition in 1932. Bauer devotes twenty-two pages to beryl alone and includes a colour plate of beryl rough and cut gems and several crystal drawings. An English translation, *Precious Stones*, completed in 1904 by Leonard J. Spencer[52], the English mineralogist, is still regarded as an authoritative work. Bauer's work is notable not only for inclusion of much information developed since Kluge's book of 1860, but also for much greater attention and accuracy to the sources of gemstones around the world. In addition it features excellent coloured lithographic plates of gemstones which are prized for faithfulness to their originals and the beauty of their colouration. Spencer's English edition is still available in facsimile reprints published by Dover Publications of New York and Charles E. Tuttle of Rutland, Vermont.

By the end of the 19th century, much had been learned about emerald and other members of the beryl family regarding physical and optical properties, chemical composition, and the types of deposits in which they were found, and crystallographic studies which defined the numerous types of faces found upon natural crystals and their geometrical relationships to one another had also been devised. Thus is seemed that emerald and beryl, among other minerals, were now fully describable and that nothing further could be learned about them unless some scientific 'breakthrough' occurred. Such a discovery was not long in coming, as will be seen below, and involved the use of certain electromagnetic radiations, called X-rays, to penetrate into mineral crystals and derive information about their inner structures that hitherto could only be surmised from external clues.

While the characteristic atomic structures for beryl and other crystalline minerals had long been suspected from such external evidence, it was not until X-rays,

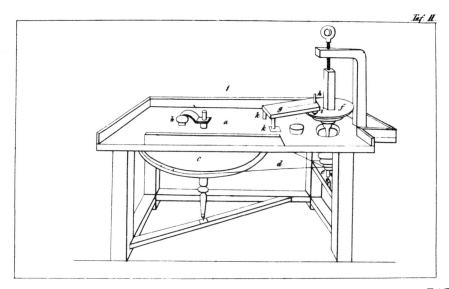

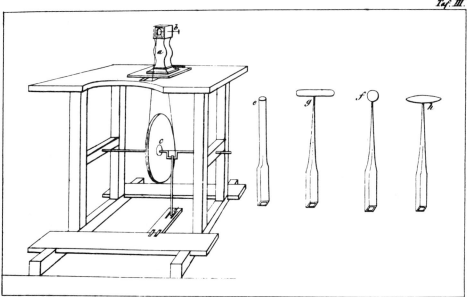

Figure 2.6 Lapidary apparatus in use in Europe in the early part of the last century. *Top:* Hand-driven lap (*right*) with device for holding a gemstone in fixed position. *Bottom:* Gem engraver's bench with a selection of cutting points. From J. R. Blum's *Taschenbuch der Edelsteinkunde* (Stuttgart, 1832) plates 2 and 3.

discovered by W. K. Röntgen (1845–1923) in 1895, were passed through crystals and their reflections photographically recorded so that the regular internal arrangement of atoms could be confirmed. This event, of great importance in the investigation of solids, came about in 1912 when the German physics students, Friedrich and Knipping, following the instructions of their professor Max von Laue

(1879–1960), who had first conceived the idea, passed a beam of X-rays through a crystal and recorded a symmetrical pattern of spots on a photographic film. This provided the first concrete evidence that the hitherto conjectured regular arrangement within crystals did in fact exist.

The significance of this experiment was not lost on the father and son team of the English physicists W. H. Bragg (1862–1942) and W. L. Bragg (b. 1890), who surmised that measurements of such spots could result in establishing the positions of the atoms within crystals. Their initial findings and methods of investigation were described in their classic treatise *X-rays and Crystal Structure,* published in 1915[53]. They proclaimed that 'instead of guessing the internal arrangement of the atoms from the outward form assumed by the crystal, we find ourselves able to measure the actual distances from atom to atom and to draw a diagram as if we were making a plan of a building' (p. 4)[53]. It is interesting to note that one of the earliest of their spot-production experiments used beryl, for plate 1 of their book shows the pattern produced by passing X-rays parallel to the long or *c*-axis of a beryl crystal. This pattern proves that the external six-fold symmetry of faces on natural beryl crystals is indeed due to a like arrangement of atoms within. Further investigations by W. L. Bragg and J. West resulted in working out the detailed structure, with findings published in 1926[54]. This structure is described and depicted in Chapter 4 and remains the accepted model.

References

1 THORNDIKE, L. *A History of Magic and Experimental Science.* 8 vols. New York: Columbia University Press. See especially vols. 1, 2, 6, and 7 (1923–59)

2 ADAMS, F. D. *The Birth and Development of the Geological Sciences.* Baltimore: Williams & Wilkins. 506 pp. (1938)

3 GESNER, C. *De Omne Rerum Fossilium.* Zurich, 8 books in one (1565)

4 KING, C. W. *The Natural History, Ancient and Modern, of Precious Stones and Gems, and of the Precious Metals.* London: Bell and Daldy. 442 pp. (1865)

5 WYCKOFF, D. *Albertus Magnus Book of Minerals.* Oxford: Clarendon Press. 309 pp. (1967)

6 BLAKE, R. P., and De VIS, H. *Epiphanius De Gemmis.* London: Christophers. 335 pp. (1967)

7 EVANS, J. *Magical Jewels of the Middle Ages and the Renaissance.* Oxford: Clarendon Press. 264 pp. (1922)

8 KING, C. W. *Antique Gems, Their Origin, Uses and Value.* 2nd ed. London: J. Murray. 498 pp. (1866)

9 ALFONSO, X. *Lapidario del Rey D. Alfonso X., Codice Original.* Madrid: Imprenta de la Iberia. ca. 200 pp. (1881)

10 KUNZ, G. F. *The Curious Lore of Precious Stones.* Philadelphia and London: J. B. Lippincott. 406 pp. (1913)

11 LEONARDUS CAMILLUS *Speculum Lapidum.* Venice. ca. 120 pp. (1502)

12 LEONARDUS CAMMILLUS *The Mirror of Stones.* London: Printed for J. Freeman. 240 pp. (1750)

13 BALL, S. H. Historical notes on gem mining. *Economic Geology* 26:681–738 (1931)

14 LOTHROP, S. K., el al. *Coclé, an Archeological Study of Central Panama. Part I: Historical Background, Excavations at the Sitio Conte, Artifacts and Ornaments.* Memoirs of the Peabody Museum of Archaeology and Ethnology, Harvard University, vol. 7. Cambridge: The Museum. 327 pp. (1937)

15 SCHUMACHER, H. A. Ueber die colombischen Smaragden. *Zeitschrift der Gesellshaft für Erdkundle* 10:38–62 (1875)

16 CANOVA, L. J. *Chivor-Somondoco Emerald Mines of Colombia.* New York: Colombian Emerald Syndicate. 30 pp. (1921)

17 CODAZZI, R. L. Minas des Esmeraldas. *Boletin de Minas y Petroleos de Colombia* (Bogotá) 1:114–43 (1929)

18 OTERO MUÑOZ, G., and BARRIGA VILLALBA, A. M. *Esmeraldas de Colombia.* Bogotá: Banco de la Republica. 133 pp. (1948)

19 TAVERNIER, J.-B. *Travels in India by Jean-Baptiste Tavernier, Baron of Aubonne* Translated by V. Ball from the original French edition of 1676. 2nd ed. Edited by W. Crooke.

2 vols. London: Oxford University Press. 335, 399 pp. (1925)

20 BANDY, M. C., and BANDY, J. A., trans. *De Natura Fossilium (Textbook of Mineralogy)*, by G. Agricola. Geological Society of America Special Paper 63. New York: Geological Society of America. 240 pp. (1955)

21 ARPHE de VILLAFAÑE, J. *Quilatador de la Plata, Oro y Piedras*. Valladolid. ca. 142 pp. (1572)

22 MOSQUERA, D. de. *Litho-Statica, Theorica, y Practica de Medir Piedras Preciosas*. Madrid: Francisco del Hierro. 202 pp. (1721)

23 BACCI, A. *Le XII Pietre Pretiose*. Rome. 148 pp. (1587)

24 ————. *De Gemmis et Lapidibus Pretiosis*. Latin translation by Wolfgang Gabelchovero. Frankfort: Matthiae Beckeri. 231 pp. (1603)

25 MORALES, G. *Libro de las Virtudes y Propiedades Maravillosas de las Piedras Preciosas*. Madrid: Luis Sanchez. 378 pp. (1605)

26 BOODT, A. B. de. *Gemmarum et Lapidum Historia*. Hanover: Typis Wechelianis. 2nd and 3rd ed., Leiden: Joannis Maire, 1636 and 1647. (1609). French translation, Lyon: Jean-Antoine Huguetan (1644)

27 LAET, J. de. *De Gemmis et Lapidibus- . . . Theophrasti Liber de Lapidibus*. Lugduni Batavorum. Also Leiden: Joannis Maire; incorporated in 3rd ed. of Boodt above. 210 pp. (1647)

28 CESI, B. *Mineralogia, Sive Naturalis Philosophiae Thesauri*. Lyon: Iacobi & Petri Prost. ca. 626 pp. (1636)

29 NICOLS, T. *A Lapidary: Or, The History of Pretious Stones*. Cambridge: Thomas Buck. 239 pp. (1652)

30 ALDROVANDI, U. *Musaeum Metallicum in Libros IIII Distributum*. Bologna: Baptiste Ferronij. 979 pp. (1648)

31 ROSNEL, P. de. *Le Mercure Indien, ou le Tresor des Indes*. Paris: Robert Chevillion. 64 pp. (1667)

32 BOYLE, R. *An Essay About the Origine and Virtues of Gems*. London: William Godbid. 185 pp. (1672)

33 SPENCER, J. J. *De Gemmis Errores Vulgares*. Leipzig: Typis Christophori Fleischeri. 40 pp. (1687)

34 PITT, R. *The Craft and Frauds of Physick Expos'd*. London: Tim. Childe. 203 pp. (1703)

35 POTT, J. H. *Lithogéognosie, ou Examen Chymique des Pierres et des Terres en Général*. Paris: J. T. Herissant. 431 pp. (1753)

36 THOMSON, T. *The History of Chemistry*. 2nd ed. London: Henry Colburn and Richard Bentley. 349, 325 pp. (1831?)

37 WALLERIUS, J. G. *Mineralogia, Eller Mineral-Riket*. Stockholm. 479 pp. (1747) French edition published in Paris (1753)

38 BRÜCKMANN, U. F. B. *Abhandlung von Edelsteinen*. Braunschweig: Fürstl. Waisenhaus-Buchhandlung; 143 pp. (1757) 2nd ed. (1773), 415 pp.; with *Beyträge zu seiner Abhandlung* [supplements], (1778); Zwote Fortsetzung [continuation] of the *Beyträge (1783)*

39 ROMÉ de LISLE, J. B. L. de. *Essai de Cristallographie*. Paris: Chez Didot. 427 pp. (1772)

40 ROMÉ de LISLE, J. B. L. de, and DUGUAT, ABBÉ. *Catalogue Systématique et Raisonné des Curiosités de le Nature et de l'Art qui Composent le Cabinet de M. Davila*. 3 vols. Paris: Chez Briasson (1767)

41 ROMÉ de LISLE, J. B. L. de. *Cristallographie, ou Description des Formes . . . du Regne Minéral*. 2nd ed. 4 vols. Paris: L'Imprimerie de Monsieur (1783)

42 BERGMAN, T. O. *Physical and Chemical Essays, Translated from the Original Latin . . . by Edward Cullen*. vol. 2. London: J. Murray. 518 pp. (1784)

43 ACHARD, F. C. *Bestimmung der Bestandtheile einiger Edelgesteine*. Berlin: Arnold Wever. 128 pp. (1779)

44 BRISSON, M. *Pesanteur Spécifique des Corps*. Paris: Imprimerie Royale. 453 pp. (1787). German edition published in Leipzig (1795)

45 VAUQUELIN, N. L. Analyse de l'aigue marine, ou béril; et découverte d'une terre nouvelle dans cette pierre. *Annales de Chimie*. 26:155–70 (1798)

46 WEEKS, M. E. *Discovery of the Elements*. 4th ed. Easton, Pa.: Journal of Chemical Education. 470 pp. (1939)

47 VAUQUELIN, N. L. Analyse de l'émeraude du Pérou. *Annales de Chimie* 26:259 (1798)

48 HAÜY, R. J. *Traité de Minéralogie*, 5 vols. Paris: Chez Louis (1801)

49 HAÜY, R. J. *Traité des Caractères Physiques des Pierres Précieuses*. Paris: Mme Ve Courcier. 253 pp. (1817)

50 BLUM, J. R. *Taschenbuch der Edelsteinkunde*. Stuttgart: Carl Hoffman. 356 pp. 2nd ed., 1834; 3rd ed. 1887, 341 pp. (1832)

51 KLUGE, K. E. *Handbuch der Edelsteinkunde*. Leipzig: F. A. Brockhaus. 561 pp. (1860)

52 BAUER, M. H. *Edelsteinkunde*. Leipzig (1896). C. H. Tauchnitz. 2nd ed. (1909); 3rd ed. revised by K. Schlossmacher (1932). 871 pp. English edition: *Precious Stones*, translated by L. J. Spencer. London: Charles Griffin and Co. (1904). 627 pp.

53 BRAGG, W. H. and BRAGG, W. L. *X-rays and Crystal Structure*. London: G. Bell and Sons. 228 pp. (1915)

54 BRAGG, W. L. and WEST, J. The structure of beryl. *Proceedings of the Royal Society of London*. A-111, pp. 691–714 (1926)

Chapter 3

Emerald and beryl in collections

This chapter describes the national collections of jewels in countries throughout the world which, of course, include emerald and beryl. Many of these collections are crown jewels which frequently date from the 16th century or even earlier.

Iran

The crown jewels of Iran are housed in a large basement vault in the National Bank of Iran, Tehran, and the exhibits are open to the public. They form what are generally conceded to be the 'richest and most dazzling single collection of jewels in the world'[1]. The beginning of the collection dates to the Savafid period (1501–1736), with the greatest enlargement due to Shah Abbas (1587–1629). He was not only largely responsible for forging the Iranian empire into a powerful state but was also a connoisseur of gems and jewels and an ardent collector. After remaining virtually unknown for several centuries, the collection was organized, cases installed, and the exhibits first opened to the public in 1960. The best descriptive catalogue of the collection, lavishly illustrated and most carefully detailed, is that of Meen and Tushingham[2].

Emeralds appear in many of the cases but are concentrated in two, of which Meen and Tushingham say 'both set and unset . . . in number, quality, and size exceed any display of emeralds known elsewhere'. After I viewed the Topkapi Museum collection in Istanbul several years ago, I thought I had seen the best, but this idea was quickly dispelled by a glance at the first few cases in the vault in Tehran. Not only are emeralds present in vast quantities, many of superb quality and individually worth many thousands of dollars, but it also becomes apparent that it would be utterly impossible to place a monetary value on the emeralds alone, not to mention the diamonds, rubies, spinels, and other gems, as well as objects of art worked in gems and precious metals.

By far the most emeralds in the collection are Columbian; indeed, Meen and Tushingham go so far as to say that they could not surely recognize any as Egyptian or Indian, while 'emeralds from the Russian Urals are present in relatively small numbers' (p. 31)[2]. The richest hoard of emeralds is in several boxes overflowing with large, rounded and polished crystals, many well over 100 carats each, accompanied by emerald-decorated jewels and rings. However, a singular emerald-jewelled box, which is 'probably the most valuable of all the jewels, apart from the Darya-i Nur [diamond]', features a solid pavé of dark-green faceted emeralds on all sides and on the lid, the latter being crowned by a single emerald of 25 × 18 mm (1 × $^{11}/_{16}$ in) estimated to weigh 25 carats. Most of the value of the box lies in the fact that the stones are of superior colour and remarkably free from flaws.

Another small box, evidently cut from a single emerald crystal, consists of a lid and bottom of emerald, each fully carved, and fastened with gold-enamel work. This exquisite object is signed by Michael Perchin, a workmaster of Fabergé. A splendid *jiqua,* or turban ornament, takes the form of a plume in precious metals, paved overall with diamonds, and bearing in its centre a magnificent round cabochon emerald estimated to weigh 65 carats. A drawing of this jewel appears in *Figure 3.1.* The imperial sword, studded with large gems, contains numerous faceted emeralds, among which are two of about 100 and 110 carats. Several modern ornaments, such as the tiara of the recently deposed empress, also feature outstanding emeralds. The tiara, made by Harry Winston of New York, is set with many fine emeralds, but perhaps its most notable feature is the use of coloured

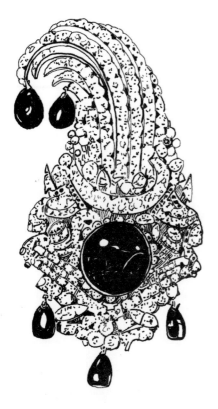

Figure 3.1 The Nadir Shah jiqua, or turban ornament, preserved in the treasury of the Crown Jewels of Iran, made of precious metals and studded with hundreds of diamonds, some small rubies, magnificent emerald drops, and a central emerald cabochon of about 65 carats. Height is 12.8 cm (5 in). (John Sinkankas).

diamonds along the headband. Emeralds, carved in the so-called 'melon' shape, are also prominent in the empress's coronation crown.

Finally, but no means least, is the jewelled globe of our planet, which is called 'The Great Globe' by Meen and Tushingham[2], who enthusiastically state that 'surely this is the most resplendent globe ever created!' This stunning object stands 108 cm (43 in) high; the rotable globe measures 45 cm (18 in) in diameter and is almost entirely covered by closely set precious stones, numbering more than 51000. The major portion is paved with emeralds because they were chosen to represent the ocean and other bodies of water. In its manufacture, 34 kg (75 lb) of gold were used. According to Meen and Tushingham, a plaque set in the north Pacific Ocean bears the inscription 'Nasir ud-Din Shah, the Sultan, Son of the Sultan, May God Perpetuate His Reign, 1291', or 1874–75 AD.

Turkey

The hoard of jewels preserved in the Topkapi Palace Museum in Istanbul is open to the public and popular with tourists, especially since the motion picture *Topkapi* publicized its treasures. Collected by past rulers of Turkey and the Ottoman Empire, the treasure includes splendid, large high-quality emeralds of Colombian origin. The famous dagger, represented in *Figure 3.2,* which was the object of theft in the motion picture, is a curved weapon whose golden handle is set with three extremely large cabochon emeralds of somewhat irregular form. Diamonds stud the spaces between these stones, and the end of the handle is fitted with a jewelled watch capped with a translucent emerald cover. The large emeralds measure about 3 to 4 cm (1¼ to 1⅝ in) and are of excellent transparency and colour, but they

Figure 3.2 The emerald-studded dagger from the collection in the Topkapi Palace Museum, Istanbul, made famous by the motion picture, *Topkapi.* It is 35 cm (13¾ in) long, and the handle is set with 3–4 cm cabochon emeralds amid diamond ornamentation and gold scroll-work. An interesting feature is the watch set in the butt and covered by a large, very clear hexagonal emerald section. A matching, jewelled scabbard accompanies the blade. (John Sinkankas).

contain a considerable number of flaws. This weapon was made as a present from Sultan Mahmud I (1696–1754) of Turkey to Nadir Shah (1688–1747), according to one account[3], but the official guidebook[4] states that the dagger, among other gifts, had been sent from Nadir Shah to Turkey, not the other way around.

One of the most impressive objects in the Topkapi Palace Museum is a pendant of gold, studded with diamonds and tassled with strings of pearls, with the central portion occupied by three dark green cabochon emeralds retaining the original hexagonal crystal form (see *Figure 3.3*). Meen[5] took optical measurements from a distance and determined these stones to measure about 53 mm (2⅛ in) across and the two others, set below that, about 46 mm (1¹³⁄₁₆ in). This splendid jewel was sent by Sultan Abdul Hamid I (1725–1789) to the Prophet's Tomb in Medina in the 18th century, but it was later returned to Turkey.

Figure 3.3 Magnificent emerald, gold, diamond, and pearl pendant, among the jewels formerly belonging to the Sultans of Turkey and on exhibit in the Topkapi Palace Museum, Istanbul. As is apparent from the shapes, the three large emeralds were cut from cross-sections of enormous Colombian emerald prisms. The top emerald shows traces of a borehole suggesting that it may have been half of a much thicker slice. This stone is about 5 cm (2 in) diameter. (John Sinkankas).

Other Topkapi emeralds include an astonishing 'egg-size' single hexagonal crystal, hollowed out and polished all over to form a container, and mounted in jewelled gold as a pendant. It is said to have been sent to Medina by Sultan Ahmed I (1589–1617), but returned to Istanbul by Fahrettin Pasha[4]. Other large and fine emerald objects are also on display, but one of the most intriguing, especially to the lapidary who looks upon it as potential gem material, is an enormous polished hemisphere of Colombian emerald that is so dark in hue that it appears black. It measures approximately 102 × 90 mm (4¹⁄₁₆ × 3⅝ in) and weighs 6550 carats! Even larger is a flattish cabochon, also almost black in appearance, which weighs 16 300 carats. Unfortunately, these stones were too far away in poor light to be able to judge more accurately their gem quality.

Among the personal jewels accumulated by Abdul-Hamid II, Sultan of Turkey from 1876–1909, which were sold at auction in Paris in 1911[6], are several splendid pieces featuring large emeralds. These include a 'grand devant de corsage' or corselet of three rows of large pear-shaped cabochon emeralds suspended from precious metal links studded with diamonds (*Figure 3.4*). The piece contains forty-two emeralds, many of which are nearly 2.5 cm (1 in) in length. Unset emeralds in the collection included a cabochon of 45.29 carats and a 'rondelle', pierced in its centre, weighing 92.25 carats.

Figure 3.4 Devant de corsage, or breast ornament, made of cabochon and drop emeralds with diamonds, approximately 28 cm (11 in) across. Once the property of Abdul-Hamid II, Sultan of Turkey, it was sold in Paris in 1911 after his exile.

USSR

Remnants of Tsarist treasures are preserved in the armoury of the Kremlin in Moscow. Among the pieces is the fur-rimmed conical cap of Vladimir Monomakh, Grand Prince of Kiev during the 12th century. The gold filigree ornamenting the cap is set with gems, among them several large rectangular step-cut emeralds[7]. The gold bow of Tsar Mikhail, made in the Kremlin Armoury in 1628, is studded with over 700 sapphires, rubies, zircons, diamonds, and emeralds, the latter alone numbering 135 and weighing an aggregate 184 carats. Five of the stones weigh 40 carats each, two are 10 carats each, and sixteen together weigh 60 carats.

Fine, dark green emeralds appear as studs on the gold-enamel covers of a gospel, which weighs altogether 26 kg (56 lb). In another work of art, dating from the reign of the third Romanov tsar, Feodor Alexeivich (1676–1682), an enormous heart-shaped cabochon emerald forms a mitre directly over the crown of an enamelled figure of Christ. Despite their similarity to typical Columbian emeralds, Duncan[7] (p. 116) maintained that 'these stones probably came from the emerald mines in the Ural Mountains which had been worked since the earliest recorded Russian times' (!) and 'it is most unlikely that any of these gems came from the great Muzo mines of Columbia'. He advances no evidence for these statements, however.

Figure 3.5 Left: Catherine the Great's emerald, weighing between 70 and 80 carats, surrounded with rows of rose-cut and brilliant-cut diamonds (outer row). It is owned by J. & S. S. De Young, Inc., jewellers of Boston, Massachusetts. (Sketched after an advertising photograph). *Right:* Step-cut emerald of superb colour and clarity set in a gold-silver mounting with large round diamonds and numerous small diamonds studding the leaves. The gem measures 3.6 × 3.25 cm (ca. 1½ × 1⁵⁄₁₆ in) and weighs 136.5 carats. It is a former Tsarist treasure and is now in the Diamond Fund of the USSR. (John Sinkankas).

In 1980, a splendid faceted emerald set in a diamond-studded brooch, shown in *Figure 3.5,* was purchased by J. and S. S. De Young, jewellers, of Boston. The piece had been given by Catherine the Great as a wedding gift to a member of the Prussian Hohenzollern family, thence it passed through a number of noble owners until it was purchased by the Boston firm. The weight of the stone is between 70 and 80 carats.

Among modern emeralds in the USSR Diamond Fund in Moscow, pride of place is taken by a magnificent rectangular step-cut Columbian emerald, 36 × 32.5 mm

($1^7\!/_{16}$ × $1^5\!/_{16}$ in) in size, weighing 136.5 carats (*Figure 3.5*). It has surprisingly few flaws and is mounted in a pierced gold and silver frame decorated with diamonds. The work is attributed to the second quarter of the 19th century[8]. Fersman[9], however, gave the weight as 135.25 carats, noting at the same time that the gem is fine quality but 'rubbed', and that it was mounted during the reign of Tsar Nicholas I in about 1830.

Other outstanding emeralds mentioned by Fersman include a great cracked Uralian stone of about 245 carats; Colombian cabochons of 153.75, 65, 28.80 carats; and step-cut gems of high quality of 42.035, 41.50, and 40 carats, the last bearing an inscription in Persian characters. Referring to an early catalogue of Russian crown jewels, Lord Twining[10] mentioned a drop emerald of 110 carats, a sévigné set with three emeralds of 140, 174.10, and 21.90 carats, and an aquamarine of 231.65 carats set in a medallion.

No discussion of Russian jewellery can omit mentioning the use of beryl gems by the great court jeweller Carl Gustavovich Fabergé (1846–1920), who is noted both for his imaginative designs and his faultless workmanship. One of his best-known pieces is a small, beautifully detailed miniature of the famous equestrian statue of Peter the Great in Nevsky Prospekt, Leningrad. It measures only 50 mm (2 in) across, and has a base made from an emerald[11]. The 'Swan Egg', one of his masterpieces, presented to Alexandra Feodorovna by Nicholas II in 1906, contains a large section of pale aquamarine forming the 'lake' on which floats a platinum swan whose wings, tail, and feet move when a concealed motor is wound. The whole fits into the egg and is the 'surprise' for which Fabergé's eggs were noted[12]. One of the prizes of the Fabergé collection of Lillian Thomas Pratt, housed in the Virginia Museum in Richmond, USA, is a rock crystal egg enclosing miniature paintings of the Tsarist residences. These are hinged to a central shaft which is rotated by means of a large, fine Uralian emerald at its apex.

Austria

The Holy Roman Empire crown jewels, which are on exhibit in the Weltliche Schatzkammer, or secular treasury, in the Hofburg, Vienna, include the elaborate gem-studded crown of István Bocskay (1557–1606), who received the crown from Sultan Achmed I[10]. A number of emeralds are used in its decoration but are not identified as to source.

In the collections of the Kunsthistorisches Museum in Vienna is a fine altar-piece, shown in *Figure 3.6,* in which part of the religious scene depicted is 'Jacob's Well', made from a large emerald crystal. Another fascinating object is a 492 carat oval faceted aquamarine mounted in a swivel-stand (*Figure 3.7*).

The most important royal jewels belonged to the Austrian Hapsburgs. Considered personal rather than state treasures, they were removed by Emperor Charles I (Karl Franz Josef, 1887–1922) when he abdicated in 1918. These are listed and described by Twining[10] (p. 14–16), and include a suite of emerald jewellery, known as the Maria Theresa emeralds, which had formed a large corsage made for Empress Maria Theresa (1717–1780) and which was later worn by

Figure 3.6 A remarkable house altarpiece or shrine ascribed to the Florentine court workshops and made for the Grand Duke of Tuscany, Ferdinand I (1549–1605). Its size is 38 × 23 cm (15 × 9 in). The frame consists of rock crystal, gold, and enamel and surrounds a pietre dure (stone mosaic or inlay) scene in the Holy Land with Christ and a samaritan before Jacob's Well, the latter made from a single large emerald crystal. *Courtesy Kunsthistorisches Museum, Vienna.*

Empress Maria Lousia, wife of Leopold I. During the 19th century, the corsage was dismantled and the emeralds reset in a diadem, corsage, necklace, two bracelets, two slides, and a watch with chatelaine, the watch being set within an oval case made from a single emerald crystal.

Ball[13] stated that in about 1875 an emerald weighing 2005 carats was among the crown jewels and valued at \$58 000. The fate of this stone is unknown and Twining does not mention it.

Figure 3.7 Oval faceted aquamarine of 492 carats exhibited in the Weltliche Schatzkammer in Vienna.
It is mounted in a swiveling gold setting; provenance unknown, possibly Russian, dated to about 1600.
The stone is not flawless but contains inconspicuous liquid-filled feather inclusions, some minute tubular
inclusions, and faint colour zones. *Courtesy Kunsthistorisches Museum, Vienna.*

Germany

Two treasuries in Germany contain remarkable collections of jewels and precious
objects once owned by royal families. The largest and most important collection is
in the Grüne Gewölbe or 'Green Vaults' of Dresden in the German Democratic
Republic.

The collection commenced with Augustus the Strong (1670–1733), the ruler of
Saxony, who, as a connoisseur and ardent collector, lost few chances to acquire or
commission marvellous examples of lapidary and goldsmith art. Emeralds are
prominent in many of the objects. One of particular interest, recently sent to the
United States for exhibit, is a statue of a black boy holding a tray on which rests a
large stone studded with natural Colombian emerald crystals of large size. Far more
emeralds in cut form may be seen in the 'Emerald Suite', on display in the eighth of
the treasury rooms, in which cut emeralds are inset in pendants, buckles, drops,
studs, a cane top, and two swords. This collection is described in Menzhausen's
detailed historical work[12], notable for its many illustrations.

The second great collection, in the Treasury of the Residenz in Munich, represents the precious objects assembled by members of the ruling Wittelsbach family of Bavaria. Its most important pieces are described and illustrated in Twining[10] and in the detailed catalogue of Thoma and Brunner[14]. Easily the most splendid object, perhaps one of the greatest examples of the goldsmith's art ever created, is the statuette of St. George and the Dragon, made in about 1590 from gold, silver, gilt, and gemstones. The horse's body is beautifully carved from a single piece of agate, equipped with trappings of enamelled and gem-set gold. St. George, made of gem-studded and enamelled gold, sits astride the horse holding a sword of rock crystal aimed at the dragon at the horse's feet. The dragon is green enamel and studded with many fine emeralds. This remarkable statuette is mounted on an elaborately decorated plinth and the whole is 50 cm (20 in) tall, 34.2 cm (13½ in) long and 19.8 cm (8 in) wide. In the same room is a splendid example of 16th century jewellery, a ceremonial necklace made of enamelled gold links set with gems, among which are a number of large and fine green stones. These stones, faithful imitations in green glass, were substituted for the original emeralds some time after 1931, according to museum officials. They are identified as emeralds by Twining[10] but Thoma and Brunner[14] correctly identify them as copies.

Another large emerald in this collection is part of a rosary made from gold and diamonds. The emerald measures about 3×4 cm ($1\frac{1}{4} \times 1\frac{1}{2}$ in) and has facets over its entire upper surface. A matching piece on the other side is green glass. Emeralds are also set in the hilt of the Bavarian Imperial sword, in the garniture of the Order of St. George, and in other objects. The collection formerly contained a number of fine and large unset emeralds, according to a catalogue of 1879[10] (p. 38), including gems of 80, 70, 52, and $27^{13}/_{16}$ carats, and an uncut emerald of 120 carats which was acquired in 1565 and was thus one of the first Colombian emeralds to pass into hands other than Spanish. In 1931, on behalf of the Treasury, Christie's of London auctioned off nine emeralds from the collection totalling 476 carats and fetching the round sum of £19 000. None of these gems were less than 28 carats; the largest, hexagonal in outline, of 'magnificent' quality and weighing 98.98 carats, sold for £3000[10]. Were these the emeralds taken from the ceremonial necklace mentioned above?

Among other German royal treasures, Twining mentions the German Imperial Crown, fitted with a large, fine emerald in one of its side panels, an aquamarine said to have been in the clasp of Napoleon's coronation mantle, and other large emeralds set in jewels and ornaments in the treasures of the Prussian royal house.

Italy

The largest and most important emeralds in Italian collections are those in the Vatican Museum which have been used to ornament papal tiaras, although a pair of very early crowns made for King Agilulf (ca. 600 AD) and his Queen, Theodolinda of Lombardy, employed emeralds among other stones in their decoration[10] (p. 417). The earliest emerald-ornamented tiara was that of Pope Boniface VIII (papacy, 1294–1303) which contained forty-three balas rubies, seventy-two sapphires, and forty-five *praxini* (emeralds). Much later, the tiara of Pope Julius II (papacy, 1503–1513) was decorated with the largest recorded emerald ever used in these headpieces, a hemispherical stone engraved with the legend 'Gregorius XIII Pont. Opt. Max'. It was attached to the apex of the tiara, to which was added a gold cross. This gem is shown in a watercolour sketch in Twining[10] (p. 380) as being carved in fluted style, but in another photograph (plate 114), which shows the gem on top of the tiara of Pius VI, it is seen to be almost spherical in shape and smoothly polished. Some accounts[15] give the dimensions as 5.5 cm (2¼ in) in diameter and 3 cm (1¼ in) in height. However, it is obvious from Twining's illustration that it cannot be more than about 25 mm (1 in) in diameter. Twining also said that the stone was Egyptian in origin, of fine dark green colour, and that the engraving was done in 1503. If the last date is correct, the stone could not have been Colombian, and it may be one of the very few large and fine emeralds from Egypt.

This particular emerald has a most interesting history. It was among the treasures taken from the Vatican to meet the enormous sum demanded by Napoleon under the terms of the Treaty of Tolentino in 1797. All major papal tiaras had to be dismantled and the stones removed, and the large emerald passed into the hands of the French. In 1804, when Pius VI agreed to travel to Paris to anoint Napoleon, the Vatican treasury was so depleted that no fitting tiara could be made from what was left. Informed of this regrettable state of affairs, 'Napoleon made good the omission by ordering a new one which he gave to the Pope as a present', and which included the large emerald[10]. A detailed contemporary description of the tiara gave the weight of the emerald as about 1000 carats. The tiara is still in the Papal Treasury and retains the large emerald, although many other stones have been removed and replaced over the years.

France

The collection in the Louvre in Paris contains an example of early use of emeralds in a gold pectoral, suspended from a chain, which is set with a large black stone scarab ornamented with pearls and emeralds. It is dated to the 3rd or 4th century AD, and is remarkable for the fact that the chain employs short beads of emerald, almost rondelles in shape, that were obviously cut from basal sections of Egyptian crystals[16]. Twining[10] mentioned that emeralds were commonly used in early French royal jewels. At the time of her death in 1372, Queen Jeanne d'Evreux owned many jewels, the best having been given to the Convent of Grands Carmes, Paris, in 1349. Among other objects, she left a crown set with emeralds and a 'coronel' largely decorated with these stones.

In 1811, Napoleon presented to his second wife, Marie-Louise of Austria (1791–1847), a magnificent emerald and diamond tiara when she bore him a son. The tiara outlasted his reign and remained in the hands of the Hapsburgs until it was sold by Van Cleef & Arpels of New York. At this time it was broken up and the large and fine emeralds placed in modern settings. The entire suite, originally containing 79 emeralds and 1015 diamonds, was valued at $1 million.

In 1887, the major portion of the French Royal Crown jewels were dispersed through auction in Paris, at which time several pieces rich in emerald gems were sold[17]. The finest of the lot was a diadem studded with 1031 diamond brilliants weighing altogether 176 carats and 40 large and small emeralds totalling 77 carats in weight. This piece was the favourite jewel of Empress Eugenie (1826–1920), wife of Napoleon III, and was bought by a certain Mr. Bachrach at the auction for 49000 francs.

A most remarkable lapidary object, now in the Louvre in Paris, is a jewelled map of France presented by Tsar Nicholas II to President Loubet as a token of goodwill to the French people. About 1 m (3 ft) square, it is a mosaic composed entirely of Russian gem and ornamental stones representing political divisions and cities. An emerald valued at 900 roubles was used to designate the city of Marseilles. This map was exhibited in the Russian section of the Art Industry Building at the Paris Exposition of 1900[17].

Spain

In regard to Spanish royal treasures, Twining (p. 579)[10] stated that 'strictly speaking there are no Spanish crown jewels', almost everything in the way of personal ornamentation being considered private rather than public property. In only one place does Twining mention a significant object in which emeralds were used, that being the Emerald Crown of Blanche of Anjou, wife of King James II, who reigned in the late 13th and early 14th centuries. Of course, the emeralds were not Colombian. Considering that the Spanish were the ones to discover and exploit the enormously rich emerald deposits of Colombia and that they controlled both production and distribution of the stones, the paucity of emeralds among the treasures of Spain is perplexing. A necklace of twenty-five large emeralds was said to have been presented to the King of Spain as a gift from the administrators of the Muzo mines, and other important emerald gifts were made later[13]. Apparently all of these were sold or otherwise disposed of, because no trace of them exists. As mentioned before, the royal houses of Spain seemed uninterested in amassing jewels, even though opportunities to do so must have been abundant.

The most important precious object in Spain in which emerald figured prominently was the elaborate jewelled gold crown made for the statue of the Virgen del Sagrario in the Cathedral of Toledo, the work of a jeweller of that city, one Don Diego Alejo de Montoya. He is said to have begun his task in 1574 and completed the crown twelve years later. Miro's illustration[19] (p. 135) shows that it is studded with several large gems, the largest and most important being a spherical emerald of 40 mm (1⅝ in) diameter placed on top (*Figure 3.8*). According to Miro, the emerald was 'prime colour, limpid and brilliant'. The crown was stolen from the cathedral in 1869 and never recovered. Kunz[20] suggested that even before that date the emerald ball had been substituted by one made of green glass. Kunz relates the story that in 1809 during the French occupation, Marshal Andoche Junot, when shown the crown by church officials, tore the emerald from its setting and remarked

Figure 3.8 The gold crown used on ceremonial occasions to adorn the image of the Virgen del Sagrario and preserved in the cathedral of Toledo, Spain. The large, spherical emerald at the apex measures 40 mm (1⅝ in) diameter and is of 'prime colour, limpid and brilliant'. Height of crown 27 cm (10¾ in), diameter 22 cm (8¾ in). From an engraving in J. I. Miro's *Estudio de las Piedras Preciosas* (Madrid, 1870).

to the horrified bystanders that 'this belongs to me!' Presumably Junot had the ball recut into smaller stones because it was never seen again.

Portugal

Among the modest crown jewels still preserved in Lisbon, only a corsage ornament, in the shape of ribbons tied in a bow, contains significant emeralds. It is described[10] as being 'set with 28 emeralds of 301.44 carats including one stone of 47.81 carats in the centre; and brilliants weighing 195.72 carats, the largest being 23.89 carats'. This jewel was the property of Queen Maria Anna of Austria, consort of John V (1689–1750), and was fabricated in the first half of the 18th century.

England

Emeralds are not conspicuous among the gems employed in the Crown Jewels of England; in fact, compared with the exceptionally large and fine diamonds, they pale into insignificance. However, the Imperial Crown of India, made in 1911 at a cost of £60 000, contains nine emeralds of the highest quality, including a very fine cabochon of 36 carats mounted in the front of the headband. Another very fine, but considerably smaller emerald is set in the centre of the diamond-studded cross at the top[10]. The king's sceptre and orb, made for Charles II in the 17th century, are adorned with emeralds, and a very fine emerald of considerable value is set in the scabbard of the state sword.

Among the Coronation Jewels, many large, important emeralds may be noted, the most remarkable, or at least the most curious, being a girdle of cloth around which are fastened elaborately carved gold panels, studded with diamonds, pearls, and emeralds. Each of the panels contains nineteen very large flat emeralds, four of which are carved. Twining's illustration (p. 186)[10] shows that most stones were cut from hexagonal cross-sections, almost certainly from large Colombian crystals. These stones 'were originally set in the trappings of a horse belonging to Maharajah Ranjit Singh and were remounted as a girdle by his successor, Maharajah Shere Singh'. The girdle was acquired in India by the East India Company and given to Queen Victoria in 1851; it is presently displayed in the Indian Room of Buckingham Palace.

Among the personal jewels of Queen Elizabeth II, large and important emeralds are abundantly represented. A splendid tiara, consisting of interlocked loops of

Figure 3.9 The beautiful emerald and diamond tiara of Queen Elizabeth II, consisting of fifteen interlinked circles in which are suspended magnificent emerald drops, graduated in size and interchangeable with an equivalent set of graduated pearl drops. *Crown copyright reserved.*

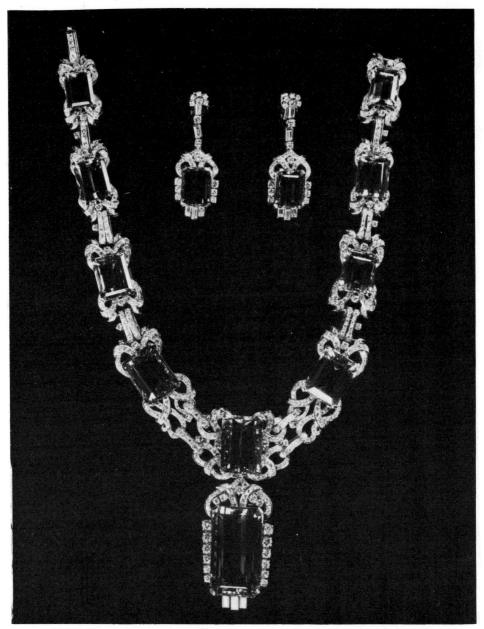

Figure 3.10 The Brazilian aquamarine necklace and earrings presented to Queen Elizabeth II by the President and people of Brazil. *Crown copyright reserved.*

precious metal studded with diamonds, is one of the most impressive pieces (*Figure 3.9*). The centre opening in each of the fifteen loops is occupied by a dangling pear-shaped emerald cabochon, each about 25 mm (1 in) in length. These can be removed and drop-shaped pearls substituted[21]. Another splendid piece is a necklace containing nine cabochons of fine dark colour. It is specially remarkable for a large pendant cabochon of emerald, alongside which is placed a marquise diamond, the sixth gem cut from the Cullinan. Queen Mary liked to wear a set of jewels in which emeralds were a prominent feature, including the necklace just described, and a large stomacher set with emeralds even larger than those in the necklace. This latter piece contains the fifth gem cut from the Cullinan. With this set was commonly worn a brooch of two rows of diamonds encircling an enormous dark-coloured emerald of hexagonal outline[21].

Though less precious, an equally remarkable piece of jewellery belonging to the Queen is an elaborate necklace featuring nine graduated step-cut blue aquamarines of exceptional colour (*Figure 3.10*). These were presented to the Queen by the president and people of Brazil. They are matched in a tiara and a pair of earrings, also set with aquamarines of similar quality. According to Young[21], the stones for the necklace 'had taken the Brazilians a whole year to collect, for stocks of the gems were low and a fine match was deemed necessary'. Furthermore, 'the Queen was so delighted with it that she had made a small tiara of aquamarines and diamonds which she wore with it'. In 1958, the people of Brazil supplemented this gift with a bracelet set with seven aquamarines among hundreds of small diamonds clustered into crowns.

The Natural History Museum in London contains the finest and largest pink faceted morganite gem known from the Malagasy Repulic. It is brilliant-cut, in the

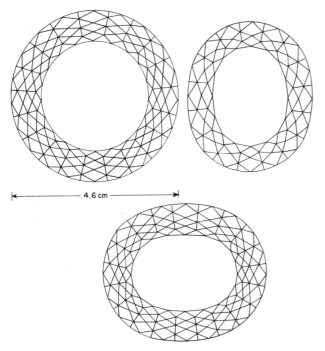

|← ——— 4.6 cm ———— →|

Figure 3.11 Three very large faceted gems cut from aquamarine, part of the Townshend Collection in the Victoria and Albert Museum, London. The round stone, the largest, weights about 331 carats and is sea-green in colour. To its right is another weighing about 197 carats of a yellow-green colour, while the bottom stone is fine sea-green and weighs about 293 carats. (John Sinkankas).

style known as 'antique', and weighs 598.7 carats (see *colour plate 14*). Another splendid beryl gem is an oval step-cut aquamarine from Russia, sea-green in colour and flawless, weighing 879.5 carats[22]. Next door, in the Geological Museum, an exceptional collection of cut and rough gems features an unusual chatoyant aquamarine cabochon weighing 114 carats and a remarkable brown step-cut beryl weighing 9.08 carats[23].

The Victoria and Albert Museum also contains remarkable beryl gems, especially those in the Townshend Collection, which were left to the museum under the terms of Townshend's will[24]. Several examples are shown in the line drawings of *Figure 3.11*. These were formerly in the Henry Philip Hope Collection, best known for having once contained the celebrated Hope diamond, now housed in the National Museum of Natural History in Washington, DC. The Hope specimens have been catalogued by Hertz[25]. Hertz described the large round brilliant gem shown in *Figure 3.11* as 'extraordinarily fine . . . beautiful sea-green colour, with a slight admixture of yellow, though, nevertheless, of a pure and decided tint; this beautiful gem is of the highest effulgence, and of the greatest perfection'. However, the largest Hope aquamarine is not owned by the museum and I have been unable to discover its whereabouts. According to Hertz, it weighed 5 ounces, 17 pennyweights, 12 grains (about 645 carats) and was cut in oval brilliant style. No sources for the roughs for these gems are given, but presumably they are Russian in origin.

One of the more remarkable gems in the Townshend Collection is the 'fixed star' emerald cabochon shown in *Figure 3.12*. Unlike normal stars, such as those observed in star sapphires, which are caused by reflections from numerous bundles of parallel fibres and which appear to move as the gem is tilted, the dark-coloured symmetrically arranged inclusions in the Townshend gem neither reflect much light nor move.

Figure 3.12 Remarkable 'fixed star' emerald in the Townshend Collection, formerly part of the Hope Collection, in Victoria and Albert Museum, London. The dark bands are formed of inclusions arranged symmetrically around the *c*-axis. Diameter about 12.5 mm (4 in). *Courtesy Victoria and Albert Museum.*

Also among the Hope Collection was surely one of the most remarkable examples of lapidary art ever created, namely the 'sword handle' that once blonged to Joachim Marat (1767?–1815), the famous French cavalry commander who married Napoleon's sister and ultimately was made King of Naples. He earned the additional title of the 'Dandy King' for his love of ostentation and for his foppishness in dress, the sword handle being an instance in which ornamentation was deemed more important than utility. This object was described in Hertz's catalogue[25] as 'a matchless aquamarine . . . cut all around with long facets which cross each other obliquely; it is of the most beautiful sea-green colour, and of the utmost perfection'. (See *Figure 3.13*). The mounting for it was made from 'fine gold, ornamented with brilliants, turquoise and garnets, and a most beautiful carbuncle on top; it is four inches long'. The weight was given as 3 ounces, 6 pennyweights (approximately 422 carats). This gem has not been recorded since it was sold out of the Hope Collection.

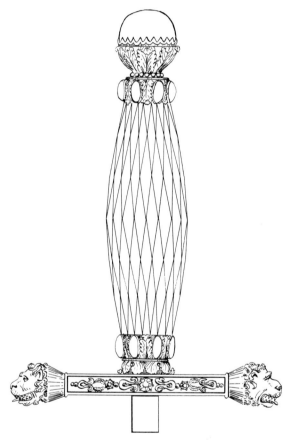

Figure 3.13 A masterpiece of the lapidary's art, a magnificent faceted aquamarine, about 10 cm (4 in) long, formerly owned by Marat and later set into a jewelled sword handle by Henry Philip Hope. After plate 15 in B. Herz, *A Catalogue of the Collection . . . Formed by Henry Philip Hope* (London, 1839). (John Sinkankas).

The Hope Collection also contained a fine square cushion-cut brilliant emerald, measuring approximately 31 mm (1¼ in) across. Hertz gives the weight as 532³⁄₁₆ grains (approximately 172 carats). It is 'most extraordinarily large and beautiful . . . from the East Indies [*sic*] . . . of a fine light green tint . . . it has two flaws in the interior, but which are scarcely visible'. Hertz says it 'formerly adorned the turban of Tippoo Saiib [Tipu Sahib (1751–1799), Sultan of Mysore]'.

USA and Canada

On the whole, the National Museum of Natural History in Washington, DC, holds the best collection of cut beryl gems, many of which are on display in the Hall of Gems. Fine emerald gems are to be found in the 'Spanish Inquisition necklace', so named because it is thought to have been made during that period. In addition to its fine emeralds, it contains a series of large, stubby briolettes of diamond which, with the emeralds, are bored through with suspension holes! The largest emerald in the necklace is about 24 × 15 mm (1 × ⅝ in) and weighs about 60 carats[26],[27] (*colour plate 18*).

A splendidly barbaric emerald necklace of Persian design, donated by Majorie Merriweather Post, features twenty-four baroque stones of good quality, the largest measuring about 23 × 20 × 15 mm (¹⁵⁄₁₆ × ¹³⁄₁₆ × ⅝ in). Another Post gift, also antique Persian, is a brooch fitted with large carved emeralds. The major central stone is 33 × 31 × 14.5 mm (1⁵⁄₁₆ × 1¼ × ⅝ in) and is engraved on one side with script stating 'the servant of Shah Abbas' and with floral decoration on the other. This gem is exhibited at Hillwood, the estate of the Post family, in Washington, DC.

An anonymous donation to the museum, a superb step-cut Colombian emerald, measures 22.2 × 19.4 × 11.8 mm (⅞ × ¾ × ½ in) and weighs 37.82 carats (it originally weighed 38.38 carats before recutting to its present form). Set in a ring, and described by Desautels[26] as being possibly 'the finest single large emerald in America', it is said to have been owned by the rulers of Baroda in India for several centuries. The 'Maximilian emerald', a step-cut gem of 21.04 carats, also donated by Post, was reputedly worn by Ferdinand Maximilian Joseph, the first and only emperor of Mexico (1864–67). Another Post gem is a fine, clear emerald weighing approximately 31 carats. Another notable gem, donated by Mrs. Stewart Hooker, was once set in a belt buckle that belonged to Abdul-Hamid II (1842–1918), the last Sultan of Turkey[28]. It is a remarkably clear, square, step-cut of 75 carats (see *colour Figure 20*).

Other museum holdings include a very large emerald of 157.5 carats, cut in oval brilliant style, and an oval cabochon of Colombian emerald weighing 117 carats. A recent addition to the collection is the 858 carat Gachalá emerald, named after its source in Columbia, donated by the late Harry Winston, and consisting of single, terminated stubby prism with glassy faces[29].

Besides the emeralds, the Natural History Museum collection includes many fine and large gems of aquamarine, golden beryl, and morganite, among other varieties[26],[30],[31]. The largest aquamarine, a step-cut gem of 'more green than blue' colour, cut in scissors style, weighs 1000 carats. There are also a pale blue Russian aquamarine of 263.5 carats, a 187 carat fine blue step-cut gem of Brazilian material, a pale blue gem from Maine of 66.3 carats (Isaac Lea Collection), and a beautiful, clean blue aquamarine of 911 carats from Brazil. The rare aquamarines of Idaho are represented by a pale cut gem, very clean, weighing 108 carats.

The best morganite, from Brazil, is rich pink in colour and weighs 235.5 carats, while two others, cut from morganite rough from the White Queen mine in San Diego County, California, weigh 122.2 and 113 carats. Among the largest of all beryl gems is the flawless golden, somewhat greenish-tinged step-cut gem of 2054 carats, cut by the author (see *Figure 3.14*). It is believed to be the largest cut golden beryl in existence. Another unusual golden beryl in the collection, a cat's-eye of 43.5 carats, was also cut by the author from Madagascar rough.

Figure 3.14 An enormous golden beryl cut gem from Brazil. Weighing 2054 carats and measuring 10.5 cm (4⅛ in) in length, it is believed to be the largest cut golden beryl in existence. It was cut by the author from a simple prism of beryl, the base of which appears on the left and the termination at the right. The thin slab in the foreground was cut from one of the prism faces to eliminate inclusions. The gem, now in the collection of the National Museum of Natural History, Washington DC, is flawless. *Courtesy Smithsonian Institution.*

In New York, the gem hall in the American Museum of Natural History contains large and important beryl specimens, among them the famous Patrizius, Patrice, or St. Patrick's emerald crystal from Chivor, Colombia, a sketch of which is shown in *Figure 3.15,* and a dark green Russian crystal of 28 000 carats. A fragment of a dark blue aquamarine crystal, weighing 6 kg (13 lb) is also on exhibit and an object of continual envy on the part of lapidaries. Among cut aquamarines are a fine blue step-cut of 144.51 carats, another of 400 carats, and a greenish-blue faceted oval of 737 carats[32]. Several pale aquamarines of Russian origin are also included, one weighing 271 carats. Morganites include a fine Brazilian step-cut of 235 carats, but it is overshadowed in terms of colour by a superb step-cut gem from Madagascar material that weighs 123.58 carats. In a daring robbery in October 1964, thieves broke into the old mineral room and removed the 737 carat and 400 carat aquamarines as well as several carved Indian emeralds, but the gems were later recovered[32].

In Chicago, the Field Museum of Natural History contains the largest aquamarine so far cut from United States material, a 137 carat square brilliant of pale blue colour, from rough found near Stoneham, Maine; it is sketched in *Figure 3.16.* There is also a fine Siberian aquamarine gem, said to be from the Hope Collection, weighing 341 carats[33].

Elsewhere, excellent cut beryls are in the collection of the Los Angeles County Museum. On April 5, 1979, the *San Diego Union* carried a story and photographs

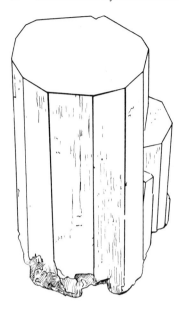

Figure 3.15 The 'Patrizius' emerald crystal, found at Chivor in 1921 by Fritz Klein and named by him after St. Patrick, patron saint of Ireland. It is 8 cm (3¼ in) tall, about 5.5 cm (2¼ in) in diameter, and weighs 630 carats. The crystal is terminated by a large face of *c*{0001} and bounded on the sides by almost equally developed faces of first order prism *m*{1010} and second order prism *a*{1120}. After a colour plate in Klein's *Smaragde unter dem Urwald* Berlin: Oswald Arnold, 1941). (John Sinkankas).

of an enormous greenish aquamarine step-cut gem that was prepared from a 6021 carat Brazilian aquamarine crystal by Pala Properties International of Fallbrook, California. The finished gem, claimed to be the largest cut aquamarine in existence, weighs 2594 carats and is valued at $120 000.

In Canada, the Royal Ontario Museum in Toronto contains fine beryl gems, but the largest and perhaps most interesting is a scissors-cut stone weighing 1625 carats[34]. When cut, it was a superb orange colour. Unfortunately, the colour of the morganites from this particular deposit in Brazil fades, and in time the hue changes to a stable pink colour.

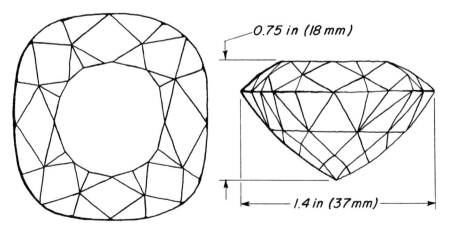

Figure 3.16 Sketch of a 137-carat pale blue aquamarine of fine quality cut from a crystal found near Stoneham, Maine, and now in the Gem Hall, Field Museum of Natural History, Chicago. After a sketch by G. F. Kunz. (John Sinkankas).

MISCELLANEOUS AMERICAN BERYLS

The largest cut emerald from a North American deposit is a fine-coloured, step-cut gem of 13.14 carats prepared from North Carolina material, which, according to Crowingshield[35], is indistinguishable from similar coloured bright Muzo emeralds valued at $1500 to $2000 per carat. The gem was sold in 1971 for an undisclosed amount to R. Santangelo, an investment banker of New York City, and valued by Henry B. Platt, Vice President of Tiffany & Company at $100 000.

In recent decades, several fine emerald necklaces have reappeared, such as the one shown in the December 29, 1953, issue of *Life* magazine and owned at the time by Van Cleef & Arpels of New York. According to the story, it once belonged to a Polish countess who was in love with Andrzey Bonwentura Kosciuszko, the Polish patriot who went to America in 1776 to serve in the Revolutionary Army. To aid the cause, the countess gave the necklace to Benjamin Franklin while he was envoy in Paris. Franklin stored the necklace in a bank, but it disappeared during the French Revolution and was not seen again until 1850 when it was offered for sale in a pawnshop. Another historical emerald necklace, recently in the hands of Cartier's of New York, was depicted by Baerwald and Mahoney[36]. The prize stone was a very dark green emerald set in a pendant, cut in rectangular step-cut style and weighing 107 carats. It was reputed to have belonged to Tsar Alexander II (1818–1881).

It is claimed that the popularity of aquamarine increased greatly in the United States when it was made known that Alice Roosevelt, Theodore Roosevelt's daughter, received from Vice-President Taft a faceted heart-shaped aquamarine upon her marriage to Nicholas Longworth in the White House in 1906. In 1935, President Franklin D. Roosevelt and Mrs. Roosevelt visited Brazil and were presented, as a token of friendship between Brazil and the United States, with a magnificent flawless step-cut aquamarine of fine blue colour, weighing 1847 carats. This gem is on exhibit in the Roosevelt Museum, Hyde Park, New York. The custom of giving aquamarines to important visitors to Brazil was repeated in 1947 when another fine blue gem, set in a brooch, was given to Mrs. Harry S. Truman when she and the president visited the country to participate in the Pan-American Conference.

South America

The devastating plague that swept over the west coast of South America in 1590 decimated the population of many cities but curiously passed by the city of Popoyan, Colombia. Its citizens, taking this as a sign of celestial favour, expressed their gratitude by commissioning a gold and emerald crown to be placed atop an effigy of the Virgin Mary in their cathedral. Known as the Crown of the Andes, it is said to have been carved from solid masses of gold weighing over 100 lb (46 kg), with the finished weight 12 lb (5.5 kg). There are 453 emeralds altogether weighing 1521 carats, with the principal stone being the Atahuallpa Emerald of 45 carats set in the central arch directly beneath the apex cross (*Figure 3.17*). Dangling from the arches are seventeen pear-shaped emeralds weighing from 12 to 24 carats each.

Figure 3.17 Crown of The Andes, commissioned in 1593 and occupying the complete efforts of twenty-five goldsmiths over a period of six years. There are 453 emeralds set into the crown or suspended as drops from the arches. Total weight of the emeralds is 1521 carats. (John Sinkankas).

The subsequent history of the crown is adventurous, and it is remarkable that the crown survived at all. In 1650, for example, British pirates raided Popoyan and seized the crown, but they later yielded it to the Spanish. During the War of Independence in Colombia in 1812, the crown changed hands several times but always was returned to the city. In 1909, however, cathedral officials decided to sell the crown to raise funds for hospitals and orphanages, a promising purchaser being Tsar Nicholas II. Delays in approval of the sale by the Vatican prevented the crown from becoming available until 1914, by which time Russia was embroiled in war and no sale was possible. In 1936, a syndicate headed by Chicago jeweller Warren J. Piper purchased the crown and sent it around the United States in exhibitions to which admission fees were charged. Finally, in 1963, according to contemporary newspaper accounts, the crown was sold at auction in London to a Dutch jeweller for $155000. Its present status is uncertain.

Elsewhere in Colombia, the Church of San Ignacio in Bogotá treasures a gold monstrance made over 250 years ago which is notable for its jewelled decorations.

It stands 80 cm (32 in) tall and weighs 8.3 kg (19 lb, 3 oz) and is studded with 1485 native emeralds valued at $2 million in 1928. Other gems include 28 diamonds, 13 rubies, 62 pearls, 168 amethysts, a sapphire, and a large topaz. A cross on top is set with 22 large faceted emeralds, and a huge cabochon emerald is placed at its foot. In an unusual touch, the golden wings of an angel on the monstrance are overlaid with an enamel made from powdered emeralds. Because the predominant colour is green, Colombians called the monstrance 'La Lechuga' or 'the lettuce'[37].

Modern emerald and beryl jewellery

The dispersal of vast quantities of emeralds from the treasuries of Indian rulers resulted in many of the stones being employed in modern pieces of jewellery, like that shown in *Figure 3.18,* in which irregular or 'baroque' emeralds, probably already drilled with suspension holes at the time of setting in the necklace, were combined with circlets of diamond-studded precious metal to make up an attractive design.

More typical of modern designs are the pieces shown in *Figure 3.19,* in which the cuts of the gems and the design are strictly formal. In such pieces, precise cutting of the gems, fully symmetrical arrangements, and the employment of platinum are common features. A minor departure from strict formality in cutting styles for emeralds is shown in *Figure 3.20,* where large and fine emeralds have been cut into pear shapes and their importance emphasized by surrounds and dangles of diamonds.

In the large and important necklace of diamonds and emeralds shown in *Figure 3.21,* step-cut emeralds have been cleverly worked into a floral design which is both impressive and pleasing to the eye. The foliage and petals are represented by numerous marquise and pear-shaped diamonds. A similar motif is employed in the upper bracelet of *Figure 3.22,* but here the emeralds are dark green, high-quality cabochons. The lower bracelet in the same figure is made more formal through employment of carefully matched and similarly cut square step-cut emeralds and marquise diamonds, all of large size. Other examples of emerald-set jewellery are shown in the colour illustrations.

The intensity of colour in dark green emeralds of top grade is such that even small examples can be effectively set in jewellery, but this is not the case with aquamarines, golden beryls, and other members of the beryl family, all of which tend to be pale in colour if cut below certain critical dimensions. In many the colour is so delicate that in stones of only several carats weight one cannot always be sure that any colour is present at all unless the stone is placed on a piece of white paper. Naturally, the most desirable specimens of these beryls are those in which the hue is most intense, but such gems are rare and command much higher prices. It is for these reasons that the majority of ordinary gem-quality beryls other than emerald are seldom cut below five carats in weight. In most cases, it is desirable to cut them to at least ten or fifteen carats to insure sufficient richness of colour. Many faintly tinted beryl crystals are found in very large sizes and from them can be cut gems of several hundred carats, often completely flawless. However, while they may

Figure 3.18 Art deco cabochon emerald and diamond necklace sold on April 22, 1980, at Christie's auction in New York for $210 000. The baroque shape of the emeralds, all of which are bored through for suspension, suggests that they may have been part of an antique Indian emerald necklace. *Courtesy Christie, Manson & Woods International Inc., New York.*

Figure 3.19 Emerald and diamond jewellery set in platinum, formerly in the Estate of Nelson A. Rockefeller and sold at Christie's auction on October 16, 1979 in New York. The ring is set with an emerald of about 8.56 carats ($95 000). The necklace contains several emeralds over 4 carats and all emeralds together weigh 37.33 carats with 64.65 carats of diamonds ($350 000). The bracelet contains 19.68 carats of emeralds and 38.73 carats of diamonds ($220 000). *Courtesy of Christie, Manson & Woods International Inc., New York.*

Figure 3.20 Emerald and diamond ear pendants, sold at auction by Christie's of Geneva on November 21, 1979, for $930 000. The pear-shaped emeralds weigh 18.11 and 18.07 carats. *Courtesy Christie, Manson & Woods International Inc., New York.*

display fairly intense colour, they are too large for jewellery and are only useful as exhibit pieces in gem collections.

The preferred cutting style for such pale-coloured varieties of beryl is the step-cut, in which light is reflected in narrow strips. Occasionally they are cut in brilliant styles or mixed cuts that combine features of both styles. However, large step-cuts are a severe test of lapidary accuracy because any appreciable deviation from parallelism between the top (crown) facets and bottom (pavilion) facets becomes easily apparent as the stone is turned about under a good light, at which time one may see reflections that are long tapered triangles instead of parallel-sided strips. These difficulties commonly result in the cutting of very large beryls in brilliant or mixed styles where slight inaccuracies are lost in the general dazzle of numerous light reflections.

Another difficulty that besets the lapidary in making step-cuts from aquamarine, golden beryl, or morganite is the devastating effect of permitting even a few tiny flaws to remain in the pre-shaped rough. If the flaws are located near the centre of the stone, they will be repeatedly reflected until the stone seems filled with lines or bands of flaws. In contrast, emeralds of appreciable size with no flaws are extremely rare, and due to the rarity of this gemstone even in small sizes, many minor flaws are acceptable, even in those cut in step-styles. Flaws in other varieties of beryl are not tolerated, however. Thus, richly coloured, accurately cut, flawless beryls, though rarely as costly as good emeralds, are nevertheless true prizes in terms of fine gems and are valued for use in first-class jewellery.

Figure 3.21 A modern necklace employing graduated step-cut emeralds with diamonds. Diameter of necklace approximately 6 inches (15 cm). *Courtesy Harry Winston, Inc., New York.*

Figure 3.22 Modern bracelets employing emeralds and diamonds. The top bracelet contains cabochon emeralds surrounded by marquise and pear-shaped diamonds, while the botton bracelet uses graduated step-cut emeralds separated by graduated marquise diamonds. *Courtesy Harry Winston, Inc., New York.*

References

1 BANK MARKAZI IRAN. *The Crown Jewels of Iran.* Tehran. 45 pp. (1964)

2 MEEN, V. B., and TUSHINGHAM, A. D. *Crown Jewels of Iran.* Toronto: University of Toronto Press. 159 pp. (1968)

3 HEINIGER, E. A., and HEINIGER, J. *The Great Book of Jewels.* Boston: New York Graphic Society. 316 pp. (1974)

4 TOPKAPI PALACE MUSEUM. *Guide Book: The Treasury Department of the Topkapi Palace Museum.* Istanbul: Kemal Cig. 64 pp. (ca. 1977)

5 MEEN, V. B. Topkapi Palace, Istanbul, Turkey. *Lapidary Journal* 20:297–302, 416–7 (1966)

6 ABDUL HAMID. *Catalogue des Perles, Pierreries Bijoux . . . dont la vente aura lieu à Paris, Nov. 1911.* Paris:n.p. 58 pp. (1911)

7 DUNCAN, D. D. *The Kremlin.* Greenwich: New York Graphic Society. 170 pp. (1960)

8 RYBAKOVA, B. A. [Treasures of the U.S.S.R. Diamond Fund]. Moscow: Sovetskii Khudozhnik. 160 pp. (1967)

9 FERSMAN, A. E. [Historical stones of the 'Diamond Treasure']. *Izvestiya Akademiya Nauk SSSR,* (Moscow), ser. 6, vol. 19, pp. 721–30 (1925)

10 TWINING, LORD. *A History of the Crown Jewels of Europe.* London: B. T. Batsford. 707 pp. (1960)

11 SNOWMAN, A. K. *Easter Eggs and other Precious Objects by Carl Fabergé: A Private Collection of Masterworks Made for the Imperial Russian Court.* Washington, DC: Corcoran Gallery of Art. 60 pp. (1961)

12 SNOWMAN, A. K. *The Art of Carl Fabergé.* London: Faber and Faber. 167 pp. (1953)

13 BALL, S. H. Some facts about famous emeralds. *Jewelers' Circular-Keystone* 88, no 10 (1924)

14 THOMA, H., and BRUNNER, H. *Schatzkammer der Residenz München.* Munich: Bayerische Verwaltung der Staatlichen Garten und Seen. 391 pp. (1964)

15 EPPLER, W. F. Berühmte Edelsteine. *Deutsche Goldschmiede-Zeitung* (Stuttgart) 52:394–99 (1924)

16 COCHE de la FERTE, E. *Antique Jewellery.* Orbis Pictus 7. Berne: Hallwag, Ltd. 8 pp., 19 pls. (1962)

17 BLOCHE, A. 1888. *La Vente des Diamants de la Couronne: son Histoire, ses Préparatifs, ses Résultats avec le Catalogue raisonné des Joyaux.* Paris: Quantin. 108 pp. (1962)

18 KUNZ, G. F. Precious Stones. Chapter in *U.S. Geological Survery Mineral Resources of the United States for 1900,* pp. 749–78 (1901)

19 MIRO, J. I. *Estudio de las Piedras Preciosas.* Madrid: Imprenta á Cargo de C. Moro. 288 pp. (1870)

20 KUNZ, G. F. *The Curious Lore of Precious Stones.* Philadelphia & London: J. B. Lippincott. 406 pp. (1913)

21 YOUNG, S. *The Queen's Jewellery: The Jewels of H. M. Queen Elizabeth II.* New York: Taplinger Publishing. 199 pp. (1969)

22 SMITH, G. F. H. *Gemstones.* 14th ed. Revised by F. C. Phillips. London: Chapman and Hall. 580 pp. (1972)

23 JOBBINS, E. A. Gemstone collections of the Geological Museum, South Kensington, London. *Lapidary Journal* 18:18–34 (1964)

24 O'DONOGHUE, M. J. The Townshend collection of precious stones in the Victoria and Albert Museum. *Journal of Gemmology* (London) 12, no. 1, pp. 1–5 (1970)

25 HERTZ, B. *A Catalogue of the Collection of Pearls and Precious Stones Formed by H. P. Hope . . .* London: Printed by William Clowes and Sons. 112 pp. (1839)

26 DESAUTELS, P. E. The National Collection of Gems in the Smithsonian Institution, 1965–1974. *Lapidary Journal* 28:84–100 (1974)

27 DUNN, P. J. Emeralds in the Smithsonian Gem Collection. *Lapidary Journal* 28:1572–5. *Smithsonian Magazine* 8 (1977), no. 9, p. 28 (1975)

28 TRAPP, F. W. The Gachala emerald shares the spotlight with the Hope diamond at the Smithsonian. *Lapidary Journal* 23:628 (1969)

29 DESAUTELS, P. E. The gemstone collection of the U.S. National Museum. *Lapidary Journal* 19:4–36 (1965)

30 DESAUTELS, P. E. *Gems in the Smithsonian.* Washington, D.C.: The Smithsonian Press. 61 pp. (1972)

31 POUGH, F. H. The gem collection of the American Museum of Natural History, New York City. *Lapidary Journal* 18:4–14, 76–81 (1964)

32 *Time Magazine.* p.23 (November 6, 1964)

33 MacFALL, R. P. The Hall of Gems of the Field Museum. *Lapidary Journal* 27:746–50, 766–771 (1973)

34 MEEN, V. B. The gem collection of the Royal Ontario Museum. *Lapidary Journal* 17:18–42 (1963)

35 CROWNINGSHIELD, R. America's largest faceted emerald. *Lapidary Journal* 25:40, 42 (1971)

36 BAERWALD, M., and MAHONEY, T. *Gems and Jewelry Today.* New York: Marcel Rodd & Co. 303 pp. (1949)

37 WOLF, B. The green treasures of the Andes. *Saturday Eveing Post,* October 11, p. 24 (1958)

Chapter 4

Crystal structures and chemical composition

Although the arrangement of atoms within the beryl crystal structure was not known until recently, both Romé de Lisle[1] (in 1783) and Haüy[2] (in 1822) concluded that beryl could be referred to the hexagonal system of symmetry. As late as 1887, however, Wiik[3] suggested that beryl was hexagonal only at high temperatures and was rhombohedral at lower temperatures, a view that failed to gain acceptance. In 1926, using the newly discovered X-ray technique, Bragg and West[4] investigated the structure and determined the model which is still accepted today.

The Beryl structure

As shown in *Figure 4.1*, looking down the principal or *c*-axis, the structure consists of rings of silicon atoms, each surrounded by four oxygen atoms in tetrahedral arrangement, all of which, incidentally, are shown much reduced in size in order to make the structure readily visible. The atoms of aluminium and beryllium have also been reduced for the same reason. The rings, shown in a view at 90° to the basal plane view, are stacked one over the other and connected by bonds between alternating aluminium and beryllium atoms. This arrangement extends throughout the entire crystal. *Figure 4.1* also shows that each aluminium atom is surrounded and bonded to six oxygen atoms while each beryllium atom is surrounded and bonded by four oxygen atoms. The abundance and uniformity of such bonds contributes to the great strength of the beryl structure and accounts for its resistance to chemical attack and such properties as hardness and toughness.

The sub-structure of silicon-oxygen tetrahedra is a very common one in the so-called silicate minerals, by far the most abundant chemical class of minerals in the earth's crust. The linked silicon-oxygen tetrahedra take various forms, that in beryl being called *cyclosilicate*, because of forming rings. However, Beus[5] (p. 86) suggested that it could also be called *tektosilicate* in view of the general uniformity of the structure, this term being used to describe a silicate structure in which the silicon-oxygen tetrahedra are more or less uniformly distributed throughout.

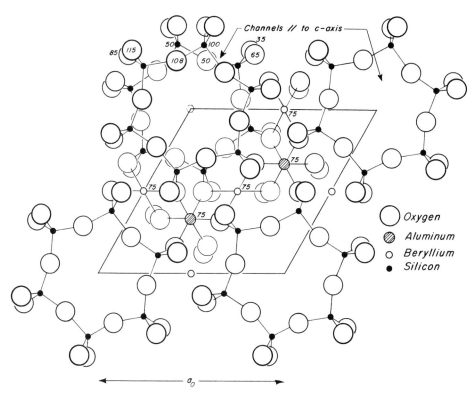

Figure 4.1 Basal projection of the ideal beryl structure showing positions of the several ions, the basic cell, and the vertical distances of the ions in relation to the unit cell dimension c_o in percents. After H. Strunz and C. Tennyson, *Mineralogische Tabellen*, 6th ed., Leipzig: Akademische Verlagsgesellschaft (1977). (John Sinkankas).

The striking feature of the structure, and one that has great significance in its chemical and physical properties, as well as in the shapes usually assumed by natural crystals (habits), is that the Si-O rings are aligned precisely over each other so that their openings form continuous channels parallel to the *c*-axis as shown in the schematic drawing of *Figure 4.3*. The vertical dashed lines pass through the centres of the channels. The distances between centres of the various atoms of the beryl structure were determined by Bragg and West[4] (p. 713) as an outgrowth of their X-ray work on the structure of beryl.

Space group and symmetry elements

Bragg and West[4] confirmed the work of Astbury and Yardley[6] that beryl belongs to the most complete class of symmetry of the hexagonal system: holosymmetric, dihexagonal-bipyramidal, with space group D_{6h}^2 in the Schoenflies notation, or P6/mcc in the Hermann-Mauguin notation. This means that if we had a completely developed beryl crystal, we would find that all of its faces are matched exactly by opposite faces, both along the sides of the crystal and along the ends. In addition to

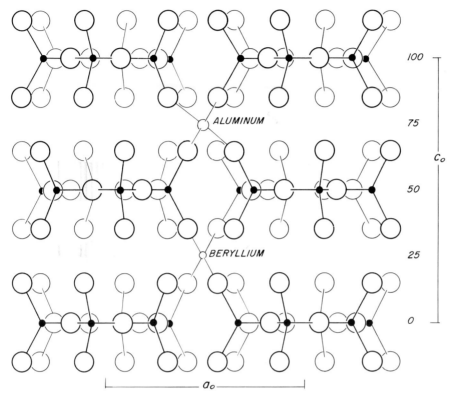

Figure 4.2 Projection of the beryl structure on first order prism plane 1010. This plane is oriented 90° to the basal plane of 0001 shown in *Figure 4.1*. The numerals along the dimension c_o correspond to those of *Figure 5.1*. After H. Strunz and C. Tennyson, *Mineralogische Tabellen*, 6th ed., Leipzig: Akademische Verlagsgesellschaft (1977). (John Sinkankas).

the usual six faces seen on by far most natural beryl crystals (hexagonal), another six faces may also be found, so that the sides of the crystal are bounded by twelve altogether (dihexagonal). Finally, the ends of the fully developed crystal may show a series of inclined faces which form pyramids, and since these develop on both ends, the term describing such development is *bipyramidal*. The numerical and letter notations given in *Figure 4.1* are a type of shorthand used to describe the elements of the symmetry in detailed, scientific writing and need not be understood any further for present purposes.

Chemical composition

Early chemical analyses of beryl by Achard[7] in 1779 and by Bergman[8] in 1780 were only crude approximations reflecting the primitive state of analytical chemistry at the time. Because of the similar chemical behaviour of beryllium and aluminium compounds, the oxides of both were counted together as 'alumina'. The fact that two distinct oxides were present was not discovered until 1798 when Vauquelin

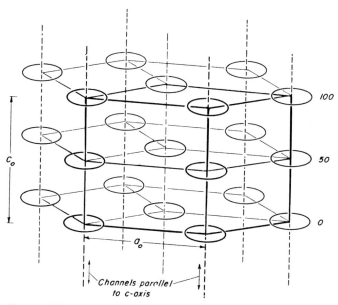

Figure 4.3 Perspective view of the unit cell structure shown in detail in *Figures 4.1 and 4.2*, showing the unit cell (dark outline) and the ring openings stacked above each other in the c-axis direction. (John Sinkankas).

published his crucial analysis of emerald. Weeks[9] (p. 250) described the discovery of the beryllium oxide as follows:

> 'The identity of beryl and emerald was not suspected until the famous French mineralogist, the Abbe Haüy, made a careful study of their crystal forms and physical properties and was so struck by the similarity of the two minerals that he asked Vauquelin to analyze them chemically'.

Vauquelin had overlooked the new oxide in an earlier analysis but corrected himself in his analysis of 1798[10] when he was able to separate and distinguish beryllia, which he named *glucina* after its sweet taste. The element itself, not yet isolated, he named *glucinum*. These names remained in use in France for many

TABLE 4.1 Vauquelin's analyses of beryls

	Beryl (1798)	Muzo Emerald (1798)	Emerald (1800)	Ideal
Silica	69.00%	64.60%	64.50%	66.9% SiO_2
Alumina	13.00	14.00	16.00	19.0% Al_2O_3
Glucina	16.00	13.00	13.00	14.1% BeO
Lime	0.50	2.56	1.60	——
Iron oxide	1.00	——	——	——
Chromium oxide	——	3.50	3.25	——
Moisture, volatiles	——	2.00	2.00	——
Total	99.50%	99.66%	100.35%	100.0%

years afterwards, but elsewhere the terms beryllium oxide, or beryllia, and beryllium were adopted.

Not only did Vauquelin discover beryllium oxide during his analysis of 'Peruvian' (Colombian) emerald, but, as his analysis showed, he found chromium, now known to be the cause of the beautiful green colour typical of emeralds.

A later analysis of Siberian aquamarine by Gmelin confirmed the presence of beryllium oxide but found no lime (calcium oxide) which ordinarily is not a significant constituent[9] (p. 251). However, an initial analysis of beryl in 1798 by Vauquelin showed the presence of lime, and, in 1800, when Vauquelin reanalyzed Colombian emerald he *again* reported lime as 'carbonate' (see his analyses in Table 5-1)[11]. By the mid-19th century, numerous analyses had been published. Two typical results by Müller[12] on beryl from Tirschenreuth fairly closely approach the 'ideal' composition given in *Table 4.1*, that is 66.7–67% SiO_2, 20.0–19.8% Al_2O_3, 13.0–13.2% BeO, and 1.0–0.8% iron oxides, for totals respectively of 100.7% and 100.8%.

Water in beryl

Water is commonly present in numerous voids in beryl crystals, some of which are large enough to see with the unassisted eye. In some crystals, the voids contain so much water that it can be seen to move when the crystal is tilted. In contrast, the water that occurs in the ring channels (see *Figure 4.1*) is invisibly trapped, and its presence, detected only at the elevated temperatures necessary for its release, caused much puzzlement to early analysts. As Deer, Howie, and Zussman[13] remark, 'even gem quality beryls may contain appreciable amounts of H_2O^+' (p. 258). Despite taking great care to select fragments free of inclusions, early analysts soon found that water and other volatiles almost invariably formed a substantial part of the analysis.

Water was first given serious consideration as a component of beryl by Penfield[14] in his classical analyses of alkali beryls published in 1884. He remarked that the water 'cannot be called accidental, for it is always present in amounts varying from 1.50 to 2.50 per cent', and he tabulated its progressive loss from beryl beginning with a 'low red' to 'white heat' and to the highest heat available to him in an air-blasted flame. Convinced that the water was integral to the composition, he proposed a formula for beryl incorporating water, a suggestion that has been adopted from time to time by other workers but which has failed to find universal acceptance. Recently, Ginsburg[15] heated beryl and found that water was slowly expelled at 800 to 900°C and that its removal did not affect the crystal structure.

Using infrared-spectroscopy methods, Wickersheim and Buchanan[16] studied water in beryl and suggested that single molecules exist in the channels. Their studies also suggested that alkali ions were present in some channels as well, and that a complex spectrum obtained on a pink beryl was due to hydroxyl (OH) groups substituting for oxygen. Nuclear magnetic resonance studies by Parè and Duclos[17] confirmed the location and orientation of water molecules in the channels but showed that such molecules were free to rotate. However, Boutin *et al.*[18] concluded that the water molecules do not rotate but rather oscillate. In a later paper, Wickersheim and Buchanan[19] enlarged on their previous findings and reaffirmed their conclusions that hydroxyl groups may substitute for oxygen in the silicate rings.

Sugitani et al.[20] found two types of water in the structure, the first as water molecules located in the spaces, 45 nm in diameter, within the channels, and the second as hydroxyl ions replacing oxygen in the rings. As shown in *Figure 4.3*, the channel holes of 45 nm are spaced 459 nm apart in the c-axis direction. More recently, Wood and Nassau[21,22] examined forty natural and ten synthetic beryls and found infrared absorption lines due to two types of water and carbon dioxide, all of which are located in the channel voids. Type I water occurs alone but Type II is associated with nearby alkali ions and is oriented as shown in *Figure 4.4*. Bakakin

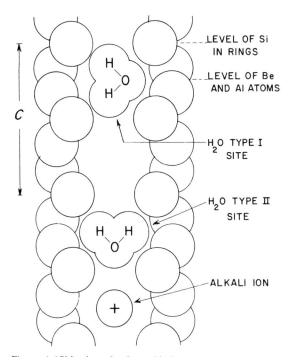

Figure 4.4 Side view of a channel in beryl, only the oxygen atoms of the wall being shown, with possible positions and orientations of water and alkali ions. After Kurt Nassau, Synthetic Emerald, *Lapidary Journal* 30 (1976):196. (John Sinkankas).

and Belov[23] also discuss the role of water and concluded that the molecules fit in the centres of the rings while either sodium or caesium ions fit within the larger voids between the rings. Two kinds of water were identified by them, the first released at low temperature (350–600°C) and the second at a much higher temperature (over 900°C).

In this connection, Nassau and Wood[21] found that a Brazilian colourless beryl, which displayed spectra of both Type I and Type II water, lost 1.6% by weight near 900°C while another colourless beryl from Brazil did not emit gases even at 1200°C, yet produced spectral absorptions indicating that some water remained in the structure. A temperature of 1350°C was required before water and CO_2 were released and the spectra indicated that none remained. An attempt to induce water to penetrate the channels of dehydrated beryl failed even after subjecting the specimen to hydrothermal treatment at 358°C and 8000 lb/in². Tests upon synthetic flux-melt beryl showed that water was absent, while in a hydrothermally grown specimen lacking alkalis, only spectra of Type I water were obtained. In a later series of experiments, Nassau and Wood[24] examined the remarkable anhydrous red beryl of Utah, which occurs in cavities in rhyolite, and inferred 'an exceptionally high temperature of formation', which precluded the incorporation of water into the structure.

Numerous analyses show the common occurrence of channel water in beryl, with quantities ranging from less than 1 weight percent to over 4% but most determination give less than 3%. Bakakin and Belov[23] (p. 487) point out that the per cent of channel water is related to the number of sites in the channels which it can occupy. In one site, it forms a complex ion with a sodium ion and in another it serves to support a large caesium ion. Furthermore, it does not merely reside inertly in the channels but serves to electrically connect the alkali ions to the structure and to confer a more complete electronic neutrality. Kleeman[25] suggested that part of the silicon atoms in the rings may be replaced by hydrogens, but the majority view is that water is present only in the channels and that its presence or absence does not affect the integrity of the structure.

Transition elements in beryl

The transition elements include iron, titanium, manganese, chromium, vanadium, scandium, cobalt, nickel, and copper, all of which have been found in beryl, but, aside from iron, mostly in small amounts. The following data are taken from Feklichev[26], Beus[5], Deer, Howie, and Zussman[13], Doelter[27], and others as indicated.

Iron (FeO). Common, from traces to as much as 3.13% (Doelter), but this very high amount is far above recent determinations as recorded in Feklichev, who gives a maximum of 1.2%; Beus gives a maximum of 0.50%; Deer, Howie, and Zussman give a maximum of 1.50%.

Iron (Fe_2O_3). Common, traces to 4.98% (Doelter), and in other earlier analyses in amounts considerably over 2%, but all are much over the amount of 1.72% recorded by Beus and the 0.96% in Deer, Howie, and Zussman. However, Feklichev gives a maximum of 2.83%. Recent analyses show Fe_2O_3 absent in many beryls, or present in amounts much less than 1%. This is a reasonable finding because the strong colouring typically induced by iron is lacking in most beryls.

Titanium (TiO_2). Rarely reported in older analyses; uncommon in recent ones. Beus, for example gives only five analyses, with a maximum quantity 0.05%.

Manganese (MnO). Rare; traces to 0.75% in Feklichev; Beus gives a maximum of 0.19%; most analyses show less than 0.20%.

Chromium (Cr_2O_3). Despite its being known as the principal colouring ion in emerald, surprisingly few emerald analyses show any chromium at all, and some analyses of non-emerald beryls which report small quantities of chromium may be in error because even very small quantites seem sufficient to induce decided emerald colour. Vauquelin found 3.50% and 3.25% chromium oxide in Muzo emeralds in 1798 and 1800 respectively, but such large quantities have not been found since. Doelter cited an analysis by Lévy who found only a trace of Cr_2O_3 in Muzo emerald and was reluctant to attribute its colour to chromium. Leitmeier[29] (pp. 309-10) recognized the difficulties in determining Cr and therefore described in detail his analytical procedure for determining this element in Habachtal emerald, which contained 0.12% Cr_2O_3. He also assembled eleven other emerald analyses, including two of synthetics (in which Cr was not found) and four of Muzo specimens, of which one contained only a trace of Cr_2O_3 and another only 0.08%. Analyses of Emmaville, New South Wales, emerald, of another Habachtal emerald, and of three Uralian emeralds all failed to detect Cr.

An analysis of a 'large quantity of emerald powder', presumably Muzo emerald, by Barriga Villalba[30] (pp. 117-9) yielded 0.26% Cr_2O_3; he noted that 'the colour of emerald is owing to the oxides of iron and chromium' and that 'a series of analyses confirm that these metals always occur in the emerald of Muzo in the following proportions, iron, Fe_2O_3—1.005%, chromium, Cr_2O_3—0.26% . . . the proportions are more or less constant, but the concentration is variable'. This view of a colouration due to the combined effect of iron and chromium is not shared by others. Beus[5] (table 39) gives an analysis by Simpson[31] (p. 198) of Poona, West Australia emerald in which was found 0.23% Cr_2O_3. Rogers and Sperisen[32] found 2.00% Cr_2O_3 in synthetic emerald and gave as a general range for emerald 0.12–0.25%.

The inconsistency of results of chromium analysis suggests that additional analyses are needed before reliable figures of Cr_2O_3 content in emerald can be established. Those analyses of emerald in which Cr was not detected may reflect more the difficulty of discriminating Cr_2O_3 from Fe_2O_3 than the absence of Cr.

Vanadium (V_2O_3). Reported very rarely, from traces to 0.9% (Feklichev); Beus (table 39, footnote) gives only one determination at 0.09%. It has been suggested that some emeralds are coloured in part by vanadium instead of or in combination with chromium, about which more will be said in Chapter 8.

Cobalt, Nickel, Copper. Very rarely reported and only in traces.

Beryl formulas

The ideal formula, $Be_3Al_2Si_6O_{18}$, is seldom confirmed by analyses of natural beryls, and by far the greater number of determinations show a small but consistent content of alkali metals and water. Attempting to reflect the empirical rather than the theoretical, Ginsburg[15] proposed the following generalization:

$$R_n^+Be_{3=1/2n}Al_2[Si_6O_{18}]\cdot pH_2O$$

where: R^+ = alkali ion, n = 0–1, and p = 0.2–0.8. For the cesium-lithium beryl vorobeyevite he proposed:

$$(Li, Na, Cs)_2Be_3Al_4[Si_6O_{18}]\cdot H_2O$$

For the same variety, Bakakin and Belov[37] (p. 490) suggested an alternative formula as follows:

$$Cs_{0.5}Be_{2.5}Li_{0.5}Al_2Si_6O_{18}\cdot 0.5H_2O$$

In an extended study of beryl compositions and isomorphous substitutions, as it pertains mainly to the introduction of alkali elements, Feklichev[26] proposed several formulas, of which the following is a generalized series-formula accommodating monovalent (singly charged) and divalent (doubly charged) ions:

$$Be_3Al_2Si_6O_{18}\text{───────────}R_1{}^+{}_{-n}R_n^{2+}Be_{2.51/2n}Al_2Si_6O_{18}$$

where: R^+ = Cs^+, Li^+, Rb^+, Na^+, K^+; R^{2+} = Ca^{2+}, Ba^{2+}, Sr^{2+}; and n = 0–1.

The above formula reflects the principal features of beryl chemistry, that is, the inverse quantitative relationship between alkalis and beryllium. Vlasov[33] (p. 98) considered this formula the most reflective of natural beryl compositions. Other suggested formulas may be found in Beus[5] (p. 96) and Deer, Howie, and Zussman[13] (p. 258).

Additionally, Bakakin and Belov[23] (p. 493–5) list numerous 'structural' formulas, grouped according to analyses of beryls from type-deposits, namely, from hydrothermal-pneumatolytic, pegmatitic, and late-pegmatitic. In these formulas, the structural ions are shown first, then channel ions, and lastly the water. A similar scheme, partitioning ions according to positions in the structure, is given in Bakakin et al.[34] (p. 130).

Stemming from their study of an unusual blue beryl from Arizona, Schaller et al.[35] (p. 691) proposed the following beryl-series formulas with end-members shown below. Water is omitted.

Standard beryl:	$Be_3R^{3+} \cdot Si_6O_{18}$
Lithium end-member:	$(Na,Cs) \cdot Be_2Al \cdot Al,Li \cdot Si_6O_{18}$
FeMag end-number:	$(Na,K,Cs) \cdot Be_3 \cdot R^{3+}R^{2+} \cdot Si_6O_{18}$

where: R^{3+} = Al^{3+}, Fe^{3+}, Cr^{3+}, Sc^{3+}; and R^{2+} = Fe^{2+}, Mn^{2+}, Mg^{2+}.

References

1 ROMÉ de l'ISLE, J. B. L. Cristallographie, ou Description des Formes . . . du Regne Minéral. 2nd ed. 4 vols. Paris: L'Imprimerie de Monsieur (1783)

2 HAÜY. R. J. Traité de Cristallographie. 2 vols. Paris: Bachelier et Huzard (1822)

3 WIIK. F. J. Mineralogische und petrographische Mittheilungen. Zeitschrift für Kristallographie und Mineralogie (Leipzig) 12; 515–7 (1887)

4 BRAGG. W. L.. and WEST. J. The structure of beryl, $Be_3Al_2Si_6O_{18}$. Proceedings of the Royal Society of London A-111, pp. 691–714 (1926)

5 BEUS. A. A. Geochemistry of Beryllium and Genetic Types of Beryllium Deposits. Edited by L. R. Page, translated by F. Lachman. San Francisco: W. H. Freeman, 401 pp. (1966)

6 ASTBURY and YARDLEY. Philosophical Transactions of the Royal Society of London A 224:221; cited in Bragg and West above (1924)

7 ACHARD. F. C. Bestimmung der Bestandtheile einiger Edelgesteine. Berlin: Arnold Wever. 128 pp. (1779)

8 BERGMAN. T. Physical and Chemical Essays. Translated by E. Cullen. Dissertation 15 of the

Earth of Gems. Vol. 2. London: J. Murray. pp. 75–119 (1784)

9 WEEKS, M. E. *Discovery of the Elements*. 4th rev. ed. Easton, Pa.: Journal of Chemical Education. 470 pp. (1939)

10 VAUQUELIN, N. L. Analyse de l'aigue marine, ou béril; et découverte d'une terre nouvelle dans cette pierre. *Annales de Chemie* 26, 155–69 (1798)

11 VAUQUELIN, N. L. Addition au mémoire précédent. *Journal des Mines* 7:97 (1800)

12 MÜLLER, H. Mineralanalysen. *Journal für Praktische Chemie* 58:180–85 (1853)

13 DEER, W. A., HOWIE, R. A., and ZUSSMAN, I. *Rock-Forming Minerals*. Vol. 1. London: Longmans. pp. 256–67 (1962)

14 PENFIELD, S. L. On the occurrence of alkalies in beryl. *American Journal of Science* 28:25–32 (1884)

15 GINZBURG, A. I. On the question of the composition of beryl. *Trudy Mineralogicheskogo Muzeya, Akademiya Nauk SSSR*. (Leningrad) 7:56 (1955)

16 WICKERSHEIM, K. A., and BUCHANAN, R. A. The near infrared spectrum of beryl. *American Mineralogist* 44:440–4 (1959)

17 PARÉ, X., and DUCLOS, P. Étude par résonance magnétique nucléaire de l'eau dans le béryl. *Bulletin de la Société Francaise de Minéralogie et Cristallographie* 87:429–33 (1964)

18 BOUTIN, H., PRASK, H., and SAFFORD, G. J. Low-frequency motions of H_2O molecules in beryl from neutron scattering data. *Journal of Chemical Physics* 42:1469–70 (1965)

19 WICKERSHEIM, K. A., and BUCHANAN, R. A. Some remarks concerning the spectra of water and hydroxyl groups in beryl. *Journal of Chemical Physics* 42:1468–9 (1965)

20 SUGITANI, Y., NAGASHIMA, K., and FUJIWARA, S. The NMR analysis of water of crystallization in beryl. *Bulletin of the Chemical Society of Japan* 39:672–4 (1966)

21 WOOD, D. L., and NASSAU, K. Infrared spectra of foreign molecules in beryl. *Journal of Chemical Physics* 47:2220–8 (1967)

22 WOOD, D. L. The characterization of beryl and emerald by visible and infrared spectroscopy. *American Mineralogist* 53:777–800 (1968)

23 BAKAKIN, V. V., and BELOV, N. V. Crystal chemistry of beryl. *Geochemistry*, no. 5, pp. 484–500 (1962)

24 NASSAU, K., and WOOD, D. L. An examination of red beryl from Utah. *American Mineralogist* 53:801–6 (1968)

25 KLEEMAN, A. W. On the analysis of beryl from Boolcoomata, South Australia. *Transactions of the Royal Society of South Australia* 68:122–4 (1944)

26 FEKLICHEV, V. G. Chemical composition of minerals of the beryl group, character of isomorphism, and position of principal isomorphous elements in the crystal structure. *Geochemistry* no. 4. 410–21 (1963)

27 DOELTER, C. *Handbuch der Mineralchemie*. Vol. 2, part 2. Dresden and Leipzig: Theodor Steinkopff, pp. 584–99 (1917)

28 LÉVY, B. Recherches sur la formation et la composition des émeraudes. *Compte Rendu de l'Academie des Sciences* (Paris) 45:877–81 (1857)

29 LEITMEIER, H. Das Smaragdvorkommem im Habachtal in Salzburg und seine Mineralien. *Tschermak's mineralogische und petrographische Mitteilungen* (Vienna) 49:245–368 (1937)

30 OTERO MUÑOZ, G., and BARRIGA VILLALBA, A. M. *Esmeraldas de Colombia*. Bogota: Banco de Republica. 133 pp. (1948)

31 SIMPSON, E. S. *Minerals of Western Australia*. Vol. 1. Perth: Government Printer. pp. 195–207 (1948)

32 ROGERS, A. F., and SPERISEN, F. J. American synthetic emerald. *American Mineralogist* 27:762–8 (1942)

33 VLASOV, K. A. *Geochemistry and Mineralogy of Rare Elements and Genetic Types of their Deposits*. Vol. 2. Jerusalem: Israel Program for Scientific Translations. pp. 67–169 (1966)

34 BAKAKIN, V. V., RYLOV, G. M., and BELOV, N. V. Correlation between the chemical composition and unit cell parameters of beryls. *Doklady Akademiya Nauk SSSR, Earth Sciences Section*, (New York) 173:129–32 (1967)

35 SCHALLER, W. T., STEVENS, R. E., and JAHNS, R. H. An unusual beryl from Arizona. *American Mineralogist* 47:672–99 (1962)

Plate 1 Doubly terminated crystal of very rare red beryl from Wah Wah Mountains, Utah; one of the largest and finest crystals found at the locality, measuring 26 × 8 mm (1 × 0.35 in). John F. Barlow Collection, Appleton, Wisconsin. (*Original watercolour by J. Sinkankas*)

Plate 2 Corroded mass of transparent morganite from Brazil, about 60 × 58 mm (2.3 × 2.25 in). Willian Larson Collection, Fallbrook, California. (*Original watercolour by J. Sinkankas*)

Plate 3 Chartreuse-coloured terminated beryl crystal, almost completely transparent and flawless, showing large first-order prism faces, large basal face and several pyramidal forms. Diamantina district, Brazil; 45 × 36 mm (1.75 × 1.4 in). William Larson Collection, Fallbrook, California. (*Original watercolour by J. Sinkankas*)

Plate 4 Emerald in mica schist matrix from Transvaal, Republic of South Africa; 90 × 75 mm (3.5 × 3 in). In collection of John Sinkankas. (*Original watercolour by J. Sinkankas*)

Plate 5 Three transparent Brazilian beryl crystals: a pale blue aquamarine; a green beryl with etched prism faces and termination corroded into smooth, rounded surfaces, and a golden beryl partly corroded, especially along incipient basal cleavage planes. Central crystal is 77 × 24 mm (3 × 1 in). Willian Larson Collection, Fallbrook, California. (*Original watercolour by J. Sinkankas*)

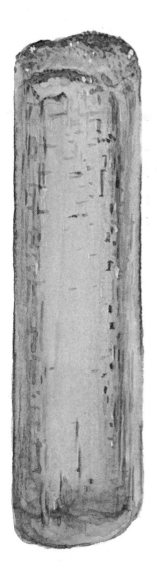

Plate 7 Two exceptional, transparent terminated aquamarine crystals from the famous Kleine Spitzkopje locality in Namibia; largest crystal is 54 × 19 mm (2.2 × 0.75 in). William Larson Collection, Fallbrook, California. (*Original watercolour by J. Sinkankas*)

Plate 8 Large gems of pink morganite (*left*), 235 carats, from Brazil, and golden beryl (*right*), 134 carats, from the Malagasy Republic. In the collections of the National Museum of Natural History, Washington, DC. *Courtesy Smithsonian Institution, Photo No. 77-14889.*

Plate 6 Magnificent transparent aquamarine crystal found in Adun Chilon, Transbaikalia, USSR; 123 × 33 mm (4.8 × 1.25 in). The crystal has been deeply corroded, so that all surfaces are covered with smooth etch marks and the terminations display numerous small peaks. Willian Larson Collection, Fallbrook, California. (*Original watercolour by J. Sinkankas*)

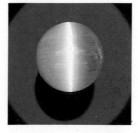

Plate 9 Cat's-eye aquamarine gem of 54.6 carats cut from Brazilian material; collections of the National Museum of Natural History, Washington, DC. *Courtesy Smithsonian Institution, Photo No. 79-420A.*

Plate 10 Greenish-golden beryl step-cut gem of 2054 carats (*left*); the largest of its kind, cut from Brazilian rough by John Sinkankas. (*Right*) a superb blue aquamarine step-cut gem, also Brazilian material; 911 carats. Both gems in the collections of the National Museum of Natural History, Washington, DC. *Courtesy Smithsonian Institution, Photo No. 77-14443. (Original watercolour by J. Sinkankas)*

Plate 11 Superb, doubly terminated morganite crystal from the White Queen Mine, Hiriart Hill, Pala, San Diego County, California; collection of David Wilber, Fallbrook, California. The crystal is bounded by broad faces of c{0001} with large faces of the first order prism and several pyramidal faces apparent. On cleavelandite matrix; crystal about 5 × 4.5 cm (2 × 1.75 in). *Courtesy Harold & Erica Van Pelt, Photographers, Los Angeles.*

Plate 12 Fine blue transparent aquamarine crystal of 19 kg (42 lb), 59 × 38 cm (23 × 15 in) found in 1979 in Jaqueto, Bahia, Brazil; now owned by Hans Stern, Jewelers, Rio de Janeiro. All surfaces are completely etched. *Photograph courtesy Neil Letson.*

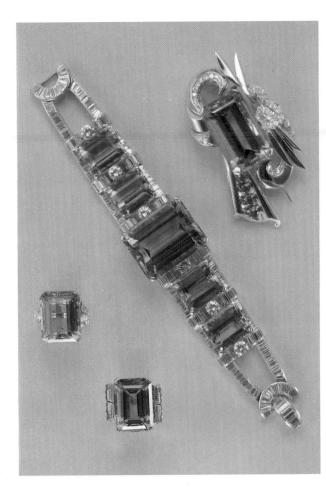

Plate 14 Superb morganite beryl in the Mineral Hall of the British Museum (Natural History), London. It was cut from Malagasy Republic material and is possibly the finest example of this variety in existence. Weight, 598.70 carats; 51 × 51 mm at the girdle and 38 mm deep. Acquired in 1913. *Photograph by Lee Boltin; courtesy British Museum (Natural History) and Peter G. Embrey.*

Plate 15 (below) The Hooker emerald brooch set with a magnificent square-cut emerald of about 75 carats; now in the collections of the National Museum of Natural History, Washington, DC. Reputedly, the stone once adorned the belt buckle of a Turkish Sultan. *Courtesy Smithsonian Institution, Photo No. 77-14194.*

Plate 13 The finest colour grade in aquamarine gems is shown in these pieces of jewellery, auctioned at Christie's in New York City, June 11–12, 1980. *Top right:* a 70-carat step-cut gem in white gold with diamonds and sapphires, $6800 (Lot 275). *Centre:* largest aquamarine is 84.68 carats, with four smaller gems; the bracelet is embellished with round and baguette diamonds, a Van Cleef & Arpels piece, $41 000 (Lot 272). *Lower left:* a superb stone of 30.85 carats, with diamonds, set in a ring, $6800 (Lot 269). *Bottom left:* a 31.04 carat gem with diamonds, set in a ring, $6000 (Lot 271). *Courtesy Christie, Manson & Woods International, Inc., New York.*

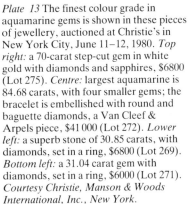

Plate 16 The Barlowe carved emeralds in the collections of the National Museum of Natural History, Washington, DC. These decorative objects were carved in India; the emerald at right was inlaid with gold and inset with small diamonds. *Courtesy Smithsonian Institution, Photo No. 77-10575.*

Plate 17 Emerald crystal with a pyrite crystal attached, from Muzo, Colombia; 25 mm (1 in) long. The emerald shows almost equal development of first and second order prisms. Julius & Miriam Zweibel Collection. *Photograph courtesy Wendell E. Wilson.*

Plate 18 Remarkable diamond and emerald necklace, dubbed 'The Spanish Inquisition Necklace' from the era in which it was made. Now in the collections of the National Museum of Natural History, Washington, DC. Astonishingly, the diamonds were bored through for suspension. The largest emerald weighs about 60 carats. *Courtesy Smithsonian Institution, Photo No. 77-10583.*

Plate 19 Emerald jewellery recently sold at auction. *Top:* bracelet with diamongs and central carved emerald of 35 mm (1.3 in) diameter, made by Van Cleef & Arpels and Vacheron-Constantin; it fetched $54 000 in June, 1980, in New York. *Left:* emerald and diamond bangle in white gold and platinum; $22 000, June, 1980, in New York. *Bottom:* a spray of brilliant-cut emeralds and diamonds in gold by Tiffany, the emeralds totalling 16.98 carats; $75 000, February, 1979, in New York. *Courtesy Christie, Manson & Woods International, Inc., New York.*

Plate 20 (*Right*) Polished baroque emeralds, fashioned in India, fastened into diamond-studded precious metal links to make this necklace; the largest is about 25 carats. Collections of the National Museum of Natural History, Washington, DC. *Courtesy Smithsonian Institution, Photo No. 77-10588.*

Plate 21 Magnificent modern necklace of carefully matched and graduated step-cut emeralds and round diamond brilliants. Approximately 150 mm (6 in) in diameter. *Courtesy Harry Winston, Inc., New York.*

Chapter 5
Physical and optical properties

Beryl is one of the most durable of all minerals. When released from its place of formation it persists virtually unchanged in the outcrops of its deposits or in the soils and gravels into which it is carried. In the stream gravels of Brazil, for example, large numbers of crystals have been found which retain traces of crystal faces despite prolonged chemical attack and abrasion with other stones. Such resistance is attributable to the crystalline structure and the strength of the bonds which retain the atoms in position.

Fracture and cleavage

Although brittle, beryl is considerably tougher than either quartz or topaz; minerals with which beryl is commonly found in alluvial deposits. Fracture surfaces are usually brilliant, smooth, and conchoidally curved like freshly broken glass. To the trained eye, the brilliance of the fresh fracture surfaces as compared to those of quartz (which tends to present a somewhat greasy luster) helps to identify this mineral. In crystals containing numerous inclusions, usually parallel to the prism faces and c-axis, the fracture surfaces across the prisms tend to be fine-granular in texture and somewhat oily in luster. Fractures parallel to prisms faces, on the other hand, seem to glitter in numerous long strip-like reflections from the surfaces of the exposed inclusion cavities.

Unlike ordinary fracture, *cleavage* in mineralogy and gemmology is used to designate a special kind of rupture: that caused by planes of weakness in the crystal structure itself, perhaps best seen in crystals of mica which can be easily split into many extremely thin sheets. Because of its compact structure, beryl can be cleaved with some measure of certainty only at 90° to its c-axis. Such a cleavage, generally indistinct and interrupted, is therefore parallel to the basal plane and has been recognized since antiquity. Tagore[1] (vol. 1, p. 412) remarked, for example, that

B–4

'the Emerald can be cloven at right angles to its axis' and that 'advantage of this is taken by the Indians, in whose ornaments flat stones of large size are often seen, –simply on this account'. Here Tagore refers to the partly developed basal cleavages which are so prominent a feature in many large Colombian emerald crystals. But they also occur in the Egyptian crystals and led to their use in beads. The development of basal cleavages in large emeralds also led to the employment of the flat sections in the typical engraved plaques of Mogul jewellery.

Basal cleavage is observed more commonly in emeralds from schist-type deposits where long, prismatic crystals are broken up by movements of the enclosing rock. (See *Colour Plate 4*, emerald crystals from South Africa). Similar segmented crystals, broken and displaced for the same reason, are commonly found in pegmatites. In contrast, crystals found in pockets or vugs seldom display cleavages and therefore provide the most perfect specimens. In addition to emeralds, beryls in which several colour phases occur within the same crystal, such as aquamarine and morganite, commonly display cleavages due to strains set up between them because of slightly differing cell dimensions in the two varieties.

The basal cleavage may be prominent due to splitting along plate-like inclusions grown parallel to the basal (terminal) plane, as is the case in the 'brown' beryl of Brazil whose body colour is actually aquamarine but whose obvious brown colour is imparted by numerous minute plates of ilmenite. When cut as cabochons with their bases parallel to the basal plane, a semi-metallic luster and a six-legged star results. Other beryl crystals may also display a similar reflection from this plane due either to solid inclusions, sometimes of haematite, or to very thin cavities containing gas or liquid.

Another cleavage plane, parallel to the prism faces was described by Lane[2], who found it to be more common than previously supposed. He described it as 'distinct' and 'about as good as that of nephelite'. In this connection, Lehmann[3] plunged heated beryls into cold water to study fracture patterns and found that many imperfect cracks developed parallel to the basal plane and many others appeared parallel to the prism faces. Similar fracture-cleavage patterns commonly occur in the beryl crystals 'frozen' in pegmatites and tend to break up the crystals into large numbers of closely interlocked cuboid fragments. Reflections from these surfaces sometimes impart a pearly luster, especially on the basal plane.

A common belief among emerald miners in Colombia is that basal cracks develop soon after crystals are taken from the ground. Pogue[4], for example, stated that 'the flaws or internal cracks . . . are not always present in the freshly mined stones, but if not they almost invariably develop soon after the specimen is removed from the enclosing rock, a result presumably caused by the strained condition of crystallization'. Olden[5], on the other hand, was firmly of the opinion that there was no basis in fact for such spontaneous decrepitation. There seems to be no reason to assume that any abrupt change in either temperature or pressure conditions occurs when these emeralds are mined, since they are found near the surface and in many cases are not even solidly enclosed in rock. The most likely explanation is that previously developed cracks were merely filled with water which rendered the crystals seemingly crack-free at the moment of exhumation but allowed these cracks to become visible when the water evaporated.

Hardness

The classical hardness assigned to beryl on the Mohs scale is 7.5–8. Auerbach[6] tested beryl and other minerals by indenting the specimens with a diamond point, and he reported the load in kilograms per mm². For beryl this proved to be 588 kg/mm². Lebedeva[7] also tested indentation hardness of thirty beryl specimens and found values between 933 and 1410 kg/mm², equivalent to 6.8 to 8.0 on the Mohs scale. Crystals containing alkalis appeared less hard as the alkali content increased. The hardness of prism faces was substantially higher than that measured on the basal plane, and, as was expected, clear crystals proved to be harder than turbid ones. Indentation hardness was also determined by Tzchorn[8] and by Gallagher[9], the latter finding on eight specimens of beryl an average Vickers hardness number, in kg/mm², of about 1300. The range fell between Vhn 1190±80 and 1450°0. Again, the hardness of prism faces exceeded that of basal faces.

As a means of discriminating beryl from quartz, especially in granitic pegmatites where these two species commonly grow side by side, hardness is of little value, quartz at H 7 on the Mohs scale being so close to beryl that no test would be convincing.

Thermal expansion

In addition to discussing the apparatus and methods for measurement of thermal expansivities, Tutton[14] (vol. 2, p. 1329) provided a comparative table of coefficients of thermal expansion for a number of minerals. From this table it can be seen that in terms of minimum linear expansion, beryl ranks behind only diamond and ahead of topaz and corundum. However, corundum displays less difference between its expansions along the c- and a-axes directions than does beryl. The extremely minute changes in dimensions experienced by diamond and corundum explain why these gems can be safely left in their jewellery mountings while undergoing repair involving strong heat. In contrast, the linear coefficient of expansion along the c-axis in quartz is almost five times as much as in beryl and along the lateral axes, almost fifteen times; thus the danger of heat-breakage in quartz is much greater than in beryl, and vastly greater than in diamond or corundum.

Thermal conductivity

The conduction of heat in beryl is not uniform and, as may be expected, it is related to crystallographic directions. This was demonstrated by Jannettaz[10], who found that if conductivity along the c-axis is taken as unity, conductivity along the lateral axes is 0.90 (later modified by him to 0.92)[11]. A recent study of thermal conductivity in beryl showed that with increasing temperature, a slight but increasing thermal conductivity occurs[12].

A convenient table of recently established thermal conductivities appeared in *Handbook of Chemistry and Physics*[13] (p. E-5), in which they are stated in terms of BTU versus time and area. The conductivity of beryl along the *c*-axis is shown to be about one-fourth greater than along the lateral axes. Conductivity along *c* increases slightly with rise in temperature, but in the lateral directions, it remains constant from 100° to 300°F.

Tutton[14] (vol. 2, pp. 1297–1301) not only explained the apparatus and methods for measuring conductivities, but also (pp. 1292–7) showed how the rates of conduction along several crystallographic directions could be visually demonstrated. A thin plate of the mineral is coated with wax and a hot metal point touched to its centre, upon which the heat radiating outward melts the wax. In the case of beryl, the melt figure is nearly circular on a plate cut across the *c*-axis but elliptical on a plate but parallel to that axis, with elongation of the ellipse along *c*.

In reporting on two commercial gem test instruments designed to identify diamonds, diamond simulants and other gems by means of their thermal conductivities, Read[15,16] indicated that emerald has a thermal conductivity in the region of 25 W/m/°C (compared with 1000–2600 for diamond and 40 for corundum).

Melting points and melts

Subjecting a thin splinter of beryl to the mineralogist's blowpipe flame results in no more than slight rounding of the sharp edges. Accordingly, in the fusibility scale which begins with stibnite (no. 1) and ends with quartz (no. 7), whose melting point is over 1700°C, beryl is given a position between 5 and 5.5. Brun[17] determined a melting point for beryl from Limoges, France, of between 1410° and 1430°C. Miller and Mercer[18] found that in heating beryl, a sinter formed first at about 1300°C, with small quantities of liquid developing at 1460°C and major melting taking place at about 1475°C. However, a clear melt could not be obtained until the temperature exceeded 1600°C. Beryl decomposed between 1475° and 1600°C and it was established that phenakite, chrysoberyl, and beryllium oxide had transiently formed. They concluded that phenakite + liquid formed at onset of beryl melting, then, as temperature increased, the phenakite decomposed and chrysoberyl + liquid formed, the latter decomposing in turn to beryllium oxide + liquid before finally melting into a clear liquid. These results are consistent with the fact that three strong structural bonds must be broken during melting, namely, those between Si-O, Al-O, and Be-O.

Riebling and Duke[19] attempted to prepare homogeneous beryl glass by melting pure BeO, Al_2O_3, and SiO_2 but without success, obtaining two-phase liquids whose boundaries were detectable in electron micrographs of the cooled melts. Munson[20] attempted to melt beryl under high pressures and found that between 15 and 50 kilobars, the decomposition products were silica, phenakite, and chrysoberyl. He claimed to have obtained clear beryl glass when a melt in excess of 2000°C was quenched at a pressure somewhat over 45.5 kbars, but quenching at lower temperatures resulted in the formation of crystalline silica with minor amounts of phenakite and chrysoberyl. At lower temperatures and pressures, some partial recrystallization of beryl took place from the melt.

The above results, coupled with the difficulties in the experimental procedures, strongly suggest that all so-called 'beryl' glasses claimed in years past to have been manufactured from melted beryl are actually mixtures of the components named, that is, quartz, phenakite, chrysoberyl, and possibly beryllium oxide. This also explains why the Verneuil flame-fusion process which works so well in the synthesis of corundums, spinels, and other minerals, has not been used for beryl. These matters are discussed at greater length in Chapter 9.

Electrical and magnetic properties

Beryl is a non-conductor of electricity. Its dielectric constant (resistance to the passage of current) was found by Curie[21] to be 6.24 parallel to the c-axis and 7.58 in the direction perpendicular to that. Fellinger[22] determined corresponding values of 6.076 and 7.023, while Takubo[23] obtained 5.76 and 6.17–6.18.

An electrical charge developed by heating (pyroelectricity) is best known in tourmaline, but Hankel[24] claims it occurs in beryl, although very weakly. He discovered positive charges on basal planes of Russian beryl crystals and negative charges on prism faces, but the results were not consistent, especially in the case of Elba beryls, which acquired positive charges on some areas of the prism faces instead of the expected negative charges. These crystals presented no external features to which this anomalous behaviour could be attributed.

The movement of a beryl crystal suspended by a thread between the poles of a magnet was studied by Knoblauch[25]. Plücker[26] found beryl to be paramagnetic negative, with the c-axis direction corresponding to the direction of least magnetic induction. Voigt and Kinoshuto[27] investigated the magnetic susceptibility of beryl and confirmed its paramagnetic nature.

Maser activity, or 'microwave amplification by stimulated emission of radiation', has been obtained in emerald and is due to the presence of the Cr^{3+} ion[28].

Density and specific gravity

By extrapolation of Fizeau's tables of coefficients of thermal expansion, Panebianco[29] concluded that beryl would attain maximum density at a temperature of $-4.7°C$. Bragg and West[30] calculated the density of ideal beryl as $2.661 \, gm/cm^3$ (or $2661 \, kg/m^3$ in International SI units), while Norrish[31] (p. 10) calculated the figure to be 2.64 and Radcliffe and Campbell[32] a figure of 2.62.

Special gravities, calculated as ratios of given weights of beryl to equal weights of water under standard conditions, range generally between 2.6–2.7 and 2.6–2.9.

The progressive increase in specific gravity with increase in alkali content is shown by Ford[33] and by Lacroix and Rengade[34]. A convenient plot of specific gravity against alkali content for numerous beryls appeared in Deer, Howie, and Zussman[35] (vol. 1, p. 262) and shows a steady rise from 2.66 for alkali-free beryl to about 2.77 for beryls containing about 28 mol % of alkalis. Lacroix [36] determined specific gravities on numerous Madagascar beryls and found the range to be 2.707–2.910, and noted that differences in value can be obtained from different parts of the same crystal. In general, those beryls obtained from muscovite-rich pegmatites are lower in specific gravity than those obtained from the lithium-bearing bodies.

TABLE 5.1 Specific gravities of beryls

Theoretical values, pure $Be_3Al_2Si_6O_{18}$	2.62 to 2.661
Maximum reported range	2.628 to 2.910
Aquamarine range	2.628 to 2.730
Emerald range	2.670 to 2.780
Alkali beryl range	ca. 2.800 to 2.910

In regard to gem beryls, especially in cut form, Webster[37] (pp. 99–125) provides values for specific gravity in the broad range of 2.68–2.90, with the following sub-ranges: aquamarine, 2.68–2.73, with an exceptional value of 2.80 for Maxixe blue beryl from Brazil; emerald, 2.69–2.78, measured on thirteen specimens from as many different localities; pink and white beryls, 2.80–2.90, with an exceptionally low value of 2.71 for one specimen. Vogel[38] examined thirteen emeralds from Colombia, Brazil, Urals, Habachtal, and Leysdorp and found values between 2.670 and 2.746, with the lowest for emeralds from Bom Jesus Dos Meiras, Brazil, and highest for emerald of Habachtal, Austria. However, an even higher value for a Habachtal emerald, namely 2.780, was determined by Jakob[39].

Numerous emerald specimens from world-wide localities were also examined by Gübelin (p. 114), who found a general range of 2.67 to 2.78, with the lowest values of 2.67–2.70 for Brazilian specimens and 2.69–2.71 for Colombian emeralds, while the highest value of 2.75–2.78 occurred in Pakistan emeralds. Barriga Villalba[41] found values for Colombian emeralds to be 2.5664 for a 'slightly green' specimen to 2.6890 for a 'pure' dark green emerald; a specimen with numerous filamental inclusions, or 'very jardin', gave 2.6769.

The estimation of specific gravities of various minerals in the field by 'hefting' of feeling the weight of a specimen in the hands is not useful in distinguishing beryl from its common and very similar associate quartz (specific gravity, 2.65), but is useful in the case of topaz, which at 3.54 is decidedly heavier. Methods for determining specific gravity are given in almost all standard mineralogical and gemmological texts, such as Webster[37].

Optical properties

Lustre

On smooth crystal faces and freshly broken surfaces, the lustre of beryl is glassy. Compared to other minerals, it resembles the lustre of quartz but is somewhat brighter, more like that of freshly broken glass without the slightly 'waxy' lustre that some fractured quartz displays.

The lustre of a polished gem is measurable in terms of its surface reflectivity according to Fresnel's simplified equation:

$$\text{reflectivity} = \frac{(n-1)^2}{(n+1)^2}$$

(where n = refracture index of the gem). The reflectivity for beryl, expressed as a percentage, is 5% and lies between that of quartz at 4.5% and that of topaz and tourmaline at around 5.7%.

Chatoyancy and asterism

The sharp, silky line, or *chatoyancy* seen in cat's-eye gems, notably chrysoberyls, is sometimes seen in beryls, but very rarely is it as distinctly defined. If several such streaks cross, the effect is called *asterism*, best known in star sapphires and rubies. Asterism in beryls is extremely rare. Both effects are due to extremely fine elongated inclusions, which may be crystals of a foreign mineral or merely voids, as is most commonly the case in cat's-eye beryls. The reflection of light from the inclusions gives rise to the optical effects, and the explanation for them is given in Goldschmidt and Brauns[42] who investigated chatoyant minerals, including a Brazilian cat's-eye beryl.

Most beryls displaying chatoyancy do so only weakly because the inclusions are neither as narrow nor as strongly reflective as they often are in chrysoberyl and corundum. Furthermore, in those beryls in which the effect is noted, especially in rather pale bluish or greenish aquamarines, other kinds of inclusions are also commonly present, which serve to scatter or absorb light and mute the display of chatoyancy. The finest cat's-eyes were cut from a rich golden beryl from Madagascar[43], but occasionally a good blue aquamarine cat's-eye appears from Brazil. Some years ago a few morganite crystals of pale pink colour were found in Brazil from which poor cat's-eyes could be cut, but only in large cabochons because the reflective tubes within were large and widely spaced. Chatoyancy in emerald is extremely rare, Henderson[44] recording a 4.56 carat gem in the Roebling collection in the US National Museum of Natural History as being one of the very few known to exist.

While ordinary chatoyancy in beryl is due to inclusions lying parallel to the c-axis, the few examples of asterism that have been recorded are due to three sets of inclusions, crossing mutually at angles of 60°, and lying in the plane at right angles to the c-axis. The earliest reliable record that could be found on such a gem is that in Greg and Lettsom[45] (p. 127), who described a star aquamarine gem cut from Mourne Mountains, Ireland, material 'exhibiting decided opalescence, and showing a six-rayed star like some varieties of corundum'. The whereabouts of this gem in unknown.

Henderson[44], in remarking on possible asterism in emerald, noted the specimen in the Townshend collection in the Victoria and Albert Museum (see *Figure 3.12*), but since this specimen only contains narrow zones of dark inclusions which cross like spokes in a wheel, it is called a 'fixed star', unlike the shimmering stars in stones in which the star is caused by reflections from numerous fibrous inclusions. Similar 'fixed' inclusions have been noted in the so-called *trapiche* emeralds of

Colombia, which will be described in Chapter 7. An editor's footnote in Henderson's article noted that 'a ten-year investigation by the G. I. A. [Gemmological Institute of America] has failed to reveal any verification of the previous occurrence of either true chatoyancy or epiasterism (asterism by reflected light) in an emerald'.

When the elongated inclusions in beryl crystals are abundant, they may contribute to a 'fibre optics' effect, that is, permit light to pass readily between the inclusions by repeated reflection from their surfaces along the c-axis direction. Thus, if a section cut across the c-axis direction is taken from a crystal and both surfaces polished, it can be placed over newsprint and the print, as if by magic, will appear on the upper surface of the polished section. This effect in beryl was noted as early as 1837 by Babinet[46], who remarked on haloes and rainbow effects observed when a pinpoint of light was passed through such a section.

Asterism of another kind had been noted in aquamarine and is due to multiple reflections from a series of minute spangles of a foreign mineral within the beryl (see *Figure 8.3*). Such spangles form upon the basal faces of the growing crystal and take up preferred orientations in respect to the beryl host. Such preferred orientation, or *epitaxy*, results in the edges of the spangles reflecting light in six-legged streaks, producing distinct but rather weak star phenomena. An aquamarine of this kind was recently found in Brazil and described by Rutland[47] and Eppler[48], the latter identifying the inclusions as extremely thin platelets of the iron-titanium mineral ilmenite. From the top of cabochon-cut gems, or looking down the c-axis, such gems appear bronze-brown in colour, but when viewed from the side, it can be seen that the inclusions occur only in very thin layers within a typical greenish-blue aquamarine host.

A remarkable star aquamarine owned by the late B. W. Anderson of England owes its star to inclusions somewhat similar to those described by Eppler[49]. In this instance, the inclusion is the sulphide mineral known as pyrrhotite, which forms six-sided flake-like crystals epitaxially orientated on the basal planes along with some chalcopyrite. The beryl itself is greenish, the star perfect but of weak intensity. Similar inclusions on basal planes include bright orange-red flakes of haematite, but these seem to provide only a beautiful orangey submetalic shimmer across the tops of cabochons, with no star.

Refraction of light

Because of its crystal structure, light rays passing through beryl are doubly refracted in all directions except that parallel to the c-axis, along which direction only single refraction occurs (see *Figure 5.1*). By convention, the index measured parallel to c is taken as the 'ordinary' or 'omega' (o) index, and in beryl it is invariably larger than the 'extraordinary' or 'epsilon' (e) index measured at right angles to the c-axis. Because of this consistent relationship, the optical sign is negative ($-$). As measurements are taken at increasing angles from the c-axis direction, the light rays split into two polarized components, diverging in value until the maximum difference is noted in the direction perpendicular to the c-axis. The difference is the double refraction or birefringence, designated 'd' or 'delta', or merely 'difference'.

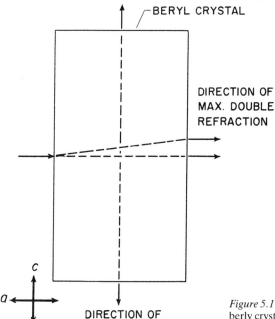

Figure 5.1 Behaviour of light passing through a
berly crystal, showing directions of single refraction
and maximum double refraction. (John Sinkankas).

From the standpoint of the jeweller interested in potential brilliancy of cut gems, the refractive index of beryl, upon which the surface reflectance component of brilliancy depends, is relatively low compared to many other gems such as spinel, corundum and particularly diamond.

Despite the low refractive index, beryl can be cut into very satisfactory gems of considerable brilliance, providing the lapidary takes care to shape the rough into proper proportions and cut the facets at the correct angles so as to achieve maximum total internal reflection as explained in Chapter 10.

Refractive index ranges

Table 5.2 shows ranges for sodium light (589.3 nm) compiled from the literature. As can be seen, there are three groups selected according to generally accepted colour varieties. The first group includes the aquamarines and other pale-coloured beryls as blue, green-blue, blue-green, yellow-green, yellow, and brownish-yellow. Some of the specimens in this group are listed as 'colourless' by their investigators but are probably not alkali goshenites, which would ordinarily have higher values. On the other hand, a number of Madagascar alkali beryls investigated by Duparc *et al.* and Lacroix are described as blue in various shades, sometimes fairly dark, or combining blue and rose in the same crystal. Despite the blue colours, which would ordinarily be associated with lower refractive indices, they are alkali beryls and hence provide higher indices. The steady rise of refractive indices with increasing alkali content is shown in *Figure 5.2*.

TABLE 5.2 Beryl refractive index ranges, (sodium light) (5893 Å)

Beryl Variety	o-ray	e-ray	Birefringence	No of Samples	Reference
Aquamarine,	1.57015–1.58234	1.56561–1.57592	0.00590–0.00693	5	50
other pale varieties	1.5691–1.5754	1.5644–1.5700	0.0046–0.0057	8	51
	1.56715–1.57924	1.56301–1.57371	0.00414–0.00553	11	52
Emerald	1.5705–1.5893	1.5656–1.5827	0.0049–0.0067	12	53
	1.57325–1.5908	1.56793–1.5839	0.00532–0.00701	10	52
	1.5712–1.5905	1.5663–1.5975	0.0049–0.007	9	54, 55
	1.602	1.592	0.010	1	66
Rose,	1.5825–1.5977	1.5761–1.5894	0.0064–0.0083	3	56
other alkali beryls	1.58455–1.59824	1.57835–1.59014	0.00620–0.00810	4	57
	1.5977–1.5977	1.5894–1.5903	0.0074–0.0083	2	58
	1.5782–1.5899	1.5725–1.5921	0.0057–0.0086	7	59, 60
	1.5974	1.5890	0.0084	1	61
	1.5860–1.5971	1.5795–1.5894	0.0065–0.0083	4	62
	1.5865–1.6021	1.5791–1.5953	0.0065–0.0069	5	63
	1.5772–1.6011	1.5717–1.59195	0.00549–0.00830	5	52
		GENERALIZED RANGES			
Aquamarine, other pale varieties	1.567–1.582	1.563–1.576	0.004–0.007		
Emerald[a]	1.570–1.591(1.602)	1.566–1.597(1.592)	0.005–0.007(0.010)		
Rose, other alkali beryls	1.577–1.602	1.572–1.595	0.007–0.008		
All varieties	1.569–1.598	1.565–1.590	0.004–0.008	64	
All varieties	1.578–1.592	1.571–1.585	0.007–0.007	64b	
All varieties	1.568–1.602	1.564–1.595	0.004–0.008	65	

[a]The extraordinarily high values shown in parentheses were determined on a Zambian emerald by Bank[66] and are 'apparently the highest hitherto known of natural emeralds'.
[b]From graph in *Figure 5.2* showing steady rise in values from pure beryl to that containing ca. 28% alkali.

Dispersion

The difference in refracting power as measured by differences in refractive indexes between the red and blue portions of the visible spectrum is called the *dispersion*. Dispersion is responsible for the flashes of pure spectral colours that are so characteristic of otherwise colourless diamond gems. Cut specimens act like miniature prisms and 'spread' the white light falling upon them into its coloured components. Compared to diamond's dispersion of 0.044, that of beryl is very low, only about 0.0090–0.0100. It is for this reason that no art of the lapidary can induce in a beryl gem the fine display characteristic of diamond and which gemmologists call the 'fire'.

Optical anomalies

Beryl possesses one principal axis (*c*) of symmetry which coincides with the single optic axis, hence beryl is optically *uniaxial*. However, almost from the first, investigations of thin sections of beryl in polarized light found that some crystals

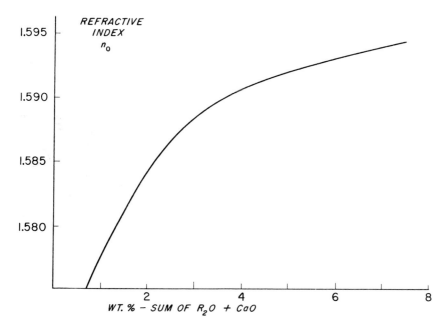

Figure 5.2 Rise in refractive index (ordinary or omega ray) with rise in content of alkalis (R_2O) and calcium oxide (CaO), the alkalis being sodium-lithium and sodium-lithium-cesium. From a graph of P. Černý and F. C. Hawthorne, Refractive indices versus alkali contents in beryl, *Canadian Mineralogist* 14 (1976):491–7. (John Sinkankas).

display features typical of biaxial minerals, or those in which two optical axes are present. In still other specimens it was found that biaxiality occurred only in certain areas, and while the morphology of beryl clearly places it in the hexagonal system, these anomalous biaxial phenomena suggested that some beryl crystals are orthorhombic.

References

1 TAGORE, S. M. *Mani-Málá, or a Treatise on Gems.* 2 vols. Calcutta: Stanhope Press. 1046 pp. (1879)

2 LANE, A. C. Prismatic cleavage in beryl. *American Mineralogist* 3:47 (1879)

3 LEHMANN, J. Contractionsrisse an Krystallen. *Zeitschrift für Kristallographie und Mineralogie* (Leipzig) 11:608–12 (1886)

4 POGUE, J. E. The emerald in Spanish America. *Pan-American Union Bulletin No. 43*, pp. 706–20 (1916)

5 OLDEN, C. Emeralds: their mode of occurrence and methods of mining and extraction in Colombia. *Transactions of the Institute of Mining and Metallurgy* (London) 21:194–209 (1911)

6 AUERBACH, F. Die Härtescala in absolutem Masse. *Annalen der Physik und Chemie* (Leipzig) ser. 3, vol. 58, pp. 257–80 (1896)

7 LEBEDEVA, S. I. [Microhardness of beryl crystals]. *Trudy Instituta Mineralogii, Geokhimii i Kristallokhimi Redkikh Elementov* (Moscow) no. 18, p. 107–15 (1963)

8 TZCHORN, G. Zur Mineralogie der Topasgänge der Scherlberge (Östtransbaikalien). *Geologie* (Berlin) 12:283–311 (1963)

9 GALLAGHER, M. J. Micro-indentation hardness of beryl. *Geological Survery of Great Britain Bulletin 25*, pp. 96–7 (1966)

10 JANNETTAZ, E. *Sur la Propagation de la Chaleur dans les Corps Cristallisés.* Paris: Gauthier-Villars. 82 pp. (1873)

11 JANETTAZ, E. Note sur la propagation de la chaleur dans les corps cristallisés. *Bulletin de la Société Francaise de Minéralogie et Cristallographie* 15:133–44 (1892)

12 KNAPP, W. J. Thermal conductivity of non-metallic single crystals. *Journal of the American Ceramic Society* 26:48–55 (1943)

13 HANDBOOK OF CHEMISTRY AND PHYSICS 51st ed. Cleveland: Chemical Rubber Co. (1971)

14 TUTTON, A. E. H. *Crystallography and Practical Crystal Measurement.* Vol. 2, London. MacMillan and Co.

15 READ, P. G. The Gemtek Gemmologist–A Test Report. *Journal of Gemmology.* Vol. XVIII, No. 7, 643–650 (1983)

16 READ, P. G. The Alpha-Test Gemstone Identifiex–A Test Report. *Journal of Gemmology.* Vol. XIX, No. 3, 261–265 (1984)

17 BRUN, A. [Melting point of beryl]. *Archives des Sciences Physiques et Naturelles* (Geneva) 12:352 (1902)

18 MILLER, R. P., and MERCER, R. A. The high-temperature behaviour of beryl melts and glasses. *Mineralogical Magazine* (London) 35:250–76 (1965)

19 RIEBLING, E. F., and DUKE, D. A. BeO · Al$_2$O$_3$ · SiO$_2$ system: structural relationships of crystalline, glassy, and molten beryl. *Journal of Material Sciences* 2:33–9 (1967)

20 MUNSON, R. A. High-temperature behaviour of beryl and beryl melts at high pressure. *Journal of the American Ceramic Society* 50:669–70 (1967)

21 CURIE, J. Recherches sur le pouvoir inducteur spécifique et la conductibilité des corps cristallisés. *Annales de Chimie at de Physique* 17:385–434; 18:203–69 (1889)

22 FELLINGER, R. Über die Dielektrizitätskonstante einiger natürlicher und synthetischer Edelsteine. *Annalen der Physik*, (Leipzig) ser. 4, vol. 60, pp. 181–95 (1919)

23 TAKUBO, J. Versuche über die Dielektrizitätskonstanten einiger Mineralien und über das elektrische Verhalten derselben bei Erhitzung. *Memoirs of the College of Science, Kyoto Imperial University*, ser. B, vol. 16, no. 2, pp. 95–154 (1948)

24 HANKEL, W. G. Über die thermoelektrischen Eigenschaften des Kalkspathes, des Berylles, des Idocrases und des Apophyllits. *Abhandlungen der königlich-sächsischen Gesellschaft der Wissenschaften, mathematisch-physische Klasse, Leipzig* 11:201–71 (1878)

25 KNOBLAUCH, H. Ueber das Verhalten krystallisirter Körper zwischen elektrischen Polen. *Annalen der Physik und Chemie* (Leipzig) 83:289–99 (1851)

26 PLÜCKER, J. On the magnetic induction of crystals. *Philosophical Transactions of the Royal Society of London, 1858*, no. 148, pp. 543–87 (1859)

27 VOIGT, W., and KINOSHUTO, S. Bestimmung absoluter Werte von Magnetisierungszahlen, insbesondere für Krystalle. *Zeitschrift für Kristallographie und Mineralogie* (Leipzig) 47:81–3 (1910)

28 GOODWIN, F. E. Maser action in emerald. *Journal of Applied Physics* 32:1624–25 (1961)

29 PANEBIANCO, H. [The maximum density of beryl]. *Revista de Mineralogia e Cristallografia Italiana* (Padua) 38:3–11 (1909)

30 BRAGG, W. L., and WEST, J. The structure of beryl, Be$_3$Al$_2$Si$_6$O$_{18}$. *Proceedings of the Royal Society of London* A-111, pp. 691–714 (1926)

31 NORRISH, K. An X-ray study of West Australian beryl. *Journal and Proceedings of the Royal Society of New South Wales* 34:1–16 (1947)

32 RADCLIFFE, D., and CAMPBELL, F. A. Beryl from Birch Portage, Saskatchewan. *Canadian Mineralogist* 8:493–505 (1966)

33 FORD, W. E. The effect of the presence of alkalies in beryl on its optical properties. *American Journal of Science*, 30:128–30 (1910)

34 LACROIX, A., and RENGADE. Sur les propriétés optiques des béryls roses de Madagascar. *Bulletin de la Société Francaise de Minèralogie et Cristallographie*, 34:123–5 (1911)

35 DEER, W. A., HOWIE, R. A., and ZUSSMAN, J. *Rock-Forming Minerals.* Vol 1. London: Longmans. pp. 256–67 (1962)

36 LACROIX, A. Sur la continuité de la variation des propriétés physiques des béryls de Madagascar, en relation avec leur composition chimique. *Bulletin de la Société Française de Minéralogie et Cristallographie* 35:200–8 (1912)

37 WEBSTER, R. *Gems.* 4th ed. (revised by Anderson, B. W.), London: Butterworths. pp. 99–125 (1975)

38 VOGEL, P. Optische Untersuchungen am Smaragd und einigen anderen durch Chrom gefärbten Mineralien. *Neues Jahrbuch für Mineralogie.* 68:401–38 (1934)

39 JAKOB, J. Drei Analysen von Beryll. *Schweizerische mineralogische und petrographische Mitteilungen* 18:607–9 (1938)

40 GÜBELIN, E. J. Gemmologische Beobachtungen am neuer Smaragd aus Pakistan. *Der Aufschluss* (Heidelberg) Sonderheft 18, pp. 111–16 (1968)

41 OTERO MUÑOZ, G., and BARRIGA VILLALBA, A. M. *Esmeraldas de Colombia.* Bogota: Banco de la Republica. 133 pp. (1948)

42 GOLDSCHMIDT, V., and BRAUNS, R. Über Lichtkreise und Lichtknoten an Kristallkugeln. *Neues Jahrbuch für Mineralogie* (Stuttgart) Beilage-Bd. 31, pp. 220–42 (1911)

43 SINKANKAS, J. Some freaks and rarities among gemstones. *Gems & Gemmology* 8:197–99 (1955)

44 HENDERSON, E. P. Cat's-eye emerald. *Gems & Gemmology* 5:222 (1955)

45 GREG, R. P., and LETTSOM, W. G. *Manual of the Mineralogy of Great Britain and Ireland.* London: John Van Voorst. 483 pp. (1858)

46 BABINET. Beiträge zur meterorologischen Optik. *Annalen der Physik und Chemie* (Leipzig) 41:128–44 (1837)

47 RUTLAND, E. H. An unusual brown beryl. *The Gemmologist* (London) 25, no. 304, pp. 191–2 (1956)

48 EPPLER, W. F. Notes on asterism in corundum-. . . chatoyancy in beryl. *Journal of Gemmology* (London) 6:195–212 (1958)

49 EPPLER, W. F. An unusual star-beryl. *Journal of Gemmology* (London) 7:183–91 (1960)

50 SCHRAUF, A. Bestimmung der optischen Constanten krystallisierter Körper. *Sitzungsberichte der Kaiserlichen Akademie der Wissenschaften, Mathematisch-Naturwissenschaftliche Classe,* 42:107–120 (1860)

51 KOHLMANN, H. Beiträge zur Kenntniss der brasilianischen Berylls. *Neues Jahrbuch für Mineralogie* (Stuttgart) Beilage-Bd. 25, pp. 135–81 (1908)

52 BÖSE, R. Optische und spektrographische Untersuchungen an Beryllen, insbesondere bei höheren Temperaturen. *Neues Jahrbuch für Mineralogie* (Stuttgart) Beilage-Bd. 70, pp. 467–570 (1936)

53 VOGEL, P. Optische Untersuchungen am Smaragd und einigen anderen durch Chrom gefärbten Mineralien. *Neues Jahrbuch für Mineralogie* (Stuttgart) 68:401–38 (1934)

54 GÜBELIN, E. J. Emeralds from Sandawana. *Journal of Gemmology* (London) 6:340–54 (1958)

55 GÜBELIN, E. J. Gemmologische Beobachtungen am neue Smaragd aus Pakistan. *Der Aufschluss* (Heidelberg) Sonderheft 18, pp. 111–16 (1968)

56 LACROIX, A. Les minéraux des filons de pegmatite à tourmaline lithique de Madagascar. *Bulletin de la Société Français de Minéralogie et Cristallographie* 31:218–47 (1908)

57 FORD, W. E. The effect of the presence of alkalis in beryl upon its optical properties. *American Journal of Science* 30:128–30 (1910)

58 LACROIX, A. Nouvelles observations sur les minéraux des pegmatites de Madagascar. *Bulletin de la Société Français de Minéralogie et Cristallographie* 33:37–50 (1910)

59 DUPARC, L., WUNDER, M., and SABOT, R. Les minéraux des pegmatites des environs d'Antsirabe à Madagascar. *Mémoires de la Société de Physique et d'Histoire Naturelle de Genéve* 36, fasc. 3, pp. 281–410 (1910)

60 DUPARC, L., WUNDER, M., and SABOT, R. Contribution à la connaissance des minéraux et des pegmatites de Madagascar. Note sur le béryl de divers gisements situés dans le environs d'Antsirabe. *Bulletin de la Société Français de Minéralogie et Cristallographie* 33:53–67 (1910)

61 DUPARC, L., WUNDER, M., and SABOT, R. Contribution à la connaissance des minéraux des pegmatites (deuxième note). *Bulletin de la Société Français de Minéralogie et Cristallographie* 34:131–8 (1911)

62 LACROIX, A., and RENGADE. Sur les Propriétés optiques des béryls roses de Madagascar. *Bulletin de la Société Français de Minéralogie et Cristallographie* 34:123–5 (1911)

63 LACROIX, A. Sur la continuité de la variation des propriétés physiques des béryls de Madagascar, en relation avec leur composition chimique. *Bulletin de la Société Français de Minéralogie et Cristallographie* 35:200–8 (1912)

64 DEER, W. A., HOWIE, R. A., and ZUSSMAN, J. *Rock-Forming Minerals.* Vol. 1, London: Longmans. pp. 256–67 (1962)

65 WINCHELL, A. N., and WINCHELL, H. *Elements of Optical Mineralogy.* Part 2, 4th ed. New York: John Wiley. 551 pp. (1951)

66 BANK, H. Sehr hochlichtbrechender Smaragd aus Sambia. *Zeitschrift der deutschen gemmologischen Gesellschaft* 29, no. 1/2, p. 101–3 (1980)

Chapter 6
Colour and luminescence

Dichroism

As described in the previous chapter, light passing through a beryl crystal is divided into two rays, the ordinary ray *o* and the extraordinary ray *e*. Both rays not only provide different refractive indexes, but they are also polarized in respect to each other. In coloured beryls, among other coloured doubly refracting minerals, each ray bears its own hue or a distinct tint of the same hue. This is the effect known as *dichroism,* or literally, 'two-colouring', or *pleochroism,* 'multi-colouring', and is caused by differential selective absorption in the gemstone. The differences in hue may be readily detected by use of the gemmological dichroscope, a small tubular instrument which contains two side by side rectangles or 'windows' of polaroid film, each turned 90° to the other in respect to polarity. The function of the polaroid film is to suppress the colour of one ray and allow the colour of the other ray to pass through. A small magnifying lens in the tube enlarges the window images and enables easy comparison of the hues. Alternatively the dichroscope may employ a polished section of optically pure calcite (Iceland Spar) whose strong double refraction produces side-by-side images or windows of the two sets of polarised rays.

When held against a cut gem or rough specimen of beryl and rotated, different colours will appear in the windows at some point during the rotation. However, if the specimen is viewed in the direction of the *c*-axis, along which the light rays do not divide, the same colour appears in both windows. Elsewhere, the incoming light ray is split into two polarized rays and each can be examined at leisure, the dichroscope tube being turned until the maximum contrast is obtained. Such contrasts naturally depend on the intensity of the colour to begin with, but even in weakly coloured specimens it is often possible to see distinct differences in the hues. (In addition to its usefulness in gem identification, the dichroscope is also helpful to the lapidary in selecting the best way to cut a gem for the finest colour).

TABLE 6.1 Dichroic colours in beryl

Apparent colour	Dichroic colours		Intensity
Green (emerald)	Yellowish green	Bluish green	Weak to distinct
Green (other than emerald)	Colourless or slightly yellowish	Bluish green	Weak to distinct
Green	Colourless	Very pale green	Weak
Green (Maxixe type)[a]	Green	Yellow	Distinct
Greenish blue	Colourless	Pale bluish green	Distinct
Greenish blue	Pale yellowish green	Pale bluish green	Distinct
Blue	Very pale yellow	Blue	Distinct
Blue	Colourless	Blue	Distinct to strong
Blue[b]	Blue	Colourless	Strong
Blue (Maxixe type)[a]	Blue	Colourless	Strong
Blue (Maxixe type)[a]	Blue	Pale pink	Strong
Yellow	Yellowish green	Pale bluish green	Very weak
Yellow	Greenish yellow	Yellow	Distinct
Yellow	Pale yellow	Lighter yellow	Weak
Pink (morganite)	Yellowish pink	Pink	Weak to distinct
Pink (morganite)	Pale pink	Pale bluish pink	Weak to distinct
Red (Utah)	Yellowish red	Purple red	Distinct
Violet[c]	Colourless	Violet	Distinct

[a]K. Nassau, Examination of Maxixe-type blue and green beryl, *Gems & Gemmology* 14:131.
[b]B. W. Anderson, *Gem Testing*, 8th ed. (London: Butterworths, 1971), p. 235, Madagascar material.
[c]R. Webster, *Gems*, 3rd ed. (London: Butterworths, 1975), pp. 815–16.
Other information from personal observation and from other authorities.

Table 6.1 lists the apparent colours of beryls, showing the dichroic hues and the intensities that may be expected.

In the following paragraphs the ions responsible for production of colour in beryls will be identified. In general, there is significant correlation between colour and composition, and, as will be seen some validity can be given to the use of colours as varietal designations in beryl and as clues to chemical composition.

Colour zoning

Many beryl crystals are uniformly coloured for the most part, but others are zoned in various patterns reflecting changes in chemical composition during growth. In emerald, for example, the most common type of zoning occurs as a lighter-hued or even colourless core that is enveloped by outer zones of darker colour. As shown in the examples in *Figure 6.1*, several zones may develop, and even more complex patterns may occur. Striking examples of colour zoning in emerald crystals are shown in a colour plate in Klein[1] and in Barriga Villalba[2].

Colourless cores are responsible for the generally pale hue of North Carolina emeralds. Brazilian beryl deposits also furnish many crystals which are aquamarine at the base and colourless to pink at the top, indicating progressive incorporation of alkali elements in their composition. Some recent finds of morganite display outer zones of pink material and inner zones of blue or grayish beryl, sometimes in striking contrast. Another type of zoning in aquamarines is shown in the top crystal

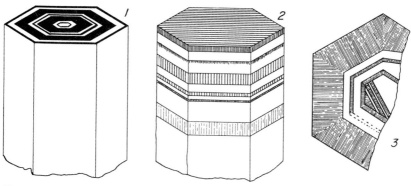

Figure 6.1 Types of colour-zoning in Leysdorp emerald crystals, after J. M. LeGrange, 'The Barbara Beryls', *Transactions of the Geological Society of South Africa* 32 (1929). 1. Zones of colourless or faintly pink alternating with green zones. 2. Less commonly, zones of varying intensity green parallel to the basal pinacoid. 3. Mixed zoning, perhaps due to further growth of emerald upon a fragment of an earlier crystal in which zones were parallel to the *c*-axis, as in type 1. (John Sinkankas).

Figure 6.2 Aquamarine crystals. *Top:* Terminated, slightly worn simple hexagonal prism with narrow bands of colour parallel to the basal plane, from the Nerchinsk region, Transbaikalia, USSR; about 11.5 cm (4½ in) long. The other crystals are from Minas Gerais, Brazil. (These crystals are in the Sinkankas Collection).

in *Figure 6.2,* in which numerous narrow colour zones appear parallel to the basal plane. This type of zoning is perhaps most characteristic of certain beryls from the famous Adun Chilon deposits in the Transbaikal region of the USSR. Such zones may be various tints of blue, green, or even yellow.

Emerald colour

The first clue to the cause of colour in emerald came in 1798 when Vauquelin[3] made his landmark analysis and found chromium. From his discovery it was concluded that this element was responsible for the green colour, but differences of opinion arose among other chemists. For example, Lévy[4] found only a trace of chromium in an analysis of Muzo emerald, and he believed that the colour was due not to chromium but to some organic compound from the black calcite that accompanied the emerald. However, Wöhler and Rose[5] showed that the green colour did not disappear with strong heating as would have happened had the colour been due to an organic compound. They reiterated the view that the colour was due to chromium. Furthermore, to demonstrate the colouring influence of chromium, they prepared a series of glass melts 'doped' with a chromium salt and obtained, upon cooling, glasses coloured by greens similar to those observed in emerald. Jannettaz[6] took the step of heating a sample of emerald-bearing black schist from the Egyptian mines and found no traces of any carbon compound that could have supported Lévy's contention.

Using a spectroscope to detect typical absoption lines in light rays passed through emerald, in 1912 Moir[7] found 'hair lines' of absorptions at wavelengths of 680.5 nm and 679.5 nm, and he concluded that 'the almost unique spectra of emerald and ruby are due to chromium oxide which has been compelled to vibrate in an abnormal or constrained manner, leading to the production of narrow absorption bands in the spectrum'. He also concluded that 'the constraining substance . . . in the case of emerald is beryllium oxide[8]'.

A few years later, Wild and Klemm[9], examining emeralds from several deposits, found vanadium as well as chromium lines in the spectrum of emerald from the Urals, thus suggesting for the first time that the vanadium ion could also be responsible, in part, for the colour of this beryl variety. The presence of vanadium was confirmed spectroscopically by Fersman[10], but it was found only in dark-coloured specimens. Fersman also noted that the serpentine associated with the Uralian emeralds contained 0.23% Cr_2O_3 and that there appeared to be a correlation between the intensity of colour and increasing content of chromium oxide in the matrix of emerald. A similar correlation was suggested by Klemm[11], who expressed his conviction that Cr replaced Al in the beryl structure.

In 1934, Vogel[12] published results of an intensive study of absorptions in emerald and other minerals coloured by chromium, using polished prisms manufactured from transparent emerald, and prepared curves of absorption versus various wavelengths of light. At the same time he investigated absorptions produced by vanadium in synthetic 'green sapphire' corundum, manufactured by the I. G. Farbenindustrie in Germany, and in an alexandrite-type synthetic spinel also doped with vanadium. When the absorption curves produced by Cr and V are compared (*Figure 6.3*), it can be seen why Vogel concluded that vanadium behaved like chromium in inducing green colour.

In a somewhat similar investigation, Kolbe[13] studied colour in minerals caused by manganese, chromium, and iron, and in examining two emeralds (from an unspecified source) found maximum absorption at 620 and 616 nm, and at 6160 nm

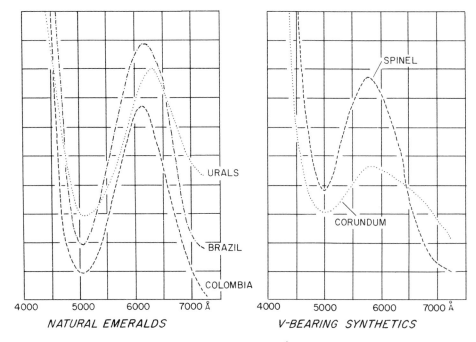

Figure 6.3 Absorption curves of light from about 4500–7500 Å (450–750 nm) in natural emeralds and vanadium-bearing synthetics, the latter showing the coincidence of the curves with those produced by chromium. After graphs by P. Vogel in Optische Untersuchungen am Smaragd und einigen anderen Chrom gefärbten Mineralien, *Neues Jahrbuch für Mineralogie* 68 (1934):401–438 (John Sinkankas).

for a specimen from Habachtal, Austria, all consistent with Vogel's findings. Absorption curves were also prepared for emerald by Grum-Grzhimailo[14], who investigated the wavelength region of 440–660 nm and noted that increasing amounts of Cr caused maximum absorption shifts from 535 nm to 630 nm and minimum absorption shifts from 480 nm to 550 nm. He suggested that pleochroism, or the difference in colours observed along differing directions in the emerald crystal, was caused by deformation of electron orbits around Cr atoms.

In 1970, Nassau and Jackson[16] confirmed the presence of both Cr and V in the trapiche emeralds of Muzo. X-ray fluorescence analyses indicated 0.10% Cr and 0.12% V in clear material. In a study of the V^{3+} ion in silicate and oxide minerals, Schmetzer[17] stated that in minerals such as beryl in which both Cr^{3+} and V^{3+} were colouring ions, the absorption curves due to each coincided for the most part, the net effect being an intensification of the green colour beyond that caused by Cr^{3+} alone.

The establishment of vanadium as a colouring ion in emerald led to a lively controversy as to whether or not vanadian emerald-like beryls should be called emerald, in spite of the fact that, as Wood and Nassau[18] pointed out, numerous emeralds are known which contain both chromium and vanadium. They suggested that if Cr is present to about 0.1% or more, the beryl could retain its classic name, and that another name be given to those in which V is the primary colouring ion.

The extensive study of causes of colour in beryls by Schmetzer *et al.* (p. 25 ff.) noted the general coincidence of absorption curves for two groups of emerald-coloured beryls, the 'Cr emeralds', containing Cr and Fe, and the 'V emeralds', containing V, Fe, and some Cr. They further noted that they could find only forty spectral studies of emeralds and suggested that this is insufficient evidence to establish any firm conclusions concerning cause of colour. Until many more analyses are performed, the relative abundances of Cr and V, perhaps as coupled with Fe, cannot be established, although it seems clear that if both Cr and V are colouring ions, both Cr emeralds and V emeralds are equally deserving of the name. It would be interesting, for example, to analyze numerous specimens of Egyptian emeralds to determine relative abundances of these elements. If vanadium is found in them, then such beryls would qualify as 'emeralds' on the basis of priority naming.

Absorption spectra for emerald are conveniently presented in Webster[20] (pp. 115, 767, 915) and more recently in Schmetzer *et al.* (pp. 25–9), the latter containing numerous references to the literature on beryl colour. For gemmological examinations with the hand spectroscope the data in Webster are perhaps more useful. He noted (p. 115) that distinct differences may be observed according to the direction in the crystal examined, or if only the *o*-ray or both *o*- and *e*-rays are being examined. Commonly, the *o*-ray shows only two narrow absorption bands in the red portion of the spectrum, the first being a doublet at 683 nm and 680 nm, the second a sharp line at 637 nm. A weak, broad absorption with vague boundaries obscures much of the yellow portion of the spectrum from about 625 nm to 580 nm, and 'there is a narrow line in the blue at 4775 Å which may only be seen in very chrome-rich stones when another line at 4725 Å may also be noticed'. When the *e*-ray is observed, however, the doublet previously mentioned appears stronger, especially the line at 683 nm, but the line at 637 nm is absent and its place taken by two diffuse lines at 662 nm and 646 nm. The latter line is bordered on the shortwave or red end by 'characteristic transparency patches', while 'the broad absorption region is now nearer to the red and much weaker, and there are no lines in the blue'.

Absorption coefficients for both rays in emerald have been calculated by Wood and Nassau[18] in relation to weight percent of Cr, with the suggestion that these may be applied to any sample to determine the approximate Cr quantity without destructive analysis. Barriga Villalba[2] (p. 115) noted in connection with colour of Colombian emeralds that while the specific gravity varies but little, it seems to 'depend on the colour', and he reported specific gravities ranging from 2.5664 for very pale material to 2.6890 for first-class, pure emerald. However, in view of the very small quantities of Cr involved in substitution for ions in the crystal structure, it is unlikely that measurable differences in specific gravity would be found in all cases. Correlation between emerald colour and density has not been made by other investigators.

That the Cr ion is not confined to emerald alone is shown by the work of Wild and Biegel[21]. The Brazilian beryls they investigated resembled aquamarines generally, but with the blue-green tint suggestive of emerald colour. When heat-treated, the colour scarcely changed, as it would be expected to do in beryls in which the principal colouring agent is iron. A spectroscopic examination showed that the colour was in part due to Cr and V.

In hand specimens of emerald and in cut gems, the differences of colour depending on which way the light rays pass through the crystal may sometimes be quite obvious. In a typical hexagonal crystal, provided it is transparent enough, one will see the decidedly bluish-green colour when looking through the sides of the prism (corresponding to the *e*-ray direction) and a yellowish-green colour when looking down the prism in the direction parallel to the prism faces (corresponding to the *o*-ray direction). These differences are less easy to see in cut gems unless they are large, and for the determination of the two colours the gemmologist's dichroscope usually is employed. This small instrument examines each ray separately, showing their colours side-by-side, making comparison easy.

In terms of cut gems, usually fashioned as step-cuts, the shape of natural crystals encourages the lapidary to cut the gem so that the table facet is parallel to the prism faces. Thus the colour seen in such a gem is largely the blueish-green prized by most connoisseurs of emeralds above the yellowish-green that would appear if the gem were cut with the table perpendicular to the *c*-axis.

Colour filters for emerald

As mentioned earlier, the light that passes through the emerald contains all wavelengths, not just green or blue-green. Other wavelengths, in the yellow, orange, and red ranges are suppressed but far from eliminated. In fact, so much red still passes that a clever optical filtering device was devised many years ago to take advantage of this phenomenon and serve as an additional means of testing emeralds, particularly to distinguish them from glass imitations and certain other simulants. Such filters are designed to absorb green but pass red, and thus make an emerald look red when viewed through the filter whereas many imitations appear some dull colour, vastly different in appearance from emerald. An early filter was devised by Wild[22], but the 'Chelsea filter', named after the Chelsea College of Science and Technology in London where it was devised in conjunction with their gemmology class by Anderson[23] and Payne, has proven to be the most satisfactory. As described by Popley[24], 'it consists of two gelatine filters, one transmitting light from 5400–7200 Å and the other 3600–5800 Å, and in addition a narrow band in the deep red. These are cemented together and the combined effect of the two filters is to transmit two bands of light, one a yellow-green (5500–5800 Å) and the other red (6850–7650 Å)'.

In use, the filter permits light of these two bands to reach the eye, giving the impression of some brownish hue if both red and green are transmitted at once, as would be the case in glass imitations. However, in emerald, the balance is upset, and the eye receives the impression that the stone is red. Webster[20] (p. 743) noted the effectiveness of the filter for dark-coloured emeralds from Colombia or the Urals, the effect being more pronounced the darker the hue, but cautioned that in South African and Indian emeralds the change to red does not take place. For this reason, and also for the fact that some other non-beryl gemstones may also appear red in the filter (Webster[20], table 9, p. 912), discretion must be employed in its use. Webster notes that the Chelsea filter may be useful in indicating synthetic emeralds since their colour is due entirely to chromium and they consequently show a remarkable ruby-red upon viewing through the filter. Another filter for emerald was developed by F. Vandrey of Göttingen and described by Gliszczynski[25], but it is rarely used.

Aquamarine, yellow beryl and goshenite

The colour traditionally associated with aquamarine, or 'water of the sea', is sea-green or pale green with decided tinges of blue. Apparently pure blue aquamarines were very rare in antiquity, and there seems little doubt that the finest of their kind have been found only in modern times. Infinite gradations in tone occur between pale green and pale blue varieties, some specimens being so pale in hue that they seem colourless until laid upon a piece of white paper. Numerous beryls verge on greenish yellow, usually weak in tint, but may pass by insensible degrees into pure yellow. Some rare specimens are yellow-green, or chartreuse, sometimes of medium intensity and very attractive. It has been found that this colour variety is susceptible to colour change if heat-treated, turning to a beautiful pure blue. A remarkable blue aquamarine, known as Maxixe-type beryl, occurs in several deposits in Brazil and furnishes the darkest of all pure-blue aquamarines. However, as will be discussed below, the colour seems to be induced by natural radiation and is easily lost by exposure to sunlight or heat.

The name goshenite was given originally to very light-coloured beryls found near Goshen, Massachusettts, which contained alkalis. Today the name signifies any colourless beryl and includes not only alkali types but also those that belong among the aquamarines because of their chemical composition and properties.

In 1934, Klang[26] published absorption curves for aquamarine-group beryls, including some yellow and green specimens, and concluded that Fe^{2+} and Fe^{3+} were responsible for the colour. Jayaraman[27] investigated blue, green, greenish blue, yellowish green, and colourless beryls from Nellore, India, and came to the same conclusion, noting further that the intensity of colour seemed proportional to the content of Fe^{3+} in blue beryls and to F^{2+} in green beryls. Borovik[28] found that scandium (Sc), the element causing the blue colour in bazzite (the scandian analogue of beryl), was present in appreciable quantities only in coloured beryls and suggested that it may be the colouring ion in some blue aquamarines. However, Mukherjee[29] examined beryls for Sc and found only extremely small amounts in a few Indian specimens and concluded that this element was not involved in their colouration.

The role of iron in colouring members of the aquamarine group was studied by Wood and Nassau[18], whose findings are summarized in *Table 6.2*. Iron as a cause of colour in beryl has also been investigated by Goldman, *et al.*[30], who conclude that Fe^{2+} occurs in channel sites and is much more powerful in causing colour (blue) than the Fe^{2+} in octahedral sites. They also attribute yellow to Fe^{3+} and note also that when both ions are present in beryls, the resultant colour depends on the

TABLE 6.2 Five types of iron in beryl

Optical Characteristic	Possible Assignment	Observed Colouration
810 nm, *o*-ray, broad band, single component	Fe^{2+} in octahedral Al site	none
810 nm, *e*-ray, broad band, more than one component	Fe^{2+} in channel site A	none
620 nm, *e*-ray, broad band, single component	Fe^{2+} in channel site B	blue
400 nm, *o* and *e* edge absorption	Fe^{3+} in octahedral Al site	yellow
374 nm, *o*; 465 nm, *o* and *e*, narrow bands	Fe^{3+} in tetrahedral Si site	none

Source: Wood and Nassau[18], p. 797.

proportions of each, thus explaining the gamut of hues that may be observed from pure blue to various shades of blue-green, green, yellow-green, and yellow (see also Rossman[31]).

Webster[20] (pp. 119, 915) discussed spectroscopic examination of aquamarines and noted that the absorption spectrum 'is not very pronounced', there being a 'somewhat broad band in the violet at 4270 Å and a feeble diffuse band in the blue-violet at 4560 Å'. Furthermore, 'the extraordinary ray, which can be isolated by the use of a polaroid disc, shows these bands more strongly, and, in such conditions, there may be detected a narrow and delicate absorption line in the middle green at 5370 Å . . . seen in natural greenish aquamarines, and in yellow and colourless beryls, but is not seen in the heat treated blue aquamarines'.

From absorption studies of typical aquamarines, Schmetzer *et al.*[19] also concluded that the bluish and sea-green hues are caused mainly by divalent and trivalent iron, but found that other transition elements were also present, some contributing colour. In the case of divalent manganese (Mn^{2+}), this ion occupies the same octahedral sites that Fe^{3+} does, but apparently it contributes nothing to colour. Analyses of aquamarine revealed that, in addition to iron, yellow beryl contained some Mn, green beryl contained some Cr and Mn, and blue beryl contained some V, Cr, and Mn.

The spectra of yellow, green, and blue beryls show two principal colour-causing components, a broad absorption band in the red-yellow region, possibly due to charge transfers between Fe^{2+} in tetrahedral sites and Fe^{3+} in octahedral sites, and a strong absorption towards the blue-violet. If the latter is present alone, the resultant colour is yellow; if the first absorption band is present alone, the colour is blue; if both bands are present, the colour may range through an infinite number of shades between yellow and blue, including the various greens caused by their blending. In some yellow Brazilian beryls titanium is present as Ti^{3+} and occupies octahedral sites in the structure.

As observed through the dichroscope, differences in colour noted along the *o*-ray and *e*-ray directions are weak but distinct. In blue aquamarines, the colour is generally blue and very pale blue; in greenish specimens, green and paler green; and in yellow beryls, yellow and very pale yellow.

Maxixe-type beryls

In 1917, splendid dark blue beryls were found in the Maxixe mine, Piauhy region, Minas Gerais, Brazil, and at once aroused a lively demand until it was found that stones faded when exposed to light[32, 33, 34]. In about 1970 blue and green crystals of similar material came upon the market and were examined by Nassau and Wood[35, 36, 37]. It is not known if this new material is from the same locality in Brazil, but it behaved like the orginal Maxixe mine beryl in respect to loss of colour. Early work on the original Maxixe beryls gave refractive indexes of o = 1.5920 (cobalt blue) and e = 1.58442 (colourless), specific gravity = 2.805, while another source[32] gave 2.797 for the specific gravity and a composition in which the following minor constituents were present: Fe_2O_3, 0.03%; MgO, 0.25%; CaO, 0.22%; CuO, trace; Li_2O, 0.98%; Na_2O, 1.28%; Cs_2O, 2.80%; and B_2O_3, 0.39%, with ignition loss of 2.20%[35].

According to Nassau and Wood[35] (pp.1052–3) after examining beryl from ca. 1973, 'none of the colour-causing transition elements . . . [is] present in amounts large enough to explain a blue colour except in the green rough, where it is clear from the spectrum . . . that the Fe present provides only the yellow component'. They also dismissed the possible role of the alkali elements as Li, Na, K, and Cs as well as Sc in causing colour, noting their amounts are 'not unusual in beryls and cannot account for the colour either'.

The most probable cause of colour in both the blue and green varieties is a colour centre, or a defect in the structure, usually of the type where an atom is missing and the vacancy occupied by an electron. The electron is free to vibrate and, in so doing, is capable of absorbing certain wavelengths of light, with the result that the remaining wavelengths reach the observer's eye and give the sensation of colour. Such a colour centre is commonly produced by irradiation and often easily destroyed by light and heat. These centres in the new beryl have been found by Anderson[38], who used a microwave irradiation technique (electron paramagnetic resonance) to establish that 'the colour arises from different impurity ions which have lost one electron, probably by irradiation, to form CO_3 colour centres in the Maxixe-type beryl and NO_3 colour centres in the [orginal] Maxixe beryl'.

The new rough fades in light and bleaches quickly to a pale yellowish hue if heat-treated. The absorptions for the o- and e-rays of both the old and new materials were compared by Nassau and Wood[35] (p. 1034) to ordinary blue and green aquamarine. In two new specimens and one of the original find, all blue in colour, a uniform absorption appeared throughout much of the visible spectrum for the e-ray, which therefore appeared colourless in one window of the dichroscope, while for the o-ray, maximum absorption occurred in the yellow-orange-red region, with the result that much blue was transmitted and this colour was seen in the other window of the dichroscope.

The green material from the new source displayed similar absorptions, but with the important difference that intense absorption due to Fe^{3+} suppressed passage of blue light and gave better transmission in the green, thus imparting this hue to the o-ray. The e-ray, instead of being colourless, was pale yellow. Maxixe-type beryl was also examined by Schmetzer, et al.[19] (pp. 23–4) who also suggested that the colour was due to activation of a colour centre through irradiation.

Colour filters for aquamarines

Upon the suggestion of G. O. Wild, a filter for distinguishing aquamarine from similarly coloured synthetic spinels was devised by F. Vandrey, described by Gliszczynski[39]. Blue synthetic spinels absorb in the yellow of the spectrum but transmit red, while aquamarines absorb in the red but transmit green. Thus with the Vandrey filter, which transmits green and red, a synthetic spinel appears entirely red but an aquamarine appears a more or less intense emerald green. Some limitations on the use of this filter were pointed out in a subsequent article[40]. Under the Chelsea filter, aquamarines appear a distinctive green[20] (p. 912).

Heliodor

Heliodor, or literally 'sun-gilded', is a name originally applied to fine golden beryl from a pegmatite deposit near Rössing, South West Africa, by the Kolonialgesellschaft für Deutsch–Sudwestafrika sometime before 1914 in order to gain publicity for the new discovery. Much acclaim resulted as the 'new' gemstone, set in jewellery designed by the noted artist Lucas von Cranach, was presented to Kaiser Wilhelm II and his wife. Claims were made that the gemstone was unique, and several properties were set forth which were said to distinguish it from ordinary yellow beryls, among them a perceptible blue phosphorescence when irradiated with cathode rays, an 'opalescence', a weak green fluorescence, and alexandrite-like colour change between daylight and artificial light (yellow to a decided greenish tinge), and a weak radioactivity. All of these claims were investigated by Eppler[41], who systematically demolished them. Today, the name has no special significance, other than to afford an alternative for the names yellow or golden beryl.

Pink (morganite) and orange beryls

The cause of colour in pink and orange beryls has not been investigated thoroughly, most authorities assuming that the colour in pink beryls is due to manganese. Cobalt and caesium have been virtually ruled out as colouring agents in natural beryl.

Several speculations about the role of alkali ions, notably lithium and caesium, in the colouration of beryls appear in Schmetzer et al.[19] (p. 29), who also provided absorption curves for several rose beryls and two orangey ('apricot' or 'salmon') beryls from Brazil. Wood and Nassau[18] analyzed numerous pink beryls and found that manganese was one element common to all, and suggested that the cause of colour could be Mn^{2+} and Mn^{3+} substitutions for Al in an octahedral site or for either Be or Si in a tetrahedral site. However, after examining the spectra produced by rose beryls, they concluded that only Mn^{2+} was involved. Absorptions were given for the o-ray at 495 nm and 540 nm, and for the e-ray at 355 nm and 555 nm. Schmetzer et al.[19] compared Wood's and Nassau's results to their own and concluded that Mn^{2+} may be responsible for the colour in rose or pink beryls but that much work needed to be done to be certain.

In the orangey beryls, which appeared in the 1960's from Brazil, sometimes likened to the colour of apricot or salmon, Schmetzer *et al.* found Mn, V, Fe, and some Cr, with absorption in the blue region and almost uniform transmissionin wavelengths towards yellow and red. Bleaching or heat treatment of these curious beryls results in a final pink colour that seems permanent, but no explanation of the disappearance of the yellow component of the orange hue has been offered.

Red beryl (Bixbite)

Early in this century, a true red beryl was found in minute crystals in rhyolite cavities in Utah's Thomas Range. In 1912, Eppler[42] (p. 253) called it 'bixbit', apparently named after Maynard Bixby, a well-known mineral collector of Utah who had found the material and distributed specimens to collections throughout the world. The name is unfortunately sometimes confused with bixbyite, a valid species name for an entirely different mineral, also named after Bixby.

In the 1960's, similar, larger, and sometimes gem-quality crystals were found in the Wah Wah Mountains of Utah and were investigated by Nassau and Wood[43]. Spectral absorption studies revealed peaks in the 480 to 550 nm region, 'probably caused by Mn^{2+}'. The spectrum for the *o*-ray shows absorptions at 480, 510, 780, 810 and 840 nm, and for the *e*-ray at 0.425 and 0.545 microns, such absorptions being 'quite intense'.

Colour changes induced by heat

Altering the colour of gemstones by heating them is a practice of long-standing whose beginnings are lost in the mists of time. In India, for example, the natives in certain of the agate-producing areas heat-treated ordinary agates and chalcedonies to produce bright red cornelian. In Southeast Asia, the practice of heat-treating brownish and reddish zircon crystals to colourless, golden and even vivid blue is apparently very old. Much less is known in the case of beryls, except that by the Middle Ages it was established that emerald could be intensely heated, losing its colour while hot, but resuming it upon cooling. The systematic heat-treatment of other beryls seems to be a relatively recent innovation.

In 1893, Doelter[44] published his *Edelsteinkunde* and included for the first time considerable scientific information on colour changes induced in beryls through heat-treatment in oxidizing and reducing atmospheres (p. 106). For many years thereafter, he concerned himself with experiments in heat-treatment and irradiation of minerals, publishing numerous articles and several books on the subject. In his *Edelsteinkunde*, for example, he mentioned that he could readily change yellow beryls to blue by heating in an oxygen atmosphere, and that he could change the yellow component in greenish-blue beryls to blue, thus converting them to a pure blue hue. However, such beryls (but not emeralds), if heated to bright red, lost their colour entirely.

In 1888, Joly[45] reported that at a temperature of 357°C yellow and green beryls became completely colourless. Hermann[46] found that heating beryls in oxygen to about 700°C for two hours caused common yellowish-grey beryl to lose all colour but had no effect on the colour of emerald. In illuminating gas, rich in CO and therefore reducing in effect, a beryl previously heated in oxygen turned to deep gray, while an emerald seemed to pale somewhat, leading to the conclusion that the colour in common greenish and yellow beryls was caused by oxides of iron.

In the same year, Doelter[47] published results of irradiation/heat-treatment experiments and noted that emerald from Habachtal, Austria, did not lose colour even when heated to a white heat, ca. 1200°C. Other experiments by Doelter[48, 49, 50] confirmed that greenish and yellowish beryls could be changed to blue by heating in an oxygen atmosphere and could be decolourized by prolonged, strong heating. Additional confirmation of these results was given in 1923 by Wild and Liesegang[51]. In 1927, Kurbatov and Kargin[52] heated pale green beryl from Sherlova Mountain, Transbaikalia, and noted commencement of colour change from greenish to blue at about 400°C, with the change completed at the end of one hour at 425°C, or in only one-half hour at 450°C. They concluded that iron, shown to be present in an analysis, was the element involved in the production of colour.

Further results are contained in Wild[53], wherein greenish beryl, heated to 420°C changed to blue, yellow beryl heated to 400°C changed to 'light blue-white', and a 'brownish beryl' heated to 400°C changed to pink. This last specimen, unfortunately, was not further identified and may have been an alkali variety. Jayaraman[27] treated Nellore, India, beryls and found that upon subjecting greenish, greenish-blue, and greenish-yellow beryls to 500°C for five hours, all changed to blue. However, these blues, as well as other colourless beryls, did not change hue with further heating. In his opinion, the blue colour was caused by Fe_2O_3, while the green was due to FeO.

In 1941, Gavrusevich and Sarapulov[54] heated blue and green beryls, noting that below 600°C they tended to become paler, but to a very variable extent, and confirmed Doelter's conclusion that aquamarines lose colour while emeralds do not. They found that beryls heated between 800–1200°C lost their transparency, ultimately becoming opaque white and resembling porcelain.

In 1952, Frondel[55] conducted heat-treatment experiments on a variety of beryls and found that emeralds did not change colour up to 1025°C, the red beryl of Utah also remaining unchanged at this temperature, but morganite, stable in colour up to 400°C, began to bleach at 440°C in a ten-hour period, then rapidly decolourized at 495°C. A pure, golden-brown beryl without a trace of green became completely colourless when heated many hours at 250°C, with the bleaching rate dependent upon the temperature, bleaching proceeding fairly quickly at 275–300°C. Greenish-yellow, olive-brown, and yellowish-green specimens heated in the range of 250–280°C lost their yellow component and resulted in final hues of green, which then turned to blue when the specimens were heated over 280–300°C. Apparently, claimed Frondel, all greenish beryl turns blue, the latter colour first appearing in the range 280–300°C, with the rate of change increasing with rising temperature. Over 400°C the change takes place in a matter of minutes. However, if insufficiently heated, such material may retain a greenish-blue cast.

As had been found before, Frondel found that the final intensity of blue after heat-treatment depends on the intensity of the starting colour, the deeper hues producing a darker blue. In this connection, the best blue was obtained from beryls of dark oil-green or olive-green colour, while pale greenish stones provided only weak blues. The blue colour obtained by such treatment is stable up to 1025°C, as is the blue found in some untreated stones. In summary, the optimum treatment range is 400–450°C, which is high enough to produce quick results but not so high that cracking and turbidity become problems.

At very high temperatures, beryls first acquire milkiness, then become opaque white and porcelain-like in texture and appearance, accompanied by a distinct prismatic cleavage. Curiously, when overheated beryls that contain cleavage cracks, but retain sufficient translucency, are cut as cabochons oriented with the bases across the c-axis, a six-rayed star appears.

Srinivasan[56] heat-treated Nellore, India, beryls and found that blue specimens became paler when heated up to 1100°C in 100°C increments, each held for about three hours. Greenish-tinged areas began to disappear at about 200°C to form brownish patches, although those portions which were blue to begin with did not change. From 500°C to 700°C, the blue became paler and the brownish hue intensified, and at 700°C, the blue lightened with commencement of turbidity. The brownish patches remained up to 900°C, while by the time 1100°C had been reached, the specimen as a whole developed a dark gray-blue colour interspersed with brown streaks. At 1450°C the specimen fused into an ash-coloured porous mass. Nellore beryl contains iron and analyses showed a significant increase in Fe^{3+} in green and greenish-yellow samples previously heated to 500°C.

A study of heat changes in beryls conducted by Wirsching and reported by Schmetzer et al.[19] showed that blue remained unaltered, while green turned to blue and yellow turned to green. Experiments on changing colour of emerald were also conducted but the changes, if present at all, were insignificant. On the other hand, it was shown that morganites could be decolourized by heating. In a later work by the same authors[57] on colour changes in beryl, it was found that iron-free yellowish specimens changed to colourless after heating in air at 500°C for three hours, while iron-coloured blue, blue-green, green, yellow-green, and yellow samples turned to blue under the same conditions. Both Cr and V emeralds failed to change colour, or perhaps became somewhat darker with development of black flecks, but blue-green beryls containing Fe and V remained the same colour, or, if originally green, changed to blue-green. Morganite, whose colouring ion was attributed to manganese, changed to colourless, while the orange variety changed to rose or colourless. Maxixe-type specimens, selected on the basis of typical absorptions in the red region of the spectrum, were also tested but with somewhat anomalous results. For example, blue specimens, possibly already irradiated, turned to colourless or rose, but another blue specimen remained blue. A rose beryl, presumably a normal morganite except for the absorption in the red typical of Maxixe beryls, also remained rose after heating. Heating trials were also conducted on colourless varieties but without inducing any colour.

Heat-treatment methods

Despite the low coefficient of thermal expansion of beryl (see Chapter 6), which means that flawless pieces can be subjected to considerable heat without fear of cracking, precautions must be taken to prevent abrupt changes in temperature. The methods of applying heat range from those that are extremely crude to some that are quite refined, such as heating in electronically controlled ovens programmed to raise and lower temperatures gradually over set periods of time. The choice of specimens is equally important, those with obvious inclusions being likely to fracture as the inclusion contents expand, or those with fractures merely enlarging along them until the stones fall apart. It has been found best to treat cut gems because these can be examined to insure that none of these defects are present. The greatest danger is always impatience to see results and opening the oven before the contents have reached room temperature.

Among crude methods, Frondel[55] noted the practice in Brazil of embedding the stones in ordinary bread dough and baking in an oven. Another simple method involves placing the stone in a test tube, stoppering the open end with cotton, and then heating over a gas flame until the colour change takes place. Bastos[58] stated that 'about 90% of the green and pink beryls [of Brazil] are heat treated', and that the test-tube method with alcohol flame is most commonly used, it taking about 5 to 30 minutes to remove the green tinge from an aquamarine, 'according to the place where the stones came from'. He emphasized that the stones must be flawless. This treatment was also used to convert salmon-hued morganites to pure pink, but as I found out for myself, it is only necessary to place them in direct sunlight over a period of about a week to more safely accomplish the same result.

Colour changes induced by irradiation

The discovery of X-rays by Röntgen in 1895, followed the next year by the discovery of radioactive emissions from a uranium compound by Becquerel, prompted experiments to see what would happen to gemstones if they were subjected to such radiations. It was soon found that colour changes could be induced in a number of gemstones, including beryls.

An early experiment involving the effects of radium irradiation of beryl took place in 1906 when Miethe[59] subjected Colombian emerald to barium-radium bromide and noted that the colour became paler after several days and finally reached a very pale hue. The absorption spectrum was unchanged, but the bands were weaker. Heating the specimen to 250°C brought no change. Doelter[47, 48, 49, 50] used X-rays and gamma-rays from radioactive sources and found that, in general, X-rays did not substantially affect the colour of emerald even when coupled with heat treatments, Lind and Bardwell[60] found that neither natural nor synthetic emerald experienced any change in colour under alpha radiation, but a synthetic emerald exposed for a long period showed a faint green phosphorescence when heated to 200°C. Pough and Rogers[61] tested numerous gemstones under X-rays and also found that emerald was unaffected. However, electron bombardment did induce a grayish-green hue, according to a later paper by Pough[62].

Schmetzer et al.[57] found neither Cr nor V emeralds affected by X-rays, gamma rays, and electron bombardment, but they noted in some specimens a slight darkening with development of black specks upon post-irradiation heat-treatment. A reversal of the procedure brought the same results; that is, heating caused the slight changes that were observed, while the radiation produced no further changes.

In beryls coloured by iron ions, more and varied changes were experienced. Doelter found, for example, that X-rays tended to 'purify' blue and yellow colours while gamma rays tended to intensify them. As cited in Schmetzer et al.[19] (p. 21), in 1935 Andreev irradiated a brownish-orange beryl with gamma rays but found no change. Pough and Rogers[61] noted as a rule that blue aquamarines assumed light to medium green colours after irradiation with X-rays, while a colourless beryl turned pale brown; continuous irradiation of about 16 to 50 hours was necessary, however, to effect these changes. No fluorescence or phosphorescence was noted and, upon heating, the stones returned to former hues. Similar irradiation results were obtained by Mukherjee[29], namely, pale blue material turned greenish and a colourless specimen turned weak brown. Pough[62] induced unstable yellow in blue, pale blue, and colourless beryls by electron bombardment.

The irradiation/heat treatment described by Schmetzer et al.[57] (pp. 84–5) show that blue-greenish-yellowish iron-bearing beryls assume greenish to yellowish hues after X-ray and gamma-ray irradiation and electron bombardment, while some colourless specimens remained unchanged or turned pale yellow. When heat-treatment followed irradiation, all coloured samples stabilized on a blue colour. When the procedure was reversed, that is, heated first, coloured specimens turned blue and, after irradiation, turned to green or yellow. Colourless specimens either remained colourless or assumed a yellowish tinge. For beryls containing Fe + Cr and originally blue-green or green, heating produced green to yellow-green which turned blue-green after irradiation. Reversing the process caused the blue-green colours to change to green and ultimately to yellow-green after irradiation.

Schmetzer et al.[57] also tested Maxixe beryls which changed under irradiation from blue to blue-green, rose to blue, or colourless to blue. One blue sample retained its blue colour and may have been irradiated to begin with. After heat-treatment, all turned to rose or colourless, except for one blue-green specimen that turned completely blue after irradiation. The reversal of the process, however, brought some surprises, in that the already-irradiated blue beryl turned colourless or rose when heated, but when irradiated became blue again. Another blue sample which remained blue after heat-treatment also remained blue after irradiation. A rose sample and a colourless sample retained their hues after heat-treatment but turned blue after irradiation.

Maxixe-type beryls were also irradiated by Nassau[63] using gamma rays from a cobalt-60 source. He found that about 50% of possible blue colour was achieved after a dose of 46.2 megarads in 2.75 days. Close to 100% colour saturation would require about 27 days of irradiation at this level, but a 'dose' of 200 megarads gave a colour close to saturation. His results show that colour intensification is an exponential function in respect to time and that a dose of 200 megarads over a period of 12 days provided about as much colour as desired. The effect of temperature on irradiation-induced colour is extremely rapid at higher temperatures and much less at the lower temperatures. For example, at 125°C held for 3 hours, the colour intensity diminished to about 70% of its former value, while at 200°C it resulted in virtually complete colour loss after a two-hour period. An excellent summary of colour in minerals and gems was provided by Nassau[64] and includes discussion of beryl varieties. Nassau[65] has also provided a comprehensive survey of gemstones treatments which includes the beryl varieties.

Summary of colour changes

Emeralds. Colouring ions Cr, also Cr + V; stable to very high temperature; unaffected by irradiation.

Aquamarine. Colouring ions, various Fe; blue, blue-green, yellow-green; remain blue or change to blue after heat-treatment; may bleach at very high temperature; tend to reassume original greenish-yellowish hues after irradiation.

Yellow Beryl. Colouring ion Fe; usually to blue after heat-treatment; return to greenish-yellow or yellow after irradiation.

Yellow Beryl. Without Fe; colourless after heat-treatment; yellowish after irradiation.

Green Beryl. Coloured mainly with Fe but with some Cr; blue-green to green hues, the green tending to become blue-green after heat-treatment; become greenish to yellowish-green after irradiation; presence of Cr prevents entire removal of green.

Blue Maxixe-Type Beryls. Colour caused by colour centre but Fe may contribute; occurs in various blue, rose, yellow, green hues, also colourless; colourless to rose after heat-treatment, also colours tend to fade more or less rapidly in light; blue returns after irradiation but other colours may turn blue-green, the greenish component perhaps due to Fe.

Rose Beryl (Morganite). Colour may be caused by Mn; colourless after heat-treatment; yellow to yellow-orange after irradiation.

Rose Beryl (Morganite), Maxixe-Type. Remains rose after heat-treatment; turns blue after irradiation.

Red Beryl, Utah-Type (Bixbite). Colouring ion Mn; stable to very high temperature; probably stable after irradiation.

Orange Beryl. Colouring ion Mn; rose to colourless after heat-treatment; fades with exposure to light, rapidly in direct sunlight, stabilizing usually on pink; yellow to yellow-orange after irradiation.

Colourless (Goshenite). Without Fe; unchanged by heat-treatment or irradiation.

Colourless (Goshenite) Maxixe-Type. Contains a colour centre; colourless after heat-treatment; turns blue after irradiation.

Colourless (Goshenite). Contains Mn; unchanged by heat-treatment; tends towards yellow-orange after irradiation.

Luminescence

Luminescence, or the emission of light without the application of strong heating, has been reported a number of times in beryl, but the luminescence was remarkable neither for its strength, its colour, nor consistent appearance. The kind produced by rubbing one hard stone against another, or triboluminescence, has been reported only once in beryl[66]. More common is fluorescence which depends on the use of one radiation, usually ultraviolet light (invisible), to excite a response that may be visible. Other types of luminescence will now be discussed.

Experiments conducted by De Ment[67] (p. 433) elicited the comment that 'at most . . . this mineral fluoresces weakly', and he noted that the natural colour would interfere with the detection of a fluorescent colour. In shortwave UV (253.7 nm), he discovered fluorescence in various shades of green, occasionally of deep hue. Alexander[68] tested beryls under X-rays but found no response in aquamarine, emerald, and other varieties, except in morganite, in which there was a 'dull to bright' fluorescence. Some beryl from Weeks quarry, East Wakefield, New Hampshire, was found to fluoresce a faint peach colour under longwave UV (365.8 nm) by De Ment[69] and a weak yellow to 'flesh' glow in a caesium beryl from Newry, Maine.

Millson and Millson[70] (p. 432) irradiated many minerals under shortwave UV to determine persistence of phosphorescence. A goshenite from San Piero, Elba, produced a bluish-white glow for about 152 hours, while a morganite from the Gillette quarry, Haddam Neck, Connecticut, glowed pink for about 296 hours. These results are unusual, phosphorescence in beryl having been only rarely reported and never for such long durations. Lieber[71] (p. 50) tested emeralds under longwave UV and found very weak fluorescence or none at all in specimens from most localities. However, emerald from Chivor, Colombia, displayed a very weak red glow, while synthetic emeralds all fluoresced dark red. No response under UV was noted for aquamarine or morganite. Gleason[72] noted weak yellow, pale green, and pink fluorescence in beryls.

Cathodoluminescence, or light produced by irradiation with cathode rays, was found in beryl by Saksena and Pant[73]. Luminescence occurred in the red region between 615 and 650 nm, with the maximum between 630 asd 650 nm. Prolonged irradiation resulted in weakening of luminescence in the red region and the production of two bands of medium intensity at 560 to 580 nm and 435 to 490 nm, and also a weak band near 540 nm.

Infrared luminescence, invisible to the human eye and detectable only with special laboratory instrumentation, has been investigated in a large number of minerals, including beryl, by Barnes[74], who noted that 'beryl' in cloudy or opaque specimens generally gives no luminescence, but relatively clear pieces of most emerald and some aquamarine show strong infrared luminescence'. He listed emeralds from eleven deposits which produced strong response in the infrared (p. 102) and altogether tested 215 emerald and aquamarine specimens from thirty-two localities. In these, he found that 20% of specimens from thirty localities responded in the infrared but only 3% of the test specimens from ten localities produced visible light (p. 115).

It seems clear that luminescence in beryls is far from being an important property and many more specimens need to be tested before some consistent behavioral patterns emerge. Beryl specimens taken from pegmatites are especially subject to errors of interpretation because of the well-known tendency for thin films of fluorescent opal to coat fracture surfaces within these bodies. Fluorescent organic materials may also enter the outcrops of such bodies and penetrate deeply into them, not to mention those strongly fluorescent compounds that are present in modern detergents used to clean specimens.

References

1 KLEIN, F. *Smaragde unter dem Urwald.* Berlin: Oswald Arnold Verlag. 285 pp. (1941)

2 OTERO MUÑOZ, G., and BARRIGA VILLALBA, A. M. *Esmeraldas de Colombia.* Bogota: Banco de la Republica. 133 pp. (1948)

3 VAUQUELIN, N. L. Analyse de l'aigue marine, ou béril; et découverte d'une terre nouvelle dans cette pierre. *Annales de Chimie.* ser. 1, vol. 26, pp. 155–69 (1798)

4 LÉVY, B. Recherches sur la formation et la composition des émeraudes. *Compte Rendu de l'Academie des Sciences* (Paris) 45:877–81 (1857)

5 WÖHLER, F., and ROSE, G. Sur la nature colorante des émeraudes. *Compte Rendu de l'Academie des Sciences* (Paris) 58:1180 (1864)

6 JANNETTAZ, E. Note sur la calcaire noir renferment les émeraudes de Muso (Nouvelle-Grenade). *Bulletin de la Société Français de Minéralogie et Cristallographie* 15:131–3 (1892)

7 MOIR, J. Notes on the spectra of the precious emerald and other gem stones. *Transactions of the Royal Society of South Africa* 2:273 (1912)

8 MOIR, J. Spectrum-phenomena in chromium compounds. *Transactions of the Royal Society of South Africa* 7:129–30 (1918)

9 WILD, G. O., and KLEMM, R. Mitteilungen über spektroskopische Untersuchungen an Mineralien. Smaragd. *Zentralblatt für Mineralogie* (Stuttgart) 1926, Abt. A, no. 1, pp. 21–2 (1926)

10 FERSMAN, A. E. [On the nature of colour in emerald]. *Doklady Akademiya Nauk SSSR* (Leningrad) pp. 24–5 (1926)

11 KLEMM, R. Über die Färbung einigen Mineralien durch Chrom. *Zentralblatt für Mineralogie* (Stuttgart) 1927, Abt. A, pp. 267–78 (1927)

12 VOGEL, P. Optische Untersuchungem am Smaragd und einigen anderen Chrom gefärbten Mineralien. *Neues Jahrbuch für Mineralogie* (Stuttgart) 68:401–38 (1934)

13 KOLBE, E. Über die Färbung von Mineralien durch Mangan, Chrom und Eisen. *Neues Jahrbuch für Mineralogie*, Abt. A, Beilage-Bd. 69, pp. 183–254 (1935)

14 GRUM-GRZHIMAILO, S. V. [On the colouration of minerals caused by chromium]. *Trudy Instituta Kristallografii* (Moscow) 2:73–86 (1940)

15 WILD, G. O., and BIEGEL, H. Lichtabsorption am Smarad. *Achat* 1, no. 1/2, pp. 16–7 (1948)

16 NASSAU, K., and JACKSON, K. A. Trapiche emeralds from Chivor and Muzo, Colombia. *American Mineralogist* 55:416–27; correction, 55:1808–9 (1970)

17 SCHMETZER, K. A. *Vanadium III als Farbträger bei natürlichen Silikaten und Oxiden.* Inaugural Dissertation, Ruprecht-Karl-University, Heidelberg. 277 pp. (1978)

18 WOOD, D. L., and NASSAU, K. The characterization of beryl and emerald by visible and infrared absorption spectroscopy. *American Mineralogist* 53:777–800 (1968)

19 SCHMETZER, K., BERDESINSKI, W., and BANK, H. Über die Mineralart Beryll und Absorptionsspektren. *Zeitschrift der deutschen gemmologischen Gesellschaft* 23, no. 1, pp. 5–39 (1974)

20 WEBSTER, R. *Gems.* 4th ed. London: Butterworths. 1006 pp. (1983)

21 WILD, G. O., and BIEGEL, K. H. Smaragd—oder nicht? *Achat* 1, no. 10, pp. 173–4 (1948)

22 WILD, G. O. The emerald filter loupe. *The Gemmologist* (London) 4:29–30 (1934)

23 ANDERSON, B. W. Colour-filters. *The Gemmologist* (London) 4:58–9 (1934)

24 POPLEY, A. R. A useful colour-filter. *The Gemmologist* (London) 4:57 (1934)

25 GLISZCZYNSKI, S. von. Kristallviolettefilter als Spezialprüfer für Smaragde. *Achat* 2, no. 1, pp. 13–4 (1949)

26 KLANG, H. Beiträge zur Kenntnis der Absorption und Lichtbrechung von Aquamarin und einigen gelben und grünen Beryllen. *Neues Jahrbuch für Mineralogie*, Beilage-Bd. 69, Abt. A, pp. 93–116 (1934)

27 JAYARAMAN, N. A chemical study of the Nellore beryl and the cause of its colouration. *Journal of the Indian Institute of Science* 23 A:30–5 (1940–41)

28 BOROVIK, S. A. [Content of Sc in beryls and some other minerals]. *Doklady Akademiya Nauk SSSR* (Leningrad) 40:125–7 (1943)

29 MUKHERJEE, B. Colour of beryl. *Nature* (London) 167:602 (1951)

30 GOLDMAN, D. S., ROSSMAN, G. R., and PARKIN, K. M. Channel constituents in beryls. *Physics and Chemistry of Minerals* (Springer Verlag) 3:225–35 (1978)

31 ROSSMAN, G. R. Color in gems: the new techniques. *Gems & Gemology* 17:60–71 (1981)

32 WILD, G. O. [Note]. *Zentralblatt für Mineralogie*, Abt. A., pp. 38–9 (1933)

33 SCHLOSSMACHER, K., and KLANG, H. Der Maxixeberyll. I. *Zentralblatt für Mineralogie*, Abt. A, pp. 37–44 (1935)

34 ROEBLING, W., and TROMNAU, H. W. Der Maxixeberyll. II. *Zentralblatt für Mineralogie*, Abt. A, pp. 134–9 (1935)

35 NASSAU, K., and WOOD, D. L. The nature of the new Maxixe-type beryl. *Lapidary Journal* 27:1032–58 (1973)

36 NASSAU, K., and WOOD, D. L. Examination of Maxixe-type blue and green beryl. *Gems & Gemology* 14:130–33 (1973)

37 NASSAU, K., and WOOD, D. L. Examination of Maxixe-type blue and green beryl. *Journal of Gemmology* (London) 13:296–301 (1973)

38 ANDERSON, L. O. The difference between Maxixe beryl and Maxixe-type beryl: and electron

paramagnetic resonance investigation. *Journal of Gemmology* (London) 16:313–7 (1979)

39 GLISZCZYNSKI, S. von. Über ein Farbfilter als Hilfsmittel zur sofortigen Unterscheidung von Aquamarinen und aquamarinefarbenen synthetischen Spinellen. *Achat* 1, no. 12, pp. 260–1 (1948)

40 GLISZCZYNSKI, S. von. Das Verhalten der 'Ferrera'-Steine unter den Vandrey'schen Prüffiltern für Aquamarine und Smaragde. *Achat* 2, no. 2, pp. 61–2 (1949)

41 EPPLER, A. Der Heliodor. *Die Umschau* (Frankfurt a. M.) 24:497–500; also in *Scientific American Monthly*, March 1921 (1920)

42 EPPLER, A. *Die Schmuck- und Edelsteine.* Stuttgart: P. Krais. 464 pp. (1912)

43 NASSAU, K., and WOOD, D. L. An examination of red beryl from Utah. *American Mineralogist* 53:801–6 (1968)

44 DOELTER, C. *Edelsteinkunde.* Leipzig: Veit & Comp. 260 pp. (1893)

45 JOLY, J. Zerstörung der Farbe in Beryll. *Zeitschrift für Kristallographie und Mineralogie* (Leipzig) 19:484 (1891)

46 HERMANN, W. Über die Einwirkung oxydierender und reduzierender Gase auf die Färbung einiger Minerale. *Zeitschrift für anorganische und allgemeine Chemie* (Leipzig) 60:369–404 (1908)

47 DOELTER, C. Über die Einwirkung von Radium- und Röntgenstrahlen auf die Farben der Edelsteine. *Sitzungsberichte der Kaiserliche Akademie der Wissenschaften, mathematisch-naturwissen schaftliche Classe, Wien,* vol. 117, Abt. 1, pp. 819–44 (1908)

48 DOELTER, C. *Das Radium and die Farben.* Dresden: Steinkopff. 133 pp. (1910)

49 DOELTER, C. *Die Farben der Mineralien insbesonders der Edelsteine.* Braunschweig: Friedrich Vieweg & Sohn. 96 pp. (1915)

50 DOELTER, C. Über die Farben der Mineralien. *Naturwissenschaften* 8:21–7 (1920)

51 WILD, G. O., and LIESEGANG, R. E. Über die Farbes des Amethystes und die des Berylls. *Zentralblatt für Mineralogie* 24:737–40 (1923)

52 KURBATOV, J., and KARGIN, W. Über die Verwandlung der grünen Färbung des Berylls in eine Bläuliche. *Zentralblatt für Mineralogie,* Abt. A, pp. 361–2 (1927)

53 WILD, G. O. The treatment of gem stones by heat. *Rocks & Minerals* Peekskill, N.Y.) 7, no. 1, pp. 9–13 (1932)

54 GAVRUSEVICH, B. A., and SARAPULOV, T. J. [On the change of colour and optical properties of beryls on heating]. *Doklady Akademiya Nauk SSSR* (Leningrad) 31:775–8 (1941)

55 FRONDEL, C. Effect of heat on the colour of beryl. *Gemmologist* (London) 21:197–200 (1952)

56 SRINIVASAN, N. R. A study on the change in the colour of beryl on heating. *Current Science* (Bangalore) no. 12, pp. 388–9 (1957)

57 SCHMETZER, K., BERDESINSKI, W., and BANK, H. Farbveränderung von Edelsteinen der Beryllgruppe. *Zeitschrift der deutschen gemmologischen Gesellschaft* 24, no. 2, pp. 81–7 (1975)

58 BASTOS, F. M. Heat-treatment of gems. *Lapidary Journal* 17:842–4 (1963)

59 MIETHE, A. Über die Färbung von Edelsteinen durch Radium. *Annalen der Physik* (Leipzig) ser. 4, vol. 19, pp. 633–8 (1906)

60 LIND, S. C., and BARDWELL, D. C. The coloring and thermophosphorescence produced in transparent minerals and gems by radium irradiation. *Journal of the Franklin Institute* (Philadelphia) 196:375–90; also in *American Mineralogist* 8(1923):171–80, with correction in 9 (1924):35

61 POUGH, F. H., and ROGERS, T. H. Experiments in X-ray irradiation of gem stones. *American Mineralogist* 32:31–43 (1947)

62 POUGH, F. H. The coloration of gemstones by electron bombardment. *Zeitschrift der deutschen gesellschaft für Edelsteinkunde, Schlossmacher Festschrift,* pp. 71–8 (1957)

63 NASSAU, K. The effects of gamma rays on the color of beryl, smoky quartz, amethyst and topaz. *Lapidary Journal* 28:20–40 (1974)

64 NASSAU, K. The origins of color in minerals and gems. *Lapidary Journal* 29:920–28 (part 1), 1060–70 (part 2), 1250–58 (part 3) (1975)

65 NASSAU, K. *Gemstone enhancement.* London: Butterworths. 288 pp. (1984)

66 VERNADSKY, W. [Triboluminescence of beryl. *Neues Jahrbuch für Mineralogie* 1:381 (1912)

67 De MENT, J. *Fluorochemistry.* Brooklyn: Chemical Publishing Company. 796 pp. (1945)

68 ALEXANDER, A. E. X-ray fluorescence in gemstones. *The Gemmologist* (London) 15, no. 177, p. 49 (1946)

69 De MENT, J. *Handbook of Fluorescent Gems and Minerals.* Portland, Ore.: Mineralogist Publishing Co. 68 pp. (1949)

70 MILLSON, H. E., and MILLSON, H. E., Jr. Observations on exceptional duration of mineral phosphorescence. *Journal of the Optical Society of America* 40:430–5 (1950)

71 LIEBER, W. Die Fluoreszenz von Mineralien. *Der Aufschluss* (Heidelberg) Sonderheft 5. 62 pp. (1957)

72 GLEASON, S. *Ultraviolet Guide to Minerals.* Princeton: Van Nostrand. 244 pp. (1957)

73 SAKSENA, B. D., and PANT, L. M. Cathodoluminescence spectra of beryl. *Journal of Scientific & Industrial Research* 14 B:246–7 (1955)

74 BARNES, D. F. Infrared luminescence of minerals. *U.S. Geological Survey Bulletin* 1052-C, pp. 71–157 (1958)

Chapter 7

Crystallography

Axes and symmetry

Since crystals are solid objects, the system of coordinates devised by the French mathematician René Descartes (1596–1650) – thus called cartesian coordinates – was adopted for the description of the faces of crystals and their relationships to one another. The basis of the system is the use of three imaginary lines or axes which meet at a common point, representing the three dimensions of space. Thus, in a simple case, such as describing the space taken by a room in a house, one axis is vertical and would intersect the ceiling and floor while two lateral axes would intersect each of two walls. In practice, a house-builder uses such axes to set up the framework, utilizing a plumb-line to be sure the vertical structural members are truly perpendicular to the earth's surface and a spirit level to insure the horizontal orientation of floors and ceilings. For most crystals, only three such axes need be used, but in the case of minerals in the hexagonal system, including beryl, three instead of two lateral axes are more convenient, as shown in the first drawings of *Figure 7.1*.

These three axes reflect the placement or *symmetry* of the atoms in the beryl structure as depicted in *Figure 4.1*. The latter figure shows only one cell of the structure, but when such cells are snugly fitted together, as occurs in actual crystals, the geometrical object known as the *hexagonal prism* is created.

As with the walls in the room of a house, the bounding planes of developed beryl crystals, or *faces*, can all be related geometrically to the crystallographic axes as shown in *Figure 7.1*. The principal or c-axis is that which passes vertically through the crystal and is parallel to the side or prism faces. The lateral axes pass at right angles through the sides of the crystal and are oriented 60° to each other. They are labelled a_1, a_2, and a_3. The plane containing these axes is at right angles to the principal or c-axis.

In addition to their usefulness in geometrically describing orientations of crystal faces, the crystallographic axes are conveniently referred to when describing

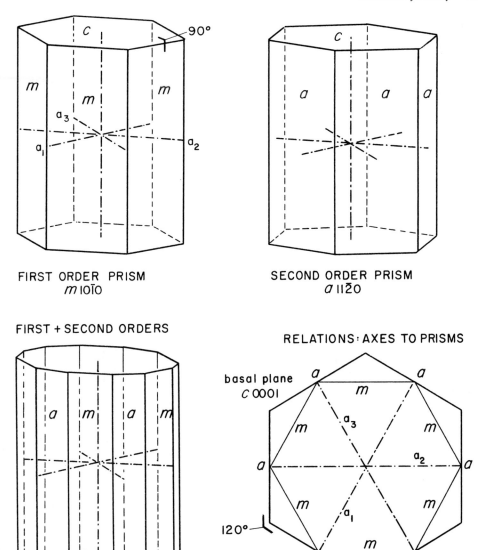

FIRST ORDER PRISM
m 10$\bar{1}$0

SECOND ORDER PRISM
a 11$\bar{2}$0

FIRST + SECOND ORDERS

RELATIONS: AXES TO PRISMS

basal plane
c 0001

120°

Figure 7.1 Fundamental prism forms of beryl. The first order prism is most often found in crystals of common beryl, aquamarine, golden beryl, and emerald, the latter often displaying only *m* and *c*. The combination of the two, namely *m* + *a*, is frequently observed in emerald crystals and also in some aquamarine and golden beryl crystals. (John Sinkankas).

certain physical properties. Thus, as noted in Chapter 6, light passing parallel to the *c*-axis is singly refracted, while that passing though the crystal elsewhere is doubly refracted. Colours also appear differently according to axial direction, and similar differences are noted in other properties according to direction. All such differences are a consequence of the fact that the atoms within the crystal are not randomly arranged but follow the patterns shown in *Figures 4.1* and *4.2*.

Before passing on to a discussion of symmetry, it should be mentioned that crystallographers now place all crystals in seven divisions according to the number of axes, their relative lengths, and their inclination to each other. These systems are the isometric or cubic, tetragonal, trigonal, orthorhombic, monoclinic, triclinic, and hexagonal, the last of concern here. All are described and explained in any standard textbook of gemmology or mineralogy.

The regularity of atomic arrangement in beryl, or symmetry, is expressed in descriptive terms and symbols. Because the elements of the symmetry are as complete as possible within the hexagonal system, beryl is classed as *normal, holosymmetric,* or *holohedral,* the last term referring to the complete symmetry in the patterns of faces. A more modern and more descriptive term for the symmetry is *dihexagonal bipyramidal.* The word *dihexagonal* means that faces can occur in pairs both along the sides of the prism and upon the pyramidal faces, as may be seen in the drawings of beryl crystals in *Figures 7.2* to *7.5.* The term *bipyramidal* refers to the fact that whatever kind of face appears upon one pyramidal termination can also appear on the other.

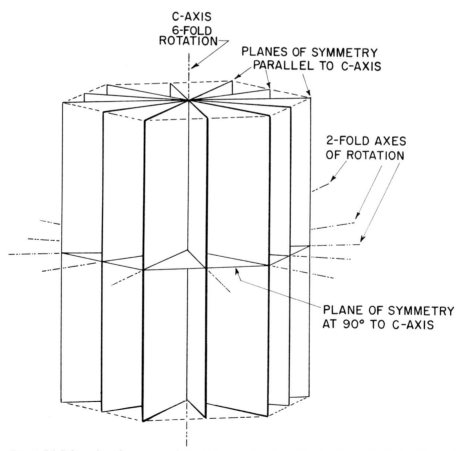

Figure 7.2 Orientation of symmetry planes and axes in beryl crystals, showing their relationships to the first order hexagonal prism (indicated in dashed outlines). (John Sinkankas).

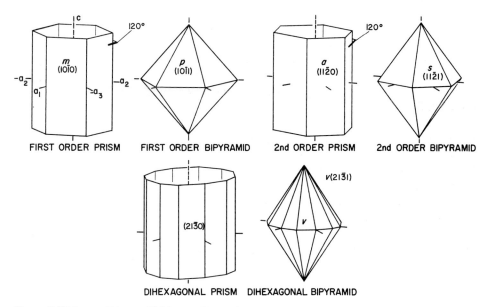

Figure 7.3 Prism and bipyramidal forms of beryl. (John Sinkankas).

The features or *elements of symmetry* for beryl are shown in *Figure 7.2*. The c-axis is the principal axis of symmetry and is six-fold, that is, the crystal can be rotated in six increments of 60°, each time exposing the same kind of atomic arrangement (and faces, if such are present). The lateral or two-fold axes, operate the same way, but now only two positions are possible in one full rotation in which the same atomic arrangement appears. Lastly, the crystal can be bisected by a series of imaginary *planes of symmetry,* of which there are six parallel to the c-axis and one parallel to the a-axis as shown in *Figure 7.2*. These are also called 'mirror' planes of symmetry because the structure and faces (if present) on one side of the plane are faithfully reproduced in the other.

Faces and forms

In crystallography, the word *face* means the natural flat plane occurring on crystals which have had the opportunity to grow without inference, usually within a cavity in rock. The word *form* is used for the collection of all possible faces of a specific type that can occur on a crystal. Thus, on the beryl crystals drawn in *Figure 7.3*, the form letter *m* designates the faces of the commonest hexagonal prism which has six and only six faces, all alike in respect to their placement to the axes, and as noted before, all exposing the identical atomic arrangement. The other very common form of beryl crystals is *c,* shown in *Figure 7.4,* which refers to faces that cut the c-axis at right angles and terminate the crystal in many specimens. There can only be two c-faces, as in *doubly-terminated* crystals, but in nature, one seldom finds both because most crystals grow from matrix and only one end is developed.

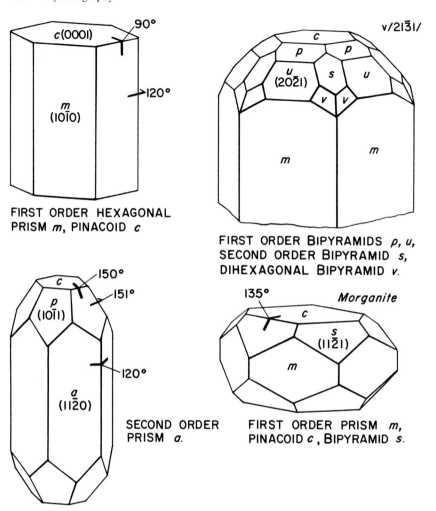

FIRST ORDER HEXAGONAL
PRISM *m*, PINACOID *c*

FIRST ORDER BIPYRAMIDS *p*, *u*,
SECOND ORDER BIPYRAMID *s*,
DIHEXAGONAL BIPYRAMID *v*.

SECOND ORDER
PRISM *a*.

FIRST ORDER PRISM *m*,
PINACOID *c*, BIPYRAMID *s*.

Figure 7.4 The most common forms found on beryl crystals. The form at the top left is typical of emerald; that at the bottom right is typical of alkali beryls. The two others are common in aquamarines. (John Sinkankas).

TABLE 7.1 Beryl crystal forms

Name	Form Letter	Number of Possible Faces	Remarks
Pinacoid	*c*	2	Also called basal pinacoid; very common
First order prism	*m*	6	Commonest face
Second order prism	*a*	6	Uncommon
Dihexagonal prism	Various	12	Uncommon
First order bipyramid	Various	12	Common
Second order bipyramid	Various	12	Common
Dihexagonal bipyramid	Various	24	Uncommon to rare

Where a single face is involved, the numerical symbols used to describe it are enclosed in parenthesis ( ), as in *Figures 7.3* and *7.4*. (An explanation of the Bravais-Miller numerical symbols can be obtained from standard gemmological or mineralogical texts). However, when a form is being discussed, these numerals are enclosed in braces { }.

Compared to some other minerals, beryl forms are few in number; only seven types are known, as indicated in *Table 7.1*.

These forms are shown in *Figure 7.3* and various combinations of these faces in *Figure 7.4*. Other combinations appear in *Figures 7.5* to *7.7*. Several of the drawings show 'dipyramid' as an alternative term to 'bipyramid', but each means the same.

Trapiche emeralds

The Spanish word *trapiche,* normally applied to cog-wheels used to crush sugar cane, came also to be applied to emerald crystals in which inclusions form a six-spoked pattern when the crystals are observed in sections across the *c*-axis. Even earlier, the Spanish name *gemelo* had been applied to these curious crystals in the belief that they were twins. Such crystals are seldom over 25 mm (1 in) long and usually less than 10 mm (½ in) wide. The unique features are a central slender hexagonal core from which radiate narrow bands of inclusions, whitish or translucent in colour. The sectors between the 'spokes' may be filled with clear emerald *Figure 7.8*. Some crystals are fully developed prisms of $m\{1010\}$, usually without good terminations, while others are incompletely filled between the rays so that these protrude noticeably and reinforce the resemblence to a cog wheel. These crystals have been found only in the Colombian deposits and no similar growths of emerald or other beryls elsewhere have been reported.

The earliest notice of trapiche emeralds was taken by Bertrand[1] in 1879, who found some among a lot of Muzo emeralds and remarked on the strange habit. They were again noticed by Codazzi[2], who likened them to cyclic twins of aragonite. In 1916 Pogue[3] depicted a trapiche crystal (p. 719) and noted that this specimen and others like it had been found recently at Muzo and that the 'carbonaceous impurities [are] disposed along crystallographic lines so as to form a six-rayed star pattern'. In another paper[4] he also stated that 'one specimen was examined optically and proved to be of the same orientation throughout; it therefore does not represent a twinned crystal as suggested by Lleras Codazzi'. Furthermore, 'its re-entrant angles are presumably the effect of solution and the disposition of the carbonaceous inclusions, the expression of crystallizing forces, as shown also, for example, in chiastolite'.

Bernauer[5] made the first thorough examination of these crystals in about 1925, having at his disposal about forty roughly prismatic crystals up to 25 mm (1 in) long and up to 30 mm (1¼ in) in diameter. Sketches showed the internal arrangement of inclusions, some surrounding a central core, but others having grown without a core. Typically the inclusions taper longitudinally (parallel to the *c*-axis). His analysis of the inclusion material showed that it departed considerably from the

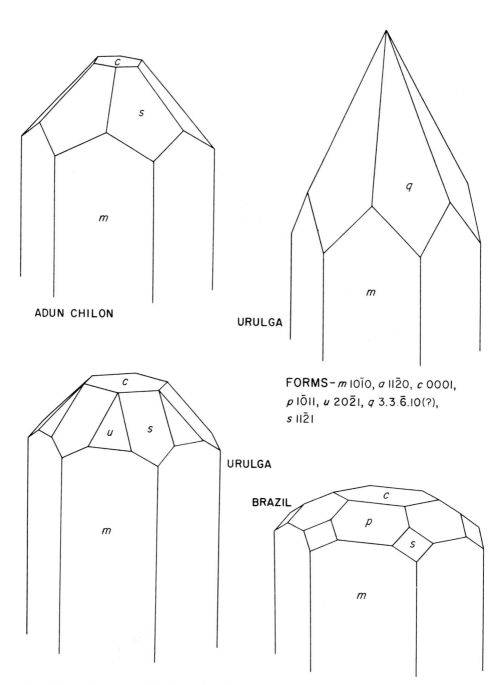

ADUN CHILON

URULGA

URULGA

FORMS — *m* 10$\bar{1}$0, *a* 11$\bar{2}$0, *c* 0001,
p 1$\bar{0}$11, *u* 20$\bar{2}$1, *q* 3.3.$\bar{6}$.10(?),
s 11$\bar{2}$1

BRAZIL

Figure 7.5 Pyramidal forms of beryl crystals. The forms *p* and *s* are very common on morganite crystals. The crystals labelled Adun Chilon and Urulga (River) are from Transbaikalia, USSR. After N. Koksharov, *Materialien zur Mineralogie Russlands,* atlas (St. Petersburg, 1853). (John Sinkankas).

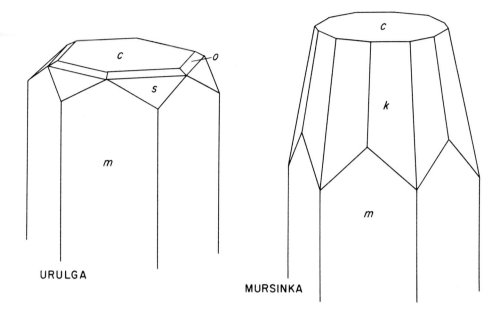

URULGA

MURSINKA

FORMS- *m* 10Ī0, *c* 0001, *u* 20$\bar{2}$1, *p* 10Ī1, *s* 11$\bar{2}$1,
v 21$\bar{3}$1, *n* 31$\bar{4}$1, *k* 42$\bar{6}$1

—MURSINKA—

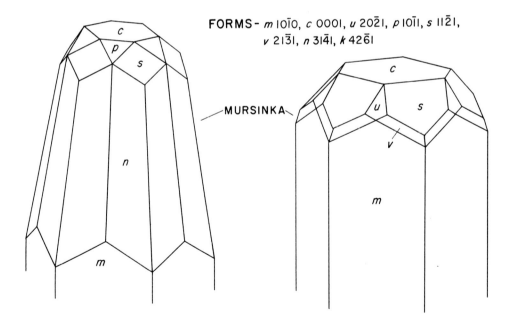

Figure 7.6 Crystals from Urulga River, Transbaikalia and Mursinka in the Urals, USSR. The very steep dihexagonal bipyramids *k* and *n* are rarely found except as rough areas along edges of terminations. After N. Koksharov, *Materialien zur Mineralogie Russlands,* atlas (St. Petersburg: 1853). (John Sinkankas).

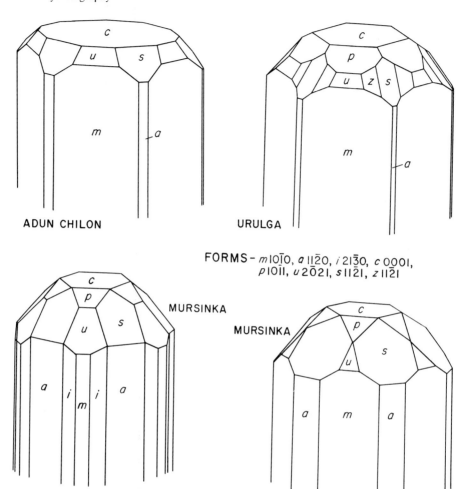

Figure 7.7 Various combinations of forms on beryl crystals, the two upper specimens from Adun Chilon and the Urulga River, Transbaikalia, the lower two from Mursinka in the Urals, USSR. After N. Koksharov, *Materialien zur Mineralogie Russlands,* atlas (St. Petersburg, 1853). (John Sinkankas).

typical emerald analysis by containing far too much Al_2O_3. Bulk specific gravity was found to be 2.680–2.701, but the figure was considered inaccurate because of the inclusions, some of which were carbonaceous. Clear splinters, however, provided values of 2.699–2.709, while the specific gravity of a plate cut completely across a crystal and containing a central core was found to be 2.648–2.691. When heated to redness, no loss of weight could be found.

Cores were rich in inclusions of calcite, dolomite, pyrite, mica, small greenish biotite-like scales, kaolin, and carbonaceous matter, the last apparently responsible for imparting a very dark shade to those areas of emerald in which it was present. The dichroism was the same as in ordinary emerald, but weaker, while refractive indexes were found of $o = 1.5690-1.5695$, $e = 1.5626-1.5640$, difference $= 0.0064-0.0056$. On plates cut parallel to the *c*-axis, he obtained

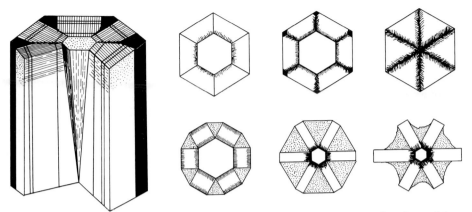

Figure 7.8 Zones of inclusions in the trapiche emeralds of Colombia. The large sectioned crystal shows zones of inclusions arranged normal to the faces of the tapering hexagonal core as well as several zones of inclusions parallel to faces of the first order prism. After F. Bernauer, Die sogenannten Smaragddrillinge von Muzo, *Neues Jahrbuch für Mineralogie* Abt. A, Beilage-Bd. 54 (1926):205–42. The smaller drawings are after K. Nassau and K. A. Jackson, Trapiche emeralds from Chivor [*recte* Peña Blanca] and Muzo, Colombia, *American Mineralogist* 55 (1970):416–27. *Top:* Three crystals with central cores surrounded by trapezodial segments, with the last two figures representing specimens in which the core tapers. *Bottom:* Three crystals with clear central cores and radiating 'spokes' of clear emerald; the triangular regions between the spokes are filled with more or less opaque albite-emerald. (John Sinkankas).

$o = 1.5687–1.5679$, $e = 1.5622–1.5623$, difference $= 0.0065–0.0056$. Bernauer concluded that the sectorial structure was due to repulsion of impurities by slowly growing crystals.

According to Scheibe[6], trapiches at Muzo occur only in the rock adjoining that in which gem emeralds occur, namely, a dark, carbonaceous shale of the Viletta Formation of Lower Cretaceous age, which is altered in places by veins containing the trapiche emeralds as a kind of 'contact' mineral. Around 1962, the crystals were found especially in the Banco Amerillo just west of Tambre Boliche, 100 m (110 yd) south of the mine buildings. More recently, trapiches were investigated by MacKague[7] and Chaudhari[8], who examined numerous small crystals averaging about 8 mm (⅓ in) long and 4 mm (³⁄₁₆ in) wide. These had cores of 'very pale green colour . . . non-pleochroic . . . decidedly of poor quality'. However, good quality emerald occurred in the sectors between the inclusion rays, each sector more or less completely separated from the prism faces of the core by a clay-like matrix which contained quartz.

The most recent study of trapiches is from the hands of Nassau and Jackson[9,10] who described crystals thought to be from Chivor but which later turned out to be from the Peña Blanca mine near Muzo. They noted that 'these have the clear centre and are distinct from the specimens from Muzo itself, which have a dark centre'. According to Tripp and Hernandez[11], the trapiches were found by a farmer in 1963 on land that is now part of the Peña Blanca property. The crystals examined by Nassau and Jackson were generally 12 mm (½ in) long and 10 mm (⅜ in) wide, although Tripp and Hernandez noted a crystal of 20 mm (¾ in) in diameter that was cut for the sake of its gem-quality core. The largest crystal seen by them was 115 × 50 mm (4⅝ × 2 in) and weighed 167 carats.

Nassau and Jackson found that all trapiche crystals were untwinned and contained white, feathery inclusions consisting of albite and beryl. The Muzo crystals were characterized by carbonaceous inclusions that sometimes outlined the core and the segments. The inclusions were even found within the segments and in the core, at times so abundantly as to make the core seem black. When heated to redness in air, the black cores changed to green 'with traces of orange-brown, presumably due to loss of the carbonaceous content'. A spectrochemical analysis showed the core to contain appreciably higher Fe, Ti, and Ca than elsewhere in the specimen.

Record-size crystals

A summary of giant crystals in pegmatite bodies, including beryl, appeared in a 1953 study made by Jahns[12]. Gedney and Berman[13] described 'star-like' groups of enormous beryl crystals from the Bumpus quarry, Maine, several of which were 120 cm (4 ft) in diameter, and one measured in place, though not fully exposed, was 4.2 m (14 ft) long. Page et al.[14] mention a crystal of 5.4 m (18 ft) long in the Bob Ingersoll quarry, Black Hills, and noted that 'the largest mass of beryl, 61 tons in weight', was mined from another pegmatite on the Bob Ingersoll property.

The Muiâne pegmatite quarry at Alto Ligonha, Mozambique, once exposed a giant crystal of sky blue colour which measured about 2.4 m (8 ft) in diameter[15]. Saint Ours[16] reported that a crystal measuring 13 m (42 ft) long and from 1.5 to 2 m (4½ to 6 ft) in diameter was found in Pegmatite A4 of the Malakialina field of Madagascar. Knorring[17] remarked on the very large crystals from Alto Ligonha, Mozambique, and noted that 'blue and pink beryls are often found together, forming large aggregates . . . some 200 tons of beryl have been mined from a single mass at Namivo mine'.

References

1 BERTRAND, E. [Muzo trapiche emeralds]. *Bulletin de la Société Française de Minéralogie et Cristallographie* 2:31 (1879)

2 CODAZZI, R. L. *Contribucion al Estudio de los Minerales de Colombia.* Bogota: Imprenta de la Cruzada. 7 pp. (1915)

3 POGUE, J. E. The emerald in Spanish America. *Bulletin of the Pan-American Union* (Washington, DC.) 43:706–20 (1916)

4 POGUE, J. E. The emerald deposits of Muzo, Colombia. *Transactions of the American Institute of Mining and Metallurgical Engineers* 55:910–34 (1916)

5 BERNAUER, F. Die sogenannten Smaragddrillinge von Muzo und ihre optischen Anomalien. *Neues Jahrbuch für Mineralogie*, Abt. A, Beilage-Bd. 54, pp. 205–42 (1926)

6 SCHEIBE, R. Die Smaragdlagerstätte von Muzo (Kolombien) und ihre náhere Umgebung. In O. Stutzer, Beiträge zur Geologie und Mineralogie von Kolumbien, IV. *Neues Jahrbuch für Mineralogie*, Vol. 54, Abt. B, pp. 419–47 (1926)

7 McKAGUE, H. L. Trapiche emeralds from Colombia. *Gems & Gemology* 11:210–3 (1964)

8 CHAUDHARI, M. W. An unusual emerald. *Schweizerische mineralogische und petrographische Mitteilungen* 49:569–75 (1969)

9 NASSAU, K., and JACKSON, K. A. Trapiche emeralds from Chivor and Muzo, Colombia. *American Mineralogist* 55:416–27; correction, 55:1808–9 (1970)

10 NASSAU, K., and JACKSON, K. A. Trapiche emeralds from Chivor and Muzo, Colombia: nature

and origin. *Lapidary Journal* 24:82, 84–6 (1970)

11 TRIPP, E. J., and HERNANDEZ, L. H. The complete trapiche emerald picture. *Lapidary Journal* 24:96–104 (1970)

12 JAHNS, R. H. The genesis of pegmatites. I. The origin and occurence of giant crystals. *American Mineralogist* 38:563–98 (1953)

13 GEDNEY, E. K., and BERMAN, H. Huge beryl crystals at Albany, Maine. *Rocks & Minerals* (Peekskill, N.Y.) 4:78–80 (1929)

14 PAGE, L. R., *et al. Pegmatite investigations 1942–1945 Black Hills, South Dakota. U.S. Geological Survey Professional Paper* 247. 228 pp. (1953)

15 MITCHELL, K. The largest beryl crystal? *The Gemmologist* (London) 28, no. 341, p. 228 (1959)

16 SAINT OURS, J. de. Étude générale des pegmatites. *Republique Malgache Rapport Annuel du Service Géologique* (Tananarive), pp. 73–87 (1960)

17 KNORRING, O. Pegmatite and related investigations. In *University of Leeds, Research Institute of African Geology, 6th Annual Report, Session 1960–61*, pp. 7–13 (1962)

Chapter 8

Inclusions

While beryl crystals are remarkable for their lack of entrapped minerals and other types of inclusions, they are by no means free of them. Such inclusions encompass solids, liquids, and gases, but also various kinds of cavities which may or may not be filled with liquid and/or solid particles.

Gemmologists are obviously interested in inclusions because too many inclusions can make otherwise good gem material worthless; they are of interest for other reasons. Certain inclusions, especially in emerald, are distinctive and sometimes can even serve to identify the particular deposit from which they came. In the case of emeralds synthisized by the high-temperature flux-melt process, the inclusions are considerably different from those found in natural emeralds because water is never present in the cavities. Inclusions also provide evidence as to the geochemical environment in which the beryl crystals grew. Finally, some inclusions greatly enhance the value of certain gem beryls, such as in the cat's-eye types where the regular array of extremely fine tubes permits the cutting of handsome and valuable gems. Another example is star beryl, in which appear numerous minute plate-like inclusions deposited upon the basal planes of growing beryl crystals and subsequently covered over by additional beryl growth. Reflections from these inclusions provide interesting if not particularly handsome gems.

According to Gübelin[1] (p. 37), inclusions may be divided among those that were present before the host crystal formed (the *protogenetic* types), those that formed contemporaneously (the *syngenetic*), and lastly, those which developed afterwards (the *epigenetic* inclusions). All three are known to occur in beryls and will be discussed in the sections below.

Protogenetic inclusions

Protogenetic inclusions are minerals which formed before the beryl and were enveloped by the beryl crystal as it grew. They commonly include pegmatite and greisen species such as quartz, albite, and mica and are generally found in the bases of the crystals at the point of attachment to cavity walls. As previously noted, some common beryl crystals in pegmatites, completely enveloped by other minerals, may have very large inclusions of quartz, feldspars, mica, black tourmaline, and apatite, forming coarsely granular masses within 'shell' or 'cored' crystals of beryl. In pegmatite cavities, alkali beryls, usually among the last species to form, may sometimes be found enclosing prisms of gemmy coloured tourmaline as well as platelets of cleavelandite and other pocket species.

In long prismatic aquamarine and golden beryl crystals, small bits of mineral matter may fall upon the growing basal faces and may not be enclosed, the beryl crystal growing so rapidly in the direction of the c-axis that a miniature 'well' is formed, the walls of which extend upward, sometimes to relatively enormous distances, without becoming bridged over by growth across the c-axis direction as shown in *Figure 8.1*. It is likely that such bridging-over is prevented by the rapidity of growth, because once such a tube begins, it is extremely difficult for nutrient matter to circulate within the tube and cause the walls to grow towards each other. Similar tubular inclusions, possibly in slower-growing crystals, do bridge over. These may be recognized by the particle of foreign mineral at their bottoms and a gradual inward-curving closure of the walls until the entire inclusion resembles a greatly elongated rain-drop.

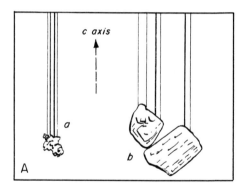 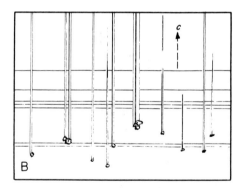

Figure 8.1 Typical inclusions in beryls. A: Solid inclusions giving rise to face-lined tubes parallel to the c-axis; irregular mass at (a) probably a clay mineral, small crystals at (b), possibly of quartz. B: Similar tubular inclusions passing through colour zones, the latter parallel to the basal plane; some tubes persist, some are interrupted, and others taper to a closure in the 'spike' on nailhead inclusions, From V. C. Feklichev, *Berill: morfologiva, sostav i struktura kristallov.* (Moscow: Izdatelstvo Nauka, 1964) and E. Gübelin, *Internal World of Gemstones: Documents from Space and Time* (Zurich: ABC Edition, 1973). (John Sinkankas).

Gaps upon the basal plane of the growing beryl crystal can also be initiated by liquid droplets, which may take the form of flattened discs or very small spheres as shown in *Figure 8.3*. The former tend to be closed over, but the latter tend to perpetuate the gaps formed by them, resulting in the very common extremely fine tubular inclusions or 'silk' that can be seen parallel to the c-axis in so many beryl crystals.

Protogenetic inclusions are especially common in emeralds grown within mica schists, as in the Egyptian, Uralian, and Rhodesian deposits. They are made up of such species as micas, actinolite, quartz, and black tourmaline, among others. Despite growing within such rock, the emerald crystals manage to thrust aside the majority of minerals and remain reasonably free of them.

Syngenetic inclusions

Typical syngenetic inclusions in beryls are mentioned by Gübelin[1], p. 51–2 and include calcite rhombs in Muzo emerald, pyrite and pyrrhotite crystals in emerald, and quartz in aquamarine and emerald. Halite crystals are common in emerald as

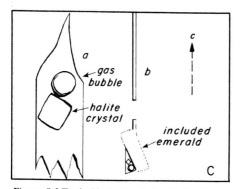
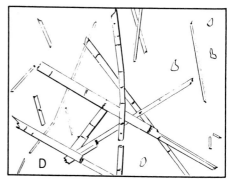

Figure 8.2 Typical inclusions in beryl. C: Characteristic inclusions in Colombian emerald; jagged liquid-filled cavities at (a) contain a gas bubble and halite crystal while at (b) an inclusion of a small emerald crystal forms a three-phase inclusion as well as an axial tube, the latter interrupted, possibly by later growth. D: Actinolite inclusions in Uralian emerald; these are randomly scattered in the crystal. From V. G. Feklichev, *Berill: morfologiya, sostav i struktura kristallov.* (Moscow: Izdatelstvo Nauka, 1964) and E. Gübelin, *Internal World of Gemstones: Documents from Space and Time* (Zurich: ABC Edition, 1973). (John Sinkankas).

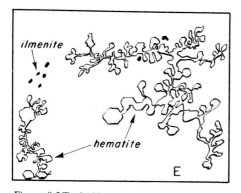
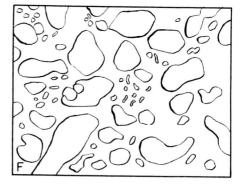

Figure 8.3 Typical inclusions in beryl. E: Extremely thin plate-like dendrites of ilmenite (black) and haematite (orange) grown upon the basal plane of aquamarine from Brazil. F: Extremely thin voids resembling flattened bubbles forming planes of inclusions parallel to the basal plane; as in E, some are epitaxial; all are so thin that vivid colours arise from those which interfere with light. From V. G. Feklichev, *Berill: morfologiya, sostav i struktura kristallov.* (Moscow: Izdatelstvo Nauka, 1964) and E. Gübelin, *Internal World of Gemstones: Documents from Space and Time* (Zurich: ABC Edition, 1973). (John Sinkankas).

shown in *Figure 8.2;* it is assumed that in this case the nutrient solution was saturated in sodium-chlorine ions which crystallized into halite with a drop in temperature.

Epitaxial growths are another kind of inclusion found in beryl crystals. The term *epitaxy* refers to minerals growing upon others in such a manner that the orientation of the epitaxial mineral is governed by the crystal structure of the host. Thus certain aquamarine crystals of Brazil contain thin platelets of ilmenite and haematite which assume parallel positions on the basal faces of the host, become entrapped, and are finally completely covered by the beryl. Because of their common orientation, such beryl crystals can be polished as cabochons with their bases parallel to the basal plane, and the reflections from the inclusions give rise to asterism or a 'star'.

Syngenetic liquid inclusions

As mentioned previously, by far the commonest inclusion in all beryls is liquid, sometimes two liquids, sometimes also gas, and occasionally small crystals grown within the liquids. Gübelin[1] (pp. 69–70) noted that the 'normal' filling is usually water, dissolved salts, traces of heavy elements, and carbon dioxide gas, the last mixed with water vapour. Among the elements detected were Na, Ca, K, Mg, Cl, and F, as well as carbonate, carbonic acid, and sulphate ions. The cavity fillings in emeralds, for example, are saline, sometimes so saturated with salts that minute crystals of halite, sylvite, and anhydrite precipitates can be observed under high magnification. In a recent study of cavity contents in Colombian emerald, Touray and Poirot[2] confirmed the presence of a saline solution, gas, halite crystals, and an unidentified mineral in the host crystal which seemed to encourage the formation of elongated inclusions trailing from the mineral particles.

Liquid inclusions can be further classified according to whether they are primary or secondary, the first being those droplets which adhere to the host beryl during growth and are subsequently trapped, and the secondary being those liquds which intrude into fractures and fissures which arise from later rupture of the host crystal. Primary liquid inclusions often appear to have no crystallographic relationship to the host and thus occur in random shapes and orientations. Commonly they form swarms which may be so dense that the crystal appears milky. In emeralds, they often resemble mossy growths, resulting in the descriptive terms of 'garden' or the French 'jardin' emeralds. Under high magnification the cavities are often jagged or 'sawtoothed' in profile and are filled with liquid, sometimes also a gas bubble, and as is common in Colombian emeralds, one or two minute halite crystals.

The numerous tubular inclusions that parallel the *c*-axis that were mentioned before, range in size from stubby cylinders to extremely long hair-like openings, usually also filled with liquid-gas and sometimes a few very small crystals of a foreign mineral. Unlike the irregular cavities mentioned above under emerald, these tend to be bounded on their sides by crystal faces and hence have been called 'negative' crystals. They tend to perpetuate themselves and for this reason may sometimes be traced unbroken throughout a long prism of beryl.

Some beryl crystals display sharp zones of clear material interspersed with zones containing large numbers of the tubular inclusions mentioned. In aquamarines, for example, numerous inclusions of this sort may be present in the lower portion but abruptly disappear near the top. Other crystals may be found in which this zoning is reversed, that is, the crystal is essentially free of inclusions near its base but contains them near the termination. This pattern seems more common in golden beryls than in aquamarines. Striking and differently coloured zones of inclusions are a particular feature of the beautiful beryl prisms from the Adun Chilon deposits of Transbaikalia, USSR, but examples may be found in many other deposits too.

The cause of this zoning may be due to changes in the velocity of crystal growth. Probably a faster-growing individual tends to entrap rather than thrust aside impurities that fall upon basal face, while the reverse applies to a slower-growing crystal. Because inclusions represent greater exposed area, subsequent corrosion of the crystal may manifest itself in deep pitting of the basal face and the development of striations on the sides of the prism due to attack on tubular inclusions close to the surface.

As we have seen, minute spherical droplets or bits of foreign mineral which fall upon the c-faces of growing beryl crystals can cause tubular development. In contrast, some droplets of fluid are discoidal in shape and, when numerous, cause a decided pearly lustre on these faces. The disc-shaped droplets are so broad that the nutrient solution is able to flow over them and cause the growing crystal to completely enclose them as shown in *Figure 8.3*.

Secondly liquid inclusions cause some of the most interesting optical displays within beryl crystals. Some seem like very thin diaphanous veils entrapped within the clear material, others like spatters of rain that fell upon glass and formed random dispersal patterns. Such inclusions generally represent former fracture openings in the host crystal, possibly due to internal stresses resulting from changes in chemical composition, or perhaps due to thermal or physical shock. In any case, the cracks were accessible to the external nutrient solution, which carried in additional beryl material and deposited it to fill the cracks. As pointed out by Laemmlein[3], cracks in beryl crystals may occur more or less parallel to basal and prismatic cleavage planes, which then 'heal' with introduction of additional material but leave traces in the form of numerous liquid-gas cavities. A particular manifestation of such planar cracks is the so-called 'feather' or 'fingerprint' pattern, representing a more or less circular original crack opening. Typically, the narrower portions of these cracks contain more inclusions than the wider parts, because it is more difficult for the solution to reach into them and deposit beryl during the 'healing' process.

Epigenetic inclusions

According to Gübelin[1], (p. 88) only ilmenite and haematite are considered epigenetic, that is, formed after the beryl host by a process of crystallizing within the beryl (exsolution). A similar process is thought to account for the silk-like crystals of rutile in star ruby and sapphire, and indeed the natural stones have been duplicated in the laboratory by a process of melting and slow cooling, upon which the deliberately added impurities capable of forming rutile exsolve to provide synthetic star gem material.

However, in nature, where virtually all beryls grow in liquid and at much lower temperatures than those that must prevail for ruby and sapphire, it seems doubtful that beryl crystals could accommodate considerable amounts of either ilmenite or rutile impurities during growth, much less allow them to form crystals within the structure afterwards. In view of the fact that both ilmenite and haematite occur in well-defined bands in crystals instead of being uniformly distributed throughout, as would be likely in a process of exsolution, it is considered that they are syngenetic in origin, that is, they grow epitaxially upon faces of the beryl host crystal and later become enclosed by additional beryl growth.

Solid inclusions

Table 8.1, Mineral inclusions in beryl, has been compiled from many sources, but it must be far from complete considering how difficult it can be to positively identify extremely small inclusions of minerals. For this reason, some entries are accompanied by a question mark, indicating an identification of doubtful validity.

Many identifications have been made visually under magnification, still the common practice, and it is only lately that identifications based on chemical composition have been possible on extremely small samples by use of the electron microprobe, an instrument that can focus a beam of electrons on an extremely small area to produce X-rays characteristic of certain elements. Quantitative as well as qualitative data may be obtained with the instrument that are often sufficient to identify the mineral. A brief discussion of the technique and its applicability to the study of inclusions in gemstones appears in Glübelin[1] (p. 23–4). Graziani and others[4,5,6,7] used the microprobe to conduct their examinations of beryl inclusions.

TABLE 8.1 Mineral inclusions in beryl

Mineral	Description	Locality
Actinolite	Rodlike crystals in emerald	Urals: Habachtal
Albite	Bladed crystals in pink beryl	Haddam Neck
Albite	In emerald	Chivor; Gachala
Albite	In trapiche emerald	Muzo
Apatite	In aquamarine	——
Apatite	In aquamarine	Brazil
Apatite	In emerald	Habachtal
Arsenolite (?)	In beryl	Elba
Beryl	In beryl	Sondalo, Italy
Beryl	In aquamarine	Brazil
Biotite	In emerald	Urals; Habachtal; Transvaal; Goiaz

TABLE 8.1 (continued)

Mineral	Description	Locality
Biotite	In beryl	Uuksu, Finland
Biotite	In aquamarine	India
Byssolite	In emerald	Bom Jesus d. Meiras
Bityite (?)	Oriented plates in beryl	Brazil
Calcite	Rhombs in emerald	Muzo
Calcite	In V-emerald	Salininha, Bahia
Calcite	In emerald	Transvaal; Urals
Calcite	In beryl	——
Carbon (?)	In trapiche emerald	Muzo
Chlorapatite	In emerald	India
Chlorite	In emerald	Habachtal
Chlorite	In beryl	Graz, Austria
Chromite	In emerald	——
Columbite	In beryl	Haddam Neck
Columbite-tantalite	In aquamarine	Pakistan (?)
Corundum	In aquamarine	Brazil
Dolomite	In emerald	Goiaz, Brazil
Epidote	In emerald	Habachtal
Epidote	In beryl	——
Epidote	In aquamarine	Brazil
Feldspar	In beryl	Elba
Feldspar	In V-emerald	Salininha, Bahia
Feldspar	In emerald	Sandawana
Fluorapatite	In aquamarine	Brazil
Fluorite	In beryl	Adun Chilon; Uuksu, Finland
Fluorite	In pink beryl	Wodgina, W. Australia
Fuchsite	In emerald	Ajmer-Merwara
Fuchsite	In aquamarine	Brazil
Garnet	In pink beryl	Haddam Neck
Garnet	In beryl	Elba
Garnet	In aquamarine	Pakistan (?)
Garnet	In emerald	Sandawana
Goethite	In beryl	Elba
Halite	In emerald	Colombia
Halite	In beryl	——
Haematite	In emerald	Habachtal; Sandawana
Haematite	In green beryl	Elba
Haematite	In aquamarine	Brazil
Haematite	In beryl	Brazil
Ilmenite	In beryl, on $c\{0001\}$	Minas Gerais
Ilmenite	In aquamarinc	Brazil
Ilmenite	In beryl	Brazil; Madagascar
Kaolin	In beryl	Sondalo, Italy
Lepidocrocite	In aquamarine	Brazil

TABLE 8.1 (continued)

Mineral	Description	Locality
Magnetite	Crystals in beryl	Lonedo, Italy
Magnetite	In aquamarine	Brazil
Mica	Plates in emerald	Urals; Transvaal
Molybdenite	Flakes in emerald	Transvaal
Muscovite	In beryl	Sondalo; Uuksu, Finland
Muscovite	In pale blue beryl	Brazil
Parisite	In emerald, pink crystals	Muzo
Pentlandite	In emerald	——
Petalite	In beryl	——
Phlogopite	In emerald	Urals
Phlogopite	In V-emerald	Salininha, Bahia
Phlogopite	In pale blue beryl	Brazil
Phlogopite	In aquamarine	——
Pollucite (?)	In beryl	Elba
Pyrite	Euhedrons in emerald	Chivor
Pyrite	In emerald	Leysdorp
Pyrite	In beryl	Lonedo, Italy
Pyrite	In beryl	——
Pyrite	In aquamarine	Brazil
Pyrrhotite	In emerald	——
Pyrrhotite	In green beryl	——
Pyrrhotite	In aquamarine	Brazil
Quartz	In emerald	Chivor; Urals
Quartz	In aquamarine	Brazil; W. Australia
Rutile	In emerald	Habachtal; Goiaz, Brazil
Talc	In emerald	Urals; Goiaz, Brazil
Talc	In V-emerald	Salininha, Bahia
Titanite	In emerald	Habachtal
Topaz (?)	In beryl	Minas Gerais
Tourmaline	In emerald	Habachtal; Urals
Tourmaline	In pink beryl	Haddam Neck
Tremolite	Acicular crystals in emerald	Habachtal; Sandawana

References

1 GÜBELIN, E. J. *Die diagnostiche Bedeutung der Einschlüsse in Edelsteinen. Schweizerische mineralogische und petrographische Mitteilungen* 28, No. 1, pp. 146–156

2 TOURAY, J. C., and POIROT, J. P. Observations sur les inclusions fluides primaires de l'émeraude, etc. *Compte Rendu de l'Academie des Sciences* (Paris), ser. D, vol. 266, no. 4, pp. 305–8 (1968)

3 LAEMMLEIN, G. Sekundäre Flussigkeitseinschlüsse in Mineralien. *Zeitschrift für Kristallographie und Mineralogie* (Leipzig) 71:237–56 (1929)

4 GRAZIANI, G., and GUIDI, G. Mineralogical study of a star-beryl and its inclusions, *Neues Jahrbuch für Mineralogie*, Monatshefte, Jg. 1979, no. 2, pp. 86–92 (1979)

5 GRAZIANI, G., and GIULIO, V. Di. Growth of an aquamarine crystal from Brazil. *Neues Jahrbuch für Mineralogie*, Monatshefte, Jg. 1979, no. 3, pp. 101–8 (1979)

6 GRAZIANI, G., and LUCCHESI, S. Einschlüsse und Genese eines Vanadiumberylls von Salininha, Bahia, Brasilien. *Zeitschrift der deutschen gemmologischen Gesellschaft* 28, no. 3, pp. 134–45 (1979)

7 GRAZIANI, G., and GIULIO, V. Di. *Neues Jahrbuch für Mineralogie*, 137, no. 3, pp. 198–207 (1979)

Chapter 9
Beryl simulants and synthetic beryls

The zeal of the miner in uncovering valuable gemstones is matched by the zeal of the imitator of gems. Imitation gems or gem simulants have been used since antiquity, but most of them were made from glass or sometimes from other stones which could be skillfully disguised to give them the appearance of valuable gemstones. It is only since the last century, when chemical composition of minerals became known, that serious attempts have been made to duplicate natural stones through the process of *synthesis,* that is, to produce substances that in every essential were identical to their natural counterparts.

Glass and other simulants

The use of green glass to make emerald simulants began soon after glass itself was discovered. According to Lucas[1] (p. 116), the exact date that glass-making began in Egypt is uncertain, but he mentioned a 'large green ball bead', inscribed with the name of Amenophis I, as certainly dating its manufacture to at least the beginning of the 18th Dynasty, or about 1600 BC.

The use of glass to imitate emerald and other beryls continued without interruption into modern times, glass makers learning how to skillfully incorporate swarms of bubbles in green paste to simulate the natural inclusions of emerald. Numerous examples of antique pastes are to be found in every major collection of jewellery.

Imitation of emerald and other precious stones reached a peak of perfection during the Renaissance. Benvenuto Cellini (1500–1571), the eminent Florentine goldsmith, boasted about his skill in detecting frauds[2] (pp. 26–7), but he also said that imitations were made not only of solid pieces of glass but from several pieces of material cemented together. For example:

'I mind me also of having seen rubies and emeralds made double, like red and green crystals, stuck together, the stone being in two pieces, and their usual name is 'doppie' or doublets'.

Unfortunately, Cellini did not make clear whether the pieces were all of glass or part-glass, or perhaps two parts of genuine gem material. Further on:

'emeralds and sapphires are also manufactured out of single stones, and this so cleverly that they are often difficult to tell, and however wonderfully they are counterfeited in colour they are so soft, that any good jeweller with the average amount of brains, can easily spot them'.

Another ancient technique of imitation involved dyeing rock crystal. The technique probably stemmed from the practice of 'oiling' rough crystals with some suitable fluid to fill in the natural cracks and thus to both enhance the colour and give an impression of flawlessness, albeit temporarily. This practice continues today.

The use of backings to heighten the colour of a mounted gemstone began much before the Renaissance, and by Cellini's time had become a standard practice. For example, Cellini[2] (p. 28) gave an alloy for making a 'green foil', consisting of 10 carats of fine copper, 6 of silver, and one of gold. A simple, highly polished gold or silver foil 'mirror' could be cleverly set beneath the gem in its mounting to reflect such light as passed through the gem. If the foil mirror were also enamelled in a suitable colour, the colour would be transmitted through the gem to counteract any natural paleness or to even impart a colour that the stone (or glass) did not have to begin with.

Other subterfuges were employed to 'improve' cut emeralds. For example, flawed gems were impregnated with an emerald-dyed wax or varnish to fill in the crevices. In some instances, an entire gem was coated with a coloured varnish or lacquer, or in the case of emeralds set in rings, a varnish applied only to the back where it could escape detection for a time. Another trick, also depending on inaccessibility, used a dyed wax to impregnate the inside surface of bead holes.

Composite gems

Composite gems, or assembled stones, also known as doublets and triplets according to the number of pieces used, were well-known by Cellini's time. The principle behind all of them is to enhance colour and/or durability. For example, in a simple type of doublet, a bright green glass base could be used to impart the necessary hue while the top could be made from a much harder natural gemstone to resist abrasion. In a triplet, two pieces of genuine pale-coloured aquamarine could be cemented together with a central layer of vividly coloured resin. Such a stone not only would be as resistant to wear as natural solid beryl, but would also produce the same refractive index if subjected to this gemmological test, although it would have to be a careless gemmologist to avoid detecting the composite structure. A very large number of composite gems have appeared on the market from time to time and are described in detail in standard gemmological treatises, Webster's[3] (pp. 135–46) being one of the most useful.

Synthetic gemstones used as beryl simulants

Synthetic gemstones are exact re-creations of their natural counterparts, possessing essentially the same crystalline structure and exhibiting the same physical and chemical properties. The earliest commercial success in synthesis came with Auguste Verneuil's 1891 discovery of the flame-fusion process for creating corundum gems in various colours, the first attempts being made to produce synthetic ruby. In brief, the process calls for dropping aluminium oxide powder, suitably doped with a colouring agent, through the intensely hot flame of an oxyhydrogen blowpipe and collecting the molten droplets upon a clay pedestal, upon which they crystallize. Experimentation soon enlarged the range of colours, including excellent replicas of the colours of various beryls.

Somewhat later, an almost equally hard synthetic spinel was manufactured which also could be produced in a large variety of colours, some of which resembled natural beryls. Fortunately, both synthetic corundum and spinel are easily distinguished from beryl when gemmologically tested.

The success of the Verneuil process naturally led to attempts to produce synthetic emeralds, but unlike the corundum which gratifyingly crystallized once its droplets had fallen onto the clay pedestal, beryl merely decomposed and the resulting glassy mixture was not this mineral at all. All attempts to create emerald by this means failed, and, as Verneuil[4] himself noted in 1911, no proof was advanced to show that emeralds had been produced by the direct melting process. Despite later claims to the contrary, this statement holds good today.

On the other hand, other approaches to the synthesis of beryl succeeded, as will be described in subsequent sections of this chapter. First, a chronology of events is provided in the following section. Certain developments have been checked against the excellent historical summary of emerald synthesis by Nassau[5].

Chronology of beryl synthesis

1848. Jacques Joseph Ebelman (1814–1852), French chemist, produced small prismatic crystals of emerald by adding emerald powder to boric acid flux[6].

1888. Paul Gabriel Hautefeuille (1836–1902) and Adolphe Jean Edmé Perrey, French chemists, grew prismatic emerald crystals in molten lithium molybdate or lithium vanadate, to which were added oxides of Be, Al, and Si[7,8,9].

1894. Hermann Traube (1860–1913), German mineralogist, grew small prisms of beryl by heating a gel approximating the composition of beryl with water[10].

1911 (?). M. Jaeger and H. Espig of I. G. Farbenindustrie, Germany, began experiments on flux-fusion emeralds[5] (p. 198), but the results were not publicized until considerably later[11,12].

1912. Richard Nacken (1884–1912), German chemist, supposedly grew hydrothermal emerald crystals, but this is now refuted[15] (p. 199); instead, they were grown in a flux-fusion bath over beryl nuclei[13].

1926. J. F. Riera obtained British Patent 271316 (Oct. 4) for synthetic aquamarine produced in lithium carbonate, lithium hydroxide, boric acid, and sodium borate fluxes, to which were added oxides of Si, Be, Al, and cobalt nitrate for colour[14].

1928. Nacken flux-fusion emerald described as hydrothermal by Van Praagh[15].

1930. Carroll F. Chatham (1914—), California chemist, made colourless flux-fusion(?) beryl crystals.[16].

1934. Emerald crystals, under the trade name 'Igmerald', were sold in small quantities from Espig's production in Germany[17]; they were described by Schiebold[18], Jaeger and Espig[19], Eppler[20], Anderson[21], and Foshag[22].

1935. A. Amstutz and A. Borloz[23] grew minute emerald crystals in BeF flux, to which were added SiO_2, Al_2O_3, and a trace of Cr.

1935. C. S. Hitchen repeated Hautefeuille and Perrey process to produce emerald crystals in lithium molybdate flux, adding 0.5% Cr_2O_3 for colour[24].

1935. C. F. Chatham grew his first emerald crystal at California Institute of Technology, Pasadena, weight ca. 1 carat[16].

1938. C. F. Chatham wrote, 'I produced a few flawless synthetic emeralds of excellent Muzo colour as early as 1938, but of very tiny size[25]'; early crystals examined by Rogers and Sperisen[16], Anderson and Payne[26], and Gübelin and Shipley[27].

1949–1952. Chatham production stabilized at 50 000 carats/year (less than 10% gem quality)[28]; 60 000 carats/year in 1951 (crystals averaged 40 carats each, 10% fine gem quality)[29]. Chatham stated, 'I might add that the largest cut stone, practically clear and of good colour, so far produced was a little over 4 carats[25].

1950. Pierre Gilson, French ceramicist, began emerald synthesis studies[5] (p. 490).

1953. Chatham delivered 1014 carat single synthetic emerald crystal to Smithsonian Institution, Washington, DC., and another only slightly less in weight to the Mineralogical Museum, Harvard University. These crystals took two years to grow (various press releases).

1957. J. Wyart and S. Šćavničăr grew minute beryl crystals hydrothermally[30].

1957. W. Van Valkenburg and E. Weir grew small hydrothermal emeralds[31].

1960. Johann Lechleitner of Innsbruck, Austria, hydrotheramlly coated precut aquamarines with synthetic emerald, producing the 'Emerita' or 'Symerald' gems[32,33,34].

1960, 1962. M. Kunitomi and H. Saito obtain Japan Patents 60–13908 and 62–16567 for hydrothermal emerald synthesis methods[5] (p. 200).

1961. W. F. Eppler, German mineralogist, produced small emerald crystals in lithium molybdate flux[35].

1961. Linde Division, Union Carbide Corp., commenced research on hydrothermal growth of emerald[5] (p. 472).

1962. R. C. Linares, A. A. Ballman, and L. G. Van Uitert grew emerald crystals in various fluxes, primarily in vanadium pentoxide[36].

1962. R. A. Lefever, A. B. Chase, and L. E. Sobon grew small emerald crystals in various fluxes; best results in molybdenum oxide[37].

1963. A. L. Gentile, D. M. Cripe, and F. H. Andres announced growth of flame-fusion emerald boules from powder of Si, Be, Al, and Cr oxides[38].

1963. Walter Zerfass of Idar-Oberstein, Germany, produced hydrothermal emerald crystals[39], but these are now recognized as flux-grown[5].

1963. Pierre Gilson produced commercial quantities of flux-grown emerald crystals[5, 40].

1964. C. M. Cobb, J. A. Adamski, and E. B. Wallis grew beryl and emerald crystals in vanadium pentoxide flux to which were added oxides of Si, Al, Be, and Cr.[41].

1964. Patents on hydrothermal synthesis methods for emerald applied for by staff members of Linde Division, Union Carbide Corp[5] (p. 472); described by Flanigen et al.[42], Pough[43, 44], and Flanigen, et al.[45].

1965. E. N. Emelyanova et al. grew hydrothermal beryl crystals in various hues by adding compounds of V, Mn, Co, and Ni to solutions[46].

1965. D. Ganguli and P. Saha grew beryl from melts of quartz, alumina, and beryllium oxide[47].

1965. W. Wilson and H. Hall, U.S. Naval Ordnance Laboratory, White Oaks, MD, claimed production of small beryl and emerald crystals from melts of beryl powder (or equivalent) under high pressure[48, 49]; perhaps glasses[5] (p. 202).

1967. S. Motoo, et al. grew emerald in lithium oxide-molybdenum oxide flux[5] (p. 200).

1968. C. Frondel and J. Ito hydrothermally synthesized bazzite[50].

1969. W. B. Wilson and H. B. Hall, granted U.S. Patent 3,473,935 for high-pressure melt synthesis of beryl.

1971. M. Kunitomi and Y. Arino obtain Japan Patents 71–25,499 and 71–25,500 for flux-fusion and hydrothermal syntheses of emeralds[5] (p. 200).

1972. M. Ushio and Y. Sumiyoshi grew emeralds in vanadium pentoxide flux[5] (p. 200).

1972. K. Kojima and Y. Arino obtain Japan Patent 72–27,639 for flux-fusion growth of emerald using vanadium pentoxide and lithium and molybdenum oxides[5] (p. 200).

1972. D. Ganguli grew very small emerald crystals from a gel at high temperature[5] (p. 200).

1973. C. Sakamoto obtained Japan patent 72–73,278 for flux-fusion emerald using alkali-molybdenum flux[5] (p. 200).

1974. H. Takubo, S. Kume, and M. Koizumi synthesized emerald in gel at high pressure[5] (p. 200).

1975. T. Matsuo and S. Marusato obtained Japan patent 75–39,697 for flux-fusion emerald in lithium oxide-molybdenum oxide flux[5] (p. 200).

Simple fusion synthesis

Despite failures to synthesize beryl by melting beryl powder or melting equivalent ingredients such as silica, alumina, and beryllia, a recent attempt was made by Gentile et al.[38], who claimed to have been successful. They reported growing two boules from a powder consisting of 16 gm BeO, 18 gm Al_2O_3, 67 gm SiO_2, and 0.5 gm Cr_2O_3. Both boules were found to be coated with an aluminium silicate compound, identified as mullite, which in itself showed that considerable alumina and silica had left the boule, thus destroying the calculated proportions needed to produce beryl. No crystal faces were found on the boules and no cleavages detected. The material was identified by X-ray diffraction and petrographic methods, the latter revealing biaxial figures in thin sections. Refractive indexes were $o = 1.561-1.562$, and $e = 1.566-1.567$. Later attempts to repeat this process and other simple fusion synthesis met with failure and produced only glass-like mixtures. Apparently beryl refuses to recrystallize as beryl when melted at atmospheric pressures.

Flux-fusion synthesis

Basically, flux-fusion synthesis involves providing a suitable melt to which are added ingredients capable of recombining to form beryl. In theory it is simple, but in practice the method is beset by difficulties.

The first flux-fusion process which promised a supply of commercial emeralds was that conducted by Jaeger and Espig in the laboratories of the I. G. Farbenindustrie at Bitterfeld, Germany, during 1924 to 1942. The name 'Igmerald' was adopted to reflect the igneous origin of the emeralds. Details of the process were first revealed by Wilke[11] in 1956 and amplified by Espig[12] himself in 1960. The essentials are as follows. A platinum vessel containing molten lithium molybdate flux is supplied with beryllia (BeO) and alumina (Al_2O_3), which, being heavier than the flux, sink to the bottom. Pieces of silica in the form of quartz (SiO_2) are floated on the top of the melt and slowly diffuse silica into the flux. Simultaneously, the beryllia and alumina also dissolve and react with the flux itself to form complex oxides which, through diffusion and convection, pass to the top of the melt where they meet and interact with the silica. So long as the three additives interact, emerald crystals form. The choice of lithium molybdate flux was governed by the fact that beryl is less soluble in it than the oxides used for its synthesis. Thus beryl tends to grow while the oxides slowly dissolve to provide the necessary nourishment within a weak but constantly saturated environment.

In previous experimentation it was found that if the ingredients were allowed to distribute themselves uniformly throughout the flux, serious oversaturation occurred with the result that a myriad of very small crystals formed instead of the desired few large ones. Oversaturation was prevented by physically separating the components, that is, keeping the beryllium and aluminium oxides at the bottom of the vessel and the quartz at the top. While this scheme worked well, it resulted in emerald crystals nucleating on the quartz, whereupon they developed numerous inclusions and tended to fracture when removed.

To ensure isolated growth of the crystals, it was found advantageous to place a platinum screen across the vessel such that it depressed the beryl seeds below the surface and provided a place against which they could float, as shown in *Figure 9.1*. A vertical platinum tube was inserted in the bath to permit addition of Be and Al

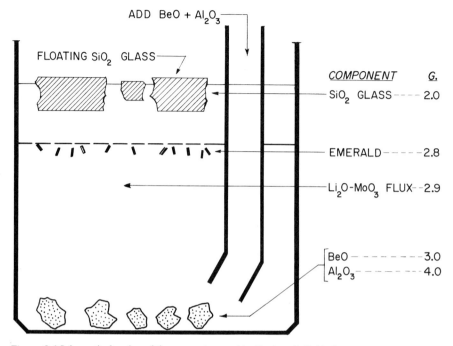

ADD BeO + Al₂O₃

FLOATING SiO₂ GLASS

COMPONENT	G.
SiO₂ GLASS ----	2.0
EMERALD -----	2.8
Li₂O-MoO₃ FLUX--	2.9
BeO ----------	3.0
Al₂O₃- ---------	4.0

Figure 9.1 Schematic drawing of the apparatus used by Espig at I. G. Farben to grow emeralds using a flux of lithium and molybdenum oxides. Based on a drawing in K. Nassau, Synthetic emerald: the confusing history and the current technologies, *Journal of Crystal Growth* 35 (1976):211–222. (John Sinkankas).

oxides as needed, but all of the quartz required for a run was supplied at the beginning. After two to four weeks, the crystals were taken out and defective places sawed off, after which they were reintroduced in the bath for further growth. Crystals of substantial size required a process time of several months, while crystals about 2 cm (¾ in) long required over a year.

Growth began in the range 640–750°C, with the optimum rate achieved at 770–800°C. In the final stages of mass-production, a growth period of twenty days was settled upon with the melt held at 800 ± 10°C. The oxides were replenished every two days, with the result that the seeds increased in weight by 20% after each run. When prismatic seeds were used, the growth rate improved. Eventually twelve furnaces were in operation to produce crystals up to 1 cm (⅜ in) long.

The properties of the new synthetic were described by Schiebold[18], Jaeger and Espig[19], Eppler[20], Anderson[21], and Foshag[22], reflecting both the interest and the concern that the appearance of these crystals aroused in the gem world. Their colour was excellent green with distinct yellow-green and blue-green dichroism. Refractive indexes were $o = 1.559$, $e = 1.566$, birefringence -0.007; specific gravity was 2.651[19]. Slightly different values were found by Eppler[20] as $o = 1.5644$, $e = 1.5606$, -0.0038, SG = 2.662; Anderson[21] found unusually strong dichroism and $o = 1.5660$, $e = 1.5647$, -0.0013, the last figure considered to be 'abnormally low', and SG = 2.66; Foshag[22] determined a strong dichroism, $o = 1.563$-6, $e = 1.560$, and SG = 2.65.

The possibility that these emeralds might be confused with natural gems led to close examination of differences that could be used in their discrimination. For example, Anderson[21] gave the following features: (a) abnormally low birefringence, specific gravity, and refractive indexes, (b) presence of strong absoption bands in the visible spectrum at 6060 Å and 5940 Å, (c) characteristic internal features such as banding and curved, crack-like markings, (d) anomalous double refraction, and (e) unusually strong dichroism. The strong absorption bands are in addition to those expected at 682.8, 679.5, 674, 662, 646 and 629.5 nm.

Eppler[20] particularly drew attention to the inclusions, pointing out the absence of the usual micas, cavities, fluids, and 'coaly' inclusions so often seen in natural emeralds. He also noted the irregular webs and veils of inclusions, some forming networks reminiscent of the cracks in aged oil paintings, that were features of the Igmerald. These inclusions appeared to contain liquid with gas bubbles. In this regard, Foshag[22] noted elongated rod-like cavities alighted in rows or 'combs', reticulated networks of veil-type inclusions, and a turbidity due to 'dirt'. He also discovered minute crystals which he could not identify but which were later described by Eppler[20] as phenakite.

Nacken emerald crystals, long claimed to be hydrothermal, are now shown to be flux-grown[5, 23]. Hydrothermal growth was erroneously ascribed due to misreading of reports of Nacken researches made in the post-World War II period (see Figure 9.2).

Chatham synthetic emeralds

The next attempt at flux-fusion synthesis of emerald, which has proved to be a commercial success, was conducted by Carroll F. Chatham of San Francisco, after much preliminary experimentation. He began synthesis experiments while still in high school and as early as 1930 grew his first synthetic beryl[16]. The first synthetic emerald crystal was grown in 1935. By 1938 he had solved the most important problem associated with his process and began marketing his production through Francis J. Sperisen, a lapidary of San Francisco. By 1948 crystals of fine Muzo colour were grown large enough and sufficiently free from flaws and inclusions to cut into gems of over 1 carat. By 1952, one faceted gem of a little more than 4 carats was recorded[35]. In 1970, Chatham established his own marketing company under the name of Chatham Created Gems, Inc. and 'kept his production capacity constant for the last ten years so as not to saturate the market[5]' (p. 488).

Chatham noted that about twelve months are required to grow the crystal[51]. These are produced in various sizes, the largest commonly being about 30 mm (1¼ in) in diameter. The polished gems range in size from several millimetres or smaller, or melée, to those of several carats or more weight, the maximum size ordinarily not exceeding 11 carats.

Crystal forms and properties of Chatham emeralds were described by Rogers and Sperisen[16], who noted that the crystals are primarily bounded by faces of the first and second order prisms, combined with the basal pinacoid. Seldom, and then only on very small crystals, do small faces of hexagonal bipyramids occur. The colour is

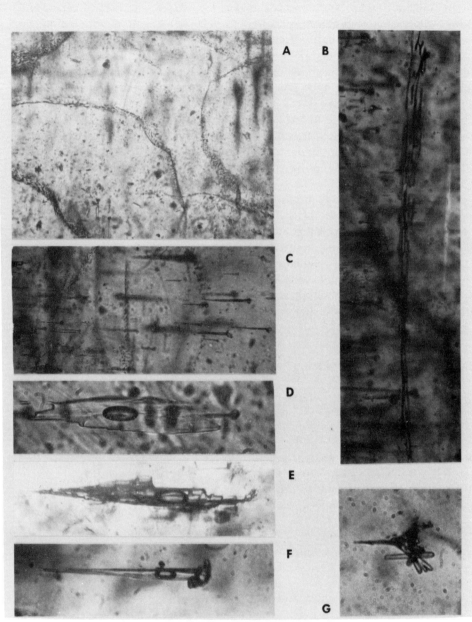

Figure 9.2 Inclusions in Nacken synthetic emeralds as observed by Dr. Kurt Nassau: A and B: Wispy or veil-like inclusions, some in long sheets. C: 'Nailhead' inclusions, growing from a solid included crystal (see also F). D and E: Two-phase inclusions resembling the gas-liquid inclusions of hydrothermal emeralds but in this case consisting of solids. F: Like E and D but commencing at a solid inclusion. G: Cluster of small prismatic crystals, probably phenakite. *Courtesy Dr. Kurt Nassau, Gems Made by Man* (Radnor, Pa.: Chilton, 1980), Fig. 11–7.

rich emerald-green, but some zoning is noted when crystals are cut through. The usual dichroic colours (yellow-green and blue-green) are apparent. Refractive indexes are $o = 1.578$, $e = 1.573$, birefringence 0.005.

Chemical analysis of early specimens indicated the presence of iron, calcium, magnesium, potassium, and sodium; when expressed as oxides, the total came to 0.14%[16]. A spectral analysis also showed lines for chromium, magnesium, titanium, calcium, and sodium. Gübelin and Shipley[27] found absorption bands at 629.5, 646, 662, 674, 679.5 and 682.8 nm, and two more at 594 and 606 nm. The entire spectrum was more intense than that noted in natural emeralds. Double refraction and patchy extinction under crossed polaroids were also noted, as well as weak dichroism. Switzer[52] found deep red fluorescence under 360 and 350 nm ultra-violet.

Inclusions also received their share of attention. Rogers and Sperisen[16] reported clusters of unidentified dark red, equant isotropic crystals as well as curved sheets, wisps, and veils of liquid-gas inclusions. Wispy inclusions were reported by Gübelin and Shipley[27]. Swarms of solid particles, wispy and feathery inclusions, systems of almost parallel rod-like inclusions, and crystals of low relief and sharp hexagonal outlines suggesting beryl were noted by Switzer[52]. Eppler[53] examined both 'Igmerald' and Chatham emeralds and found phenakite in both, mostly as groups of rounded crystals but sometimes as single stubby to elongated hexagonal prisms.

Eppler synthetic emeralds

W. F. Eppler of Germany grew emerald crystals up to 2 mm (1/16 in) in lithium molybdate flux during runs of from fourteen to seventy days. He also produced phenakite crystals which he believed to be characteristic inclusions in flux-fusion emeralds[35].

He found that the growth rate was rapid at first and the oxide components were quickly used up, with the result that in seven to ten days the crystals had attained a size of ca. 250 microns. The growth rate dropped dramatically thereafter, and in order to grow crystals to 0.5–2 mm long it was necessary to maintain the melt for a month or more.

Zerfass synthetic emeralds

According to Nassau[5] (p. 199), the Zerfass emeralds, once thought to be hydrothermal[54] have now been shown to be flux-fusion products. They were produced for a brief period in Idar-Oberstein by one of Espig's co-workers who worked for Zerfass after Espig's departure from the I. G. Farbenindustrie. Both Nassau and Flanigen, et al.[45] concur that the I. G. Farbenindustrie process was the one being used. Properties were described by Gübelin[39], but because of the extremely limited production, all are now decided rarities and the practicing gemmologist is unlikely to encounter any specimens. Refractive indexes are

$o = 1.562$, $e = 1.558$, bi-refringence 0.003–0.004, specific gravity = 2.66. In long- and shortwave UV a red glow appears. Zoned growth lines were noted and phenakite was identified as an inclusion.

Gilson synthetic emeralds

Outstanding success in producing flux-fusion emerald crystals (see *Figure 9.3*) rewarded the efforts of Pierre Gilson, French ceramist, to develop a commercially viable enterprise. These are now made in the plant of Établissements Pierre Gilson in Campagne-lez-Wardrecques near St. Omer in the Pas-de-Calais of France. The first commercial output was placed on the market in 1963[40]. Continuing refinements in the process resulted in a better product and increased quantities of cut gems and small-crystal groups. in 1977 a recent visitor to the plant quoted Gilson as saying that he then commanded 95% of the world market in synthetic emeralds[55].

Figure 9.3 Gilson emerald single crystal and cluster after ten months' growth. The large crystal measures about 63 mm (2½ in) tall and 37 × 12.5 mm (1½ × ½ in) in cross-section; several spontaneously seeded crystals are attached. The cluster crystals show development of second order prisms. *Courtesy Labratoire Gilson.*

Although details of the process have not been revealed, several qualified observers have recorded their impressions and speculations on how it works[55, 56]. The highly mechanized cutting of the stones has also been described[42]. By 1971, Gilson had adopted the use of two types of seed plates, the first being slices of natural beryl sawn parallel to the c-axis and at right angles to faces of the first order prism. These are fastened to racks with thin wire, as shown in *Figures 9.4* and *9.5*, and then immersed in the flux. In about one year's time, each plate grows to a

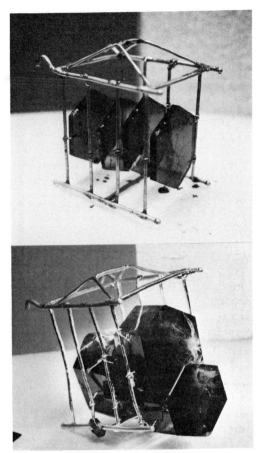

Figure 9.4 Gilson synthetic emerald crystals. *Top:* Basal section seed plates after two months' growth. *Bottom:* After ten months' growth. (*Courtesy Labratoire Gilson*).

weight of about 500 carats[41]. As emerald is accumulated, each plate assumes the cross-section of an irregular octagon bounded by two broad faces of the second order prism. This orientation of seed plate was chosen because of the faster growth rate that occurs on these faces.

Each immersion rack is fitted with five seed plates which are laterally spaced so that when growth is stopped the crystals almost touch each other[57]. According to Diehl[55], about 100 crystals were being produced each year, but not all were completely satisfactory, and the discards were returned to the flux baths as feed material.

In the second type of seed, cut across the c-axis as shown in *Figure 9.5*, the orientation exploits the rapid growth of beryl in the c-axis direction, as is typically the case in natural emerald crystals. Each crystal grows to about 4 cm (1⅝ in) in diameter and about 20 mm (¹³⁄₁₆ in) thick.

The flux, which Gilson calls his 'lava', is probably a lithium molybdate, either $LiMoO_4$ or $Li_2Mo_2O_7$, which has been identified as inclusion material in the emeralds[55]. Each tank, as well as the racks and suspending wires previously

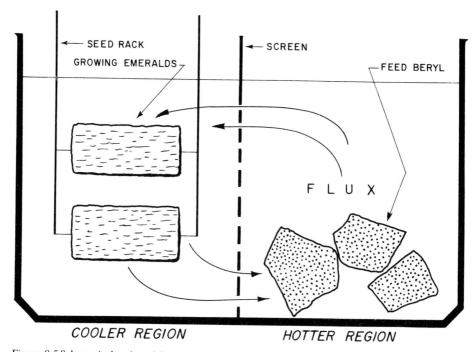

SEED RACK
GROWING EMERALDS

SCREEN

FEED BERYL

F L U X

COOLER REGION   HOTTER REGION

Figure 9.5 Schematic drawing of the apparatus used by Gilson to grow emeralds in flux. Feed beryl is dissolved in the flux and is transported to the seeds which enlarge at the rate of about 1 mm per month. Based on a drawing in K. Nassau, Synthetics in the Seventies, *Lapidary Journal* 34 (1980):58. (John Sinkankas).

mentioned, is probably fabricated from platinum or some alloy of platinum group metals. Diehl[55] supposed the tanks to be heated in such a way that slighly higher temperatures were maintained at the top of the molten flux to insure dissolution of added beryl and slightly lower temperatures maintained where crystallization took place. He also stated that the temperature in the growing region was increased by 30°C for a short period every 24 hours to dissolve away any small crystals which may have spontaneously formed on the plates. The small crystals dissolved rapidly but the large plates suffered very little loss.

None of Gilson's production of cutable emerald is sold. All of the large crystals are cut-in-plant via a remarkable assemblage of automatic lapidary devices. For example, mass-faceting machines using diamond-impregnated metal laps and drums greatly speed the production of standard shapes, including such styles as round and oval brilliants and marquises. Five standard sizes of cut gems are offered in round brilliants, oval brilliants, marquises, and the usual step-cut. The gems are classified into three quality grades according to colour, freedom from flaws, and size.

The property data, as supplied by the company itself, are refractive index, 1.558–1.575; birefringence, 0.003–0.005; dispersion, 0.014; SG 2.65–2.70. A red colour is observed under the Chelsea filter.

Fryer[58] examined older specimens and a newer type that lacked fluorescence under longwave UV. An older stone furnished $o = 1.569$, $e = 1.564 \pm 0.001$, birefringence -0.005, and SG $= 2.65\pm0.001$. This stone glowed orange-red under longwave UV. In contrast, another older stone, fluorescing red, gave $o = 1.567-1.568$, $e = 1.562$, birefringence $0.005-0.006$, and SG $= 2.65\pm0.01$. Distinct from these were results obtained on newer stones, namely, $o = 1.579$, $e = 1.571$, -0.008, SG $= 2.68-2.69$. These particular stones lacked fluorescence under UV, possibly due to the presence of iron, and they were found to be opaque to X-rays, which also suggests the presence of iron.

Inclusions in early Gilson emeralds are typical for the process. They take such forms as numerous veils and wisps of minute bubble-like or elongated bubble cavities, many containing flux, and numerous minute euhedrons of phenakite[45].

Numerous other flux-fusion attempts to grown emeralds are mentioned in the chronological table earlier in this chapter, but none resulted in commercial production.

Lennix synthetic emeralds

Synthetic flux-fusion emeralds have been produced commercially by M. Lens of France. The process was developed by Lens in the De Beers Diamond Research Laboratory, Johannesburg, South Africa[59]. The crystals grown by his process are unusual in that their habit is four-sided rather than hexagonal.

According to M. O'Donoghue[60], cut stones have a refractive index of $1.562-1.566$; birefringence, -0.004; SG $2.62-2.63$. They contain 2-phase inclusions resembling feathers and particles of flux, and a strong red can be seen through the Chelsea filter. In a total of fifty-eight natural and synthetic emeralds investigated by Schrader[61], the synthetic emeralds (including Lennix specimens) were almost free of iron.

Crescent vert synthetic emeralds

Flux-fusion synthetic emeralds have been produced commercially by the Kyocera company of Japan[59],[61]. These stones have a refractive index of $1.564-1.568$; birefringence, -0.004; SG 2.66, and appear to contain some iron as indicated by a low shortwave UV transmission factor of around 5%.

Hydrothermal synthesis

Hydrothermal methods of synthesis depend on the fact that many minerals can be dissolved in appreciable quantities in hot water under high pressures. Fundamentally, the apparatus consists of a pressure vessel in which nutrient is supplied along with water and the whole sealed and then heated. Slight differences in temperature are maintained at opposite ends of the growth chamber, the hotter end dissolving the nutrient and the cooler end causing seeds to take on additional growth. Typical apparatus and procedures are discussed by Ballman and Laudise in Gilman[63].

Richard Nacken, best known for his hydrothermal synthesis of quartz, was credited for hydrothermal growth of emerald, but, as previously mentioned, it now seems that these were actually grown in the flux-fusion process.

Lechleitner emerald-coated beryl

In 1960, a sensation was created in the gem world when Johann Lechleitner, working in Innsbruck, Austria, succeeded in hydrothermally depositing emerald on faceted seeds of beryl which needed only to be polished to finish them[32]. Such stones were given the name 'Emerita'.

No details of this work have been published, although Gübelin[33] mentioned that a weak alkaline solution, containing dissolved nutrients of silica, alumina, and beryllium oxide, was used as the fill for the pressure vessel. The vessel was heated to between 300°C and 400°C to obtain an internal pressure of 1000 bars. In early stones, the emerald layer was not over 0.5 mm thick and was found to have grown in crystallographic continuity with the underlying beryl. Some of the crystal forms taken by the emerald were of considerable complexity and beauty[33]. Later experimentation produced 'sandwich' type stones consisting of beryl-emerald slices further overgrown by emerald to intensify colour, and even fully synthetic emeralds[33, 45, 64, 65].

On the whole, the coated stones were satisfactory in terms of colour, although careless polishing could remove much of the thin emerald layer. Holmes and Crowningshield[32] determined refractive indexes of $o = 1.581$, $e = 1.575$, birefringence 0.006; Gübelin[34] found $o = 1.578–1.590$, $e = 1.571–1.583$, -0.007. Values found by Eppler[64] for the emerald overgrowth were $o = 1.581$, $e = 1.575$, and -0.006; for the 'sandwich' type they were $o = 1.570$, $e = 1.566$, and -0.004; while for the full synthetic type the values were $o = 1.574$, $e = 1.569$, and -0.005.

A more recent study giving considerably different values appeared in Bank[65]. He examined seven stones and found $o = 1.583–1.605$, $e = 1.577–1.599$, and birefringence $-0.005–0.009$. Surprisingly, Bank also found one coated 'beryl' that was actually emerald grown over a core of topaz[66]. Specific gravities recorded for the Lechleitner stones are 2.649–2.707, the less dense containing numerous core inclusions[32], 2.676–2.713[33], and 2.676–2.713[34].

Holmes and Crowningshield[32] found the absorption spectrum of early Lechleitner stones to be about the same as that observed in other emeralds, but it lacked two lines in the blue because of the thinness of the coating. Reddish fluorescence was apparent under longwave UV but was less intense than that of Chatham synthetic. Eppler[64] found that the coated stones glowed greenish under both 254 and 365 nm UV, but the full synthetic glowed only a weak dark red under the same wavelengths.

Lechleitner stones are readily identified because of the coatings and sandwich construction, which encourage the formation of minute cracks and inclusions of euclase and phenakite along the junctions. Also characteristic are core inclusions typical of natural aquamarine. According to Gübelin[33], Lechleitner had succeeded in introducing gold in his hydrothermal solution and caused deposition of minute octahedral crystals of this metal along with the emerald layers.

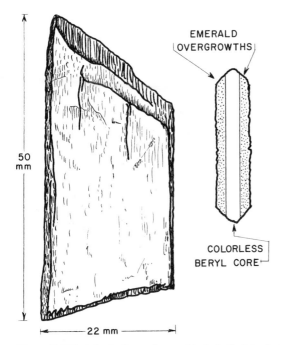

EMERALD
(OVERGROWTHS)

COLORLESS
BERYL CORE

50
mm

22 mm

Figure 9.6 Linde hydrothermal emerald. *Left:* Sketch of a tabular crystal removed from the autoclave. *Right:* Cross-section, showing emerald overgrowth upon a thin seed section of colourless beryl. After a photograph by Kurt Nassau, from Synthetic emerald: the confusing history and the current technology, *Lapidary Journal* 30 (1976):468. (John Sinkankas).

Linde hydrothermal synthesis

In 1961, E. M. Flanigen and others began research on hydrothermal synthetic emerald at the Tonawanda Research Laboratory, Linde Division, Union Carbide Corp. (see *Figure 9.6*). Although excellent emeralds were produced, the process eventually proved to be too costly to sustain itself commercially. Compared to flux-fusion emeralds, which can now be grown without interruption, the use of pressurized vessels in hydrothermal synthesis requires frequent and costly shut-downs to cool the vessels, open them, extract the contents, add new nutrients, reseal, etc.

The Linde emeralds were marketed from 1965 to 1975, although actual production ceased in 1970 due to an accumulating stock of unsold products. The company marketed cut emeralds in a 'Quintessa' line of jewellery, 'A procedure which was somewhat at odds with established jewellery trade practices', and which perhaps caused sales to be less than that needed to keep the enterprise alive.

According to Flanigen *et al.*[42],[45], the properties of the Linde product are as follows: refractive indexes, o = 1.571–1.578, e = 1.566–1.572; birefringence, 0.005–0.006; SG = 2.67–2.69 for a Cr content of 0.3–1.2%. Eppler[67] found o = 1.569, e = 1.563, −0.006, and SG = 2.67, comparing this data to B. W. Anderson's previous findings of o = 1.574, e = 1.568, −0.006, and SG = 2.69.

TABLE 9.1 Properties of synthetic emeralds

Name	Type	o (omega)	e (epsilon)	Birefringence	Specific Gravity	Chelsea Filter	Shortwave UV	Longwave UV
Chatham	Flux	1.578	1.573	0.005	2.65	Bright dull-red	Bright red	Deep red
		1.562–1.564	1.559–1.561	0.003	2.65	Glowing red	Dull bluish red	Strong red
		1.563	1.560	0.003				
		1.562	1.559	0.003				
Crescent Vert	Flux	1.568	1.564	0.004	2.66	Deep red	Deep red	None
Gilson	Flux	1.562	1.558	0.003–0.004	2.65	—	Weak olive	Olive
		1.564	1.561	0.003		Glowing red	Yellow-olive	Yellow-orange-olive
		1.562	1.559	0.003	2.65	Dull red	Mustard	
		1.569±0.001	1.564±0.001	0.005	2.65±0.01	Orange	Orange-red	
		1.567–1.568	1.562	0.005–0.006	2.65±0.01	None	Red	
		1.579	1.571	0.008	2.68–2.69		None	
'Igmerald'	Flux	1.563–1.566	1.560	0.003–0.006	2.65			
		1.559	1.566	0.007	2.651			
		1.5644	1.5606	0.0038	2.662			
		1.5660	1.5647	0.0013	2.66			
		1.562	1.559	0.003	2.65			
Lechleitner	Hydrothermal	1.581	1.575	0.006	2.649–2.707	Glowing red	Strong brick-red	Strong red
		1.578–1.590	1.571–1.583	0.007	2.676–2.713		Red	Reddish
		1.582–1.586	1.577–1.580	0.005–0.006	—			
		1.586–1.597	1.580–1.587	0.006–0.010	—			
	Full synthetic	1.577	1.571–1.572	0.005–0.006	2.67–2.69	Red	Pale red	Pale red
	Composite	1.567–1.573	1.562–1.567	0.005–0.006	2.67–2.69	Red	None	None
		1.581	1.575	0.006	2.695	Bright red	Bright red	Bright red
	Composite	1.570	1.566	0.004	2.678		Greenish	Greenish
	Full synthetic	1.574	1.569	0.005	—		Weak red	Weak red
		1.583–1.605	1.577–1.599	0.005–0.009	—		—	—

TABLE 9.1 (continued)

Name	Type	Refractive Index		Birefringence	Specific Gravity	Chelsea Filter	Shortwave UV	Longwave UV
		o (omega)	e (epsilon)					
Lennix	Flux	1.566	1.562	0.004	2.62–2.63	Red	Weak red	Red
Linares	Flux	—	—	—			None	None
Linde	Flux	1.564	1.561	0.003		Dull red or none	Dull red or none	Dull red or none
		1.564–1.572	1.561–1.563	0.003–0.005				
		1.564–1.570	1.561–1.564	0.003–0.006				
	Hydrothermal	1.571–1.578	1.566–1.572	0.005–0.006	2.67–2.69	Bright red	Bright red	Bright red
		1.571–1.578	1.566–1.572	0.005–0.006	2.67–2.69			
		1.569	1.563	0.006	2.67			
		1.574	1.568	0.006	2.69			
		1.569–1.576	1.563–1.570	0.003–0.006		Intense red	Red	Stronger red
Regency	Hydrothermal	1.576	1.570	0.006	Bright red	Dull red	Bright red	
Zerfass	Flux	1.562	1.558	0.003–0.004	2.66	Bright red	Red	Red

In colour, the Linde emeralds resemble the blue-green of Urals or Chivor crystals rather than the yellower green of Muzo stones. The blue-green, yellow-green dichroism is distinct. A bright red fluorescence appears under 365 and 253.7 nm UV, and bright red under the Chelsea filter for stones containing 0.7% Cr[43, 44, 45]. Galia[68] observed red fluorescence under UV, comparable to that noted in Chatham emerald, somewhat stronger fluorescence under longwave, and also an intense red under the Chelsea filter. Inclusions are characteristically minute liquid-gas cavity types forming elongated swarms resembling brush strokes, and irregular two-phase inclusions and spike-like cavities tapering from small phenakite crystals, the latter sometimes appearing as long-prismatic, colourless, transparent crystals[44, 45, 67].

Regency created emeralds

These are hydrothermally-grown synthetic emeralds produced by Vacuum Ventures of Pompton Lakes, New Jersey, U.S.A. M. O'Donoghue[60] reports that the stones are made using patents originally taken out by Union Carbide. Refractive index is quoted as 1.570–1.576; birefringence 0.005–0.006; SG 2.67–2.69. The stones showed a bright red through the Chelsea filter, fluoresced red under a high intensity beam of white light, and had a shortwave UV transmission factor of 23% (indicating the virtual absence of iron)[62].

Properties of synthetic emeralds

Table 9.1 compiled from the data appearing in this chapter, summarizes the properties of synthetic emeralds.

References

1 LUCAS, A. *Ancient Egyptian Materials and Industries.* 2nd ed. London: Edward Arnold & Co. 447 pp. (1934)

2 ASHBEE, C. R. *The Treatises of Benvenuto Cellini on Goldsmithing and Sculpture.* London: Edward Arnold. 164 pp. (1898)

3 WEBSTER, R. *Practical Gemmology.* 6th ed. New York: Arco Publishing. 209 pp. (1978)

4 VERNEUIL, A. Reconstructed synthetic emeralds and pearls. *The Keystone* (New York), May 1911, p. 855 (1911)

5 NASSAU, K. Synthetic emerald: the confusing history and the current technology. *Lapidary Journal* 30:196, 468, 488 (1976)

6 EBELMAN, J. J. Sur une nouvelle méthode pour obtenir des combinaisons cristallisées par la voie seche, etc. *Annales de Chimie et de Physique* 22:213–44 (1848)

7 HAUTEFEUILLE, P., and PERREY, A. Sur la réproduction de la phenacite et de l'émeraude. *Compte Rendu de l'Academie des Sciences* (Paris) 106:1800–2 (1888)

8 HAUTEFEUILLE, P., and PERREY, A. Sur la cristallisation de l'alumine et de la glucine. *Bulletin de la Société Française de Minéralogie et de Cristallographie* 13:147–9 (1890)

9 HAUTEFEUILLE, P., and PERREY, A. Ueber Berylliumsilicate. *Zeitschrift für Kristallographie und Mineralogie* (Leipzig) 21:306 (1893)

10 TRAUBE, H. Ueber die künstliche Darstellung des Berylls. *Neues Jahrbuch für Mineralogie* (Stuttgart) Beilage-Bd. 1:275–6 (1894)

11 WILKE, K. T. Die Entwicklung der Kristallzüchtung seit 1945. *Fortschritte der Mineralogie* (Stuttgart) 34:85–150 (1956)

12 ESPIG, H. Die Synthese des Smaragds. *Chem. Technik,* 12:327–31 (1960)

Chapter 10
Cutting and polishing beryl

In its clear to translucent forms, beryl is peculiarly suited to the ministrations of the lapidary. Though not as hard as diamond, ruby, and sapphire, it is still sufficiently hard that gems cut from it withstand much abuse and retain their lustre for decades. In respect to colour, the rare and beautiful emerald takes its place among the few gemstones that are considered truly precious, while the lovely limpidity of aquamarines, golden beryls, and morganites permit the fashioning of faceted gems which need take second place to few others. Furthermore, beryl possesses no easy cleavage, nor undue sensitivity to the ravages of light, which may cause colour changes, and otherwise presents no problems to the lapidary intent on shaping it into an object of beauty. In brief, it is hard, tough, and durable; it is a delight to the artisan and a pleasure to the beholder of the finished product.

Historical review

By at least 3500 BC the Egyptians were already familiar with the processes for cutting and polishing stones of all kinds. According to Lucas[1] (pp. 63–73), they had developed an impressive array of tools for stone working, ranging from those used for shaping great architectural masses to the delicate drills for boring beads. They had learned how to employ metal blades fed with grit to saw through the hardest of stones, and they also knew how to engrave fine lines on gemstones, such as those seen upon scarabs and other engraved gems.

Whether the Egyptians learned these arts from some other civilization or developed them largely within the confines of their own country is not known and perhaps never will be. In any event, much the same techniques eventually developed or spread throughout the civilized world.

By the first century AD, the arts of the lapidary were well established. Egyptian, Roman, Greek, Near-Eastern, and other cultures employed engraved gems, cabochon gems, small carvings, and other objects made from a large variety of stones and gemstones, including the emerald and other beryls. From the Middle Ages into the Renaissance, the *cabochon* style of cutting prevailed, that is, most gems meant for ornament were shaped into approximately hemispherical forms, the flattened base being set into the mounting and the curved part bulging above.

At some time during the Middle Ages it was discovered that transparent gemstones could be cut with flat surfaces or *facets* in lieu of the curved surface of the standard cabochon. Gems of this sort can still be seen ornamenting various religious and ceremonial objects, cups, caskets, and even book covers manufactured during this period. Eventually some unsung lapidary conceived the idea of cutting transparent gems with a series of facets upon the bottom of the stone as well as the top, those below acting like mirrors to reflect light back up through the stone to achieve the effect of *brilliance.*

Upon the invention of the self-reflecting facet cut, it became obvious that the best effects could be achieved in gemstones of perfect clarity, among which are the aquamarine and other beryls, which yield crystals of large size and gratifying freedom from flaws. Emeralds were also faceted, despite the fact that numerous flaws and inclusions impeded and scattered light. Nevertheless, if such imperfections were not too abundant, a beautiful glow of colour could be achieved by employing the facet cut for this gemstone.

Because no metal available to the ancients was capable of making the slightest impression on hard gemstones, including beryls, these stones had to be abraded in an indirect fashion. For example, the Egyptians used copper and iron lapidary tools, supplied with a powdered abrasive much harder than beryl. The soft metals merely dragged the abrasives along and allowed the much harder particles to do the actual cutting. Indeed it is obvious from the evidence supplied by Lucas that this method was used almost exclusively for sawing, drilling, and shaping. For soft stones, such as alabaster and marble, ordinary sand sufficed, but for beryl it was discovered that a rock known as emery, supplied from the Greek island of Naxos and from several places in Asia Minor, was effective. Much later this rock was analyzed and found to contain large amounts of corundum, a mineral much harder than beryl, thus explaining its effectiveness. Emery was well known to Theophrastus[2] (p. 115) as early as 346 BC, and he referred to it as the abrasive *par excellence* for engraving gems.

Powdered diamond, a vastly harder abrasive, may have also been in use but there is no concrete evidence available to that effect. This topic was explored by King[3] (pp. 26–7), who cited Pliny to justify his claim that diamond was used for engraving gems during the latter's lifetime, or during the early decades of the Christian era. King was of the opinion that splinters of diamond were imbedded in iron tools for the purpose of engraving the very fine lines and grooves seen in engraved gems of this period.

Despite the availability of diamond after Pliny's time, the much cheaper emery or other powdered forms of corundum continued to be the agent of choice for the sawing and shaping of beryls and other gemstones (except the diamond) into modern times. Boetius de Boodt[4] (pp. 74–85), writing in the 17th century, described the methods then in use and noted that all hard gemstones, except the diamond, were shaped on rotating tin laps and polished on tin laps charged with tripoli, a kind of very fine-grained quartz. He also mentioned diamond, but only in connection with its use for engraving.

Several hundred years later, Reinhard Blum[5] (pp. 66–81) wrote an excellent treatise on gemstones in which he gave descriptions of the lapidary's tools and abrasive and polishing agents, little of which differed materially from those described by Boetius de Boodt. Blum, for example, noted that emerald crystals were sawed by thin metal discs supplied with a slurry of emery powder suspended in oil. Roughing-out of gem shapes was accomplished on copper laps using the same abrasive. Tin, a softer metal, was used for polishing; the polishing agent was a watery slurry of either tripoli, pumice (a fine volcanic ash), or 'tin ash', better known today as tin oxide.

For some unexplained reason, aquamarines were treated differently from emerald. The roughing-out of aquamarine was done on lead instead of copper laps, and polishing was accomplished on lead with tripoli. Modern experience shows that there is no perceptible difference in the lapidary behaviour of emerald as compared to the other beryls. What works on one, works for all.

The concept that correct proportions and inclinations of facets on transparent gems could provide maximum brilliance was unknown to de Boodt. Even Blum gave only two geometrical rules to be followed in making faceted gems. He said the top or *crown* should be one-third of the total depth and the bottom part, or *pavilion*, should be two-thirds, but if the gemstone was weakly coloured, the crown should be one-fourth and the pavilion three-fourths. No scientific reason was given for these proportions, and it seems that they were arrived at by a hit-or-miss method developed through many years of cutting experience.

Poorly proportioned stones, or those cut too shallowly to reflect light from the back facets, could always be backed with a reflective metal foil, a practice which originated at least as early as the Renaissance. Today foil-backs are never used except for cheap glass stones. Instead, the lapidary attempts to obtain the maximum realizable brilliance by using the correct back facet angles and proportions.

Lapidary features of beryl

As can be seen in *Table 10.1*, in which gemstones are arranged according to increasing hardness, beryl is neither very hard nor very high in refractive index, which is a measure of the brilliancy which can be realized in a finished, correctly proportioned gem. Nevertheless, as explained above, there are compensations, and both emerald and its relatives remain highly prized gemstones.

The relatively uniform structure of the beryl crystal results in nearly uniform physical properties, as is evident from the moment the gem cutter begins to work the rough. The rough may be sawed, ground, and polished in any direction, and such cleavages as exist are produced with such difficulty that they may be ignored. Finally, the small thermal expansion permits rough to be heated safely whenever the preformed gems are to be cemented to the dopsticks by which they are to be

TABLE 10.1. Common gemstone properties compared

Mineral	hardness	Refractive index range	Remarks
Feldspar	6.0–6.5	1.52–1.589	Brittle, cleaves easily
Quartz	7.0	1.544–1.553	Good toughness, no cleavage
Beryl	7.0–8.0	1.560–1.638	Tough, no cleavage
Topaz	7.5–8.0	1.61–1.638	Hard, perfect but not easily developed cleavage
Tourmaline	6.0–6.5	1.616–1.64	Good toughness, no cleavage
Peridot	6.0–6.5	1.654–1.689	Easily chipped
Garnet	6.5–7.5	1.66–1.89	Tough, no cleavage
Spodumene	6.0–8.0	1.660–1.678	Perfect cleavage, sometimes troublesome in cutting
Spinel	7.5–8.0	1.715–1.729	Tough, no cleavage
Chrysoberyl	8.5	1.745–1.76	Very tough, no cleavage
Corundum	9.0	1.760–1.779	Very tough, no cleavage
Diamond	10.0	2.418	Extremely hard and tough despite perfect cleavage

Source: J. Sinkankas, *Gemstone & Mineral Data Book*[6] (p. 184–5, 303–7)

held during further shaping and smoothing. In sum, all these properties make beryl one of the lapidary's most favoured gemstones.

Selection of rough according to colour

For the most part, it is easy to choose suitable aquamarine, golden beryl, and morganite rough because the crystals are often smooth-faced, permitting an unobstructed view of the interiors. Even in colour-zoned crystals, the zones are seldom so pronounced that special treatment is necessary.

Usually the only requirement in choosing an orientation for the finished gem is to select the better of the two colours that may be observed through the windows of a dichroscope. (Sometimes this choice is readily apparent without the use of a dichroscope.) As discussed in Chapter 6, in some aquamarines and golden beryls there may be decided differences in colour according to crystallographic direction. That is, the colour observed when looking through the sides of the crystal prism (parallel to the lateral axes) may be different from the colour observed when looking down the length of the crystal (parallel to the *c*-axis). In the case of aquamarines, one of these colours may be stronger in tint than the other, or display a more desirable shade of blue, which many people prefer to a greenish-blue or yellowish-blue. In golden beryls, the differences generally involve shades of lighter or darker yellow, or sometimes a yellow which may be tinged with green as compared to a purer yellow seen in the other crystallographic direction. Once the desirable direction is established, the rough is shaped in such a manner that this direction passes up through the finished gem, through the top of a cabochon or through the large table facet of a faceted gem.

A more difficult choice of colour direction faces the lapidary called upon to cut emerald because many crystals which appear to be coloured uniformly are actually more or less strongly colour-zoned. Unfortunately, the zone of colour almost always appears upon the outer parts of the crystal, or exactly in those places which would be cut away in the normal course of shaping. Zoned crystals are common among the emeralds of North Carolina and Chivor and are less common in those of Muzo. Some Chivor crystals have been found which contain several alternating zones of coloured and uncoloured material that were not at all easy to detect during a cursory examination. Several examples are shown in the colour plate in Klein's book on the Chivor emerald deposits[7] (p. 64) and in *Figure 6.1*.

In most instances, zoning can be detected easily by examining the fractured base of crystals. It is here that the differences in colour are most apparent. However, in difficult cases, the only safe method is to examine the crystal in a suitable immersion fluid, as will be explained below.

A prudent rule to follow in purchasing emerald rough is to suspect colour zoning whenever relatively flawless crystals of good size, which seemingly should command a good price, are offered cheaply. They may be colour-zoned in a thin, intensely coloured layer adjacent to the prism faces, which surely would vanish at the moment of cutting, with the result that a colourless or at best pale coloured gem would be obtained.

Immersion fluids for inspecting rough

The testing of gem rough in an immersion fluid is based on the same optical principle that is at work when a piece of clear ice seems to disappear when placed in a glass of water. In both instances, the refractive index of the liquid and the solid match so closely that light passing through the fluid is prevented from being reflected from the surfaces of the solid. When a suitable liquid is chosen for immersion of beryl, the effect can be startling, to say the least, the crystals or fragments seemingly vanishing from view the moment they are plunged into the liquid. If the beryl is colourless, it may become almost invisible, but at the same time, any inclusions inside the stone become clearly visible, and if the stone is rolled from side to side, colour zoning also becomes apparent.

The liquid of choice for beryl immersion is bromoform, also called tribromoethane. $CHBr_3$, a colourless, pleasant-smelling liquid with a specific gravity of 2.89 at 20°C and a refractive index of 1.598 at 20°C. The refractive index is so close to that of beryl that the vanishing effect noted above is very conspicuous. To inspect rough, pour sufficient liquid into a colourless glass beaker (not plastic) and lower the rough into the fluid with tweezers. Because the SG of the fluid is slightly above that of beryl the rough will just barely float. For large pieces of rough, where complete immersion is impractical because of the large amount of fluid required, it is often enough to brush a bit of fluid over surfaces of the stone, thus, in effect, providing an instant 'polish' and allowing a view inside. Immersion treatments are strongly recommended for buyers of expensive beryl rough, because flaws, inclusions, and colour zoning are easily detected.

Bromoform is not ordinarily available in chemists or drug stores, but it may be obtained on special order. It is also available from suppliers of gemmological instruments and accessories such as the Gemological Institute of America in Santa Monica, California, or the Gemmological Association of Great Britain in London.

Instead of bromoform, almost any liquid reasonably close in refrative index to beryl will do. Lists of such fluids can be found in Sinkankas's *Gemstone & Mineral Data Book*[6] (pp. 331–5) in Read's *Beginner's Guide to Gemmology*[8] (p. 80) and in gemmological identification texts. Several organic oils may be used, although these by no means are cheap: anise oil (RI 1.54–1.56), cassia oil (1.58–1.60), cinnamon oil (1.59–1.60), and wintergreen oil (1.54). Lacking any of these, good results may still be obtained with such common colourless liquids as the 'flushing oils' used in automobile repair shops, kerosene, turpentine, and the colourless mineral oils sold in drugstores.

Inclusions in cut gems

Any inclusion impedes and scatters light. A large number of inclusions, as found in the 'jardin' emeralds, in which the inclusions resemble mossy growths, scatter light so completely that the reflections from back facets seem more like a green glow than anything else. As the number of inclusions diminish, the back facet reflections appear more sharply defined; in stones that contain no inclusions, the reflections are entirely crisp and clear.

A small number of inclusions can be accommodated in gems cut in brilliant style where their effect is lost amid the general dazzle provided by the multitudinous reflections from the many small facets used in this style of cutting. The worst case occurs in the severely formal step-cuts, which employ very few facets cut rigidly parallel to each other. Even the smallest inclusion is re-reflected until it becomes quite obvious, and if it is located near the bottom of the stone, it makes the gem seem cracked entirely across. If, as in the case of emeralds, some inclusions cannot be avoided, then the lapidary must be careful to place the worst of them along the outer edges of the gem and a little distance below the crown facets.

In the case of aquamarines, golden beryls, and morganites, hardly any inclusions or other flaws are tolerated. Most lapidaries prefer to cut away any included parts of the rough and accept a smaller-sized but flawless finished stone.

Chatoyant beryls

Chatoyant or cat's-eye beryls are cut from crystals which contain large numbers of very fine tube-like cavities aligned parallel to the *c*-axis. It is axiomatic that the more slender and numerous the tubes, the sharper and more brilliant the 'eye' becomes in the finished gem. It is very rare, however, that a cat's-eye beryl is cut to match the quality of the eyes found in chrysoberyl cat's-eyes or in star rubies and sapphires. Mostly the tubes in beryl are relatively coarse and the eye less perfectly developed.

Most cat's-eye beryls are cut as fairly high cabochons from bluish Brazilian aquamarine. These are very rarely intensively coloured and most of them appear quite pale. Even more rare are golden beryl cat's-eyes, but some of extremely high quality have been cut from a curious, greenish corroded beryl once found in

Madagascar. A large gem from this locality is in the collections of the Natural History Museum in Washington, D.C. Rarest of all are cat's-eyes of emerald, extremely few of these ever having been recorded. For practical purposes they are nonexistent.

To cut a cat's-eye beryl, it is necessary to orient the rough so that the tubes are parallel to the flat bottom of the cabochon. Furthermore, if the cabochon is elliptical in outline, the tubes must also run at right angles to the long axis of the ellipse. In the finished gem this will result in the streak of light or 'eye' running over the top of the cabochon from one narrow end of the ellipse to the other. If for any reason these rules are ignored, the eye will be offset to one side, the amount depending on the amount of error in the original orientation. The eye is narrower and more brilliant when the stone is sharply curved on top, and for this reason the curvature is adjusted by the lapidary so that the height is from one-third to one-half the width of the stone.

A special case of chatoyancy is the star stone, in which several streaks of light from as many separate sets of inclusions cross over atop the finished gem to form a star. In beryl, such stars have never been observed where they are due to tubular inclusions, but they have been seen where the inclusions of a foreign mineral, such as ilmenite and haematite, orient themselves upon basal planes in the growing crystal in fixed geometrical positions. This orientation is called *epitaxy* (already discussed in Chapter 8). It can provide weak stars but these are poorly reflective and never as sharp as those seen in star rubies and sapphires. Strictly speaking, they are not chatoyant stars at all but rather spangly reflections which more properly could be called a special case of *aventurescence*, or the reflection from a host of small disk-like platelets of a foreign mineral arranged in parallel planes.

The cutting of the star stones mentioned above is somewhat difficult due to the broadness of the inclusions, which form weak areas in the beryl. Care must be taken during grinding to prevent such places from chipping away and leaving deep pits which then require much sanding to remove. The procedure for orienting and cutting these stones was explained in detail by Leiper[9]. An excellent polish was obtained with a mixture of chrome oxide and Linde-A alumina powder on leather. A 20-carat gem cut by Leiper is now in the Natural History Museum, Washington, USA.

Lapidary treatment for Cabochons

For explanation of the steps required in processing beryl cabochons and carvings, the reader is referred to standard texts such as those by Sinkankas[10] and Quick and Leiper[11]. In general, all rough is sawn with very thin diamond-charged steel or bronze blades whose edges run in an oily or watery coolant. The stones are then marked for shaping and are ground on coarse and fine silicon carbide or diamond-charged wheels using water as a coolant. Further surface smoothing is done on coarse and fine flexible abrasive cloth, also supplied with water. Lastly, the gems are polished. Several types of polishers may be used, including wood, leather, hard felt, and plastic, the softer buffs usually being supplied with polishing powders such as Linde-A, chrome oxide, tin oxide, or cerium oxide suspended in a water slurry. More rapid results are sometimes possible with use of diamond powder paste on the harder buffs made from wood, plastic, or leather. Because of the strong green colour of chrome oxide, this agent is seldom used because it may disfigure the stone if it enters cracks.

For cabochon emeralds, especially those in which numerous inclusions appear, the lapidary may seal the openings to such inclusions with epoxy resin just prior to commencing polishing. This step prevents powders from entering the stone. If polishing powders enter unprotected crevices, they can be removed only with considerable difficulty. Cabochon emeralds may also be incised with a series of melon-like ridges to add attractiveness and help disguise flaws. These grooves are cut on very small abrasive wheels and smoothed with equally small sanding wheels which may be made from leather, wood, plastic, or even rubber, followed by another set of wheels supplied with a suitable polishing agent. In general, emerald cabochons are cut 'high', that is, the height nearly equals the width of the stone.

A popular method of utilizing beryls too flawed for other purposes is to tumble the fragments in barrels with water and a suitable abrasive. The process is carried on for a long period of time or until all edges and surfaces are worn smooth. After this step, which may take weeks, the stones are removed and carefully washed, then placed in another barrel with a suitable polishing agent to obtain a beautiful glass-like finish. Such tumbled gems or 'baroques' are much used in all kinds of jewellery in which an unsophisticated or even barbaric air is desired.

Beryl carvings

Beryl is readily carved using small diamond wheels to saw away unwanted parts and to further shape the carvings. Small abrasive wheels made from silicon carbide are also used for shaping, and loose silicon carbide grit applied to wood, plastic, or leather wheels is used for sanding the surfaces to a satisfactory degree of smoothness prior to polishing.

The same polishing wheels, although of a smaller size as needed to fit into small recesses, and the same polishing agents as were used for making cabochons are also employed. However, because of the generally pale colour in which beryls occur, carvings in this mineral do not stand out as well as those executed in darker gemstones or those that are only translucent. For this reason, beryl carvings are far from common. Indeed, one may see hundreds of small objects carved from quartz varieties, jades, serpentines, etc., for every one carving of beryl.

Faceted gems

In a tradition of at least three centuries duration, the emerald has been cut in a severely simple style which has become known as the 'emerald cut', that is, into a rectangular gem covered with elongated strip-like facets (see *Figure 10.1*). This cut is also known as the step cut. To protect the corners and to provide places where

165

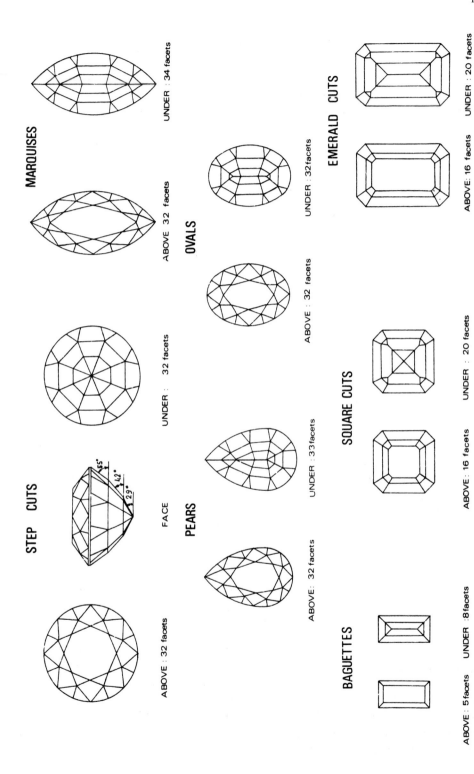

STEP CUTS

MARQUISES

ABOVE : 32 facets · UNDER : 32 facets · FACE · ABOVE 32 facets · UNDER : 34 facets

PEARS

OVALS

ABOVE : 32 facets · UNDER : 33 facets · ABOVE : 32 facets · UNDER : 32 facets

BAGUETTES

SQUARE CUTS

EMERALD CUTS

ABOVE : 5 facets   UNDER : 8 facets · ABOVE: 16 facets   UNDER : 20 facets · ABOVE : 16 facets   UNDER : 20 facets

Figure 10.1 Showing the various cuts for beryl including the popular 'emerald' or 'step' cut at the lower right-hand side and four versions of the 'brilliant' cut above

the gem may be secured by the prongs of the mounting, the corners are usually also cut off in a series of very narrow steps, thus producing an octagonal outline (see *Figure 10.2*). This style of cutting is also much used for other beryl gems such as aquamarines, golden beryls, and morganites, although many of these are also cut in brilliant style, that is, in circular or elliptical shapes, covered with a multitude of small, more or less triangular facets. Other styles may take a circular or elliptical outline with the facets cut as a series of small steps, cleverly adjusted to provide uniform coverage of the entire surface. Still other styles include the 'mixed cut' wherein one part of the gem is faceted as a brilliant and the other in steps (see the four versions of the brilliant cut in *Figure 10.1*).

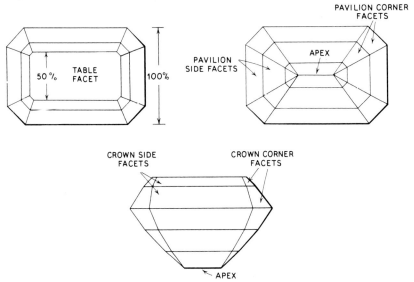

Figure 10.2 Typical proportions of the step or emerald cut. Additional facets may be added to the crown and pavilion, especially on larger stones (John Sinkankas)

The popularity of the step cut for beryls may be due in part to the fact that the usual prismatic shape of the crystals lends itself readily to this form of cutting with minimum loss of material. Certainly this consideration also affects the selection of the step cut for the cutting of emeralds. However, as previously noted, the presence of unavoidable flaws or inclusions requires employment of brilliant cuts whereby the flaws are made less conspicuous. It is probably for this reason that so many of the large aquamarines of early Russian vintage are found in brilliant style because these gems were seldom entirely free of flaws.

While the step cut is popular for large and flawless beryl gems, it is also a severe test of the lapidary's skill because all of the long and narrow facets placed upon the crown and pavilion must be exactly parallel. If they are not, the reflections from them become wedge-shaped, as is immediately apparent as the stone is slowly turned to change the pattern of reflections. Some older hand-cut gems show slight but noticeable errors, but fewer of the modern ones do because they are usually cut with the aid of accurate faceting machines.

Proportions and angles of faceted gems

The cross-section of a faceted gem resembles a reflecting prism in which the light that falls through the top of the gem is reflected back from inner facets to return to the eye, resulting in the effect known as brilliance. The angle made by the bottom pair of facets is crucial to brilliance. If the angle is incorrect, the light passes out the bottom of the stone and a dark spot is seen by the viewer instead of the desired mirror-like reflections. Only a narrow range of bottom-facet angles is available to the lapidary to maximize reflections and brilliance.

The measure of this angle has been the subject of numerous optical studies aimed at tracing paths of light within a gem and calculating the angles whereby the paths can be diverted upward. Much depends on the refractive index of the gemstone itself, the general rule being that gemstones of higher refractive index, capable of bending light more sharply, produce the greatest brilliance, while those gemstones of lower refractive index produce less. Furthermore, in the case of higher refractive index gemstones, inner reflections can result from shallower bottom angles, thus allowing these gems to be cut less deeply. This becomes apparent when two brilliant gems of the same size and style of cutting are compared, one being a diamond and the other a beryl. It will be seen that the diamond is cut to less depth while the beryl had to be cut to greater depth in order to insure upward reflection (i.e. total internal reflection) of light.

TABLE 10.2. W. F. Eppler's beryl proportions and angles

Variety	Rose beryl (Morganite)	Emerald	Aquamarine
Refractive index	0 = 1.594 e = 1.586	o = 1.582 e = 1.575	o = 1.571 e = 1.566
Pavilion depth	40.6% of diameter	41.1%	41.5%
Crown depth	27.9	28.1	28.2
Total depth	68.5	69.2	69.7
Total depth + 2% for girdle thickness	70.5	71.2	71.7
Table facet width	59.9	57.0	54.1
Pavilion angle	39.1°	39.4°	39.7°
Crown angle	54.3°	52.6°	50.8°

Source: Eppler[13], pp. 26–30

An intensive study of ideal proportions and angles for faceted gems was conducted by Maier[12], who provided a table of angles for various gemstones. For the emerald (refractive index 1.5838), the recommended angle for pavilion facets is 39°99′18″ and for the crown facets 30°47′37″. Eppler[13] provided another set of angles, based on his own calculations, as shown in *Table 10.2*.

Eppler had sample gems cut to these specifications and claimed them to be eminently satisfactory. But his specifications required cutting the crown so high that it appeared awkward when placed in mountings, and they departed so radically from the traditional proportions that no one adopted them. The proportions and angles given in *Table 10.3* remain those generally in use.

In radical departure from normal practice, Barriga Villalba and Barriga Del Diestro[18] (pp. 55–68) proposed a style of cutting for the emerald which is claimed to afford maximum brilliancy. The principle behind the cut is making the pavilion of the gem approximate the curve of a parabola, with the focal point near the bottom of the gem (*Figure 10.3*). The cross-section shows main crown facets inclined at angles of 38° to the plane of the girdle and five step facets on the pavilion inclined to this plane at angles of 62°, 55°, 47°, 36°, and 15°. In effect, the pavilion approximates the shape of a cabochon and, as one may expect, provides about the same reflectivity as may be seen in any transparent cabochon when it is turned over and viewed from the back. In such cabochons, and also in the cut proposed, light is reflected from a peripheral band but scarcely any from the centre, which therefore appears dark. The theory is attractive, but only if the light were to originate at the focal point of the parabola, which of course it does not.

TABLE 10.3. Current recommended proportions and angles for cutting beryl

Pavilion depth:	about ⅔ of diameter	
Crown depth:	about ⅓ of diameter	

Authority	Pavilion main facet angle	Crown main facet angle
Willems[14]	42°	45°
Quick and Leiper[11]	43°	42°
Sinkankas[10]	43°	40°–50°
Schlagel[15]	41°	37°
Hoffman[16]	43°	42°
Vargas and Vargas[17]	43°	42°

A new cut for emerald[19], which results in an increase in total internal reflection, and therefore in brilliance, has been developed by Menachem Serdermish, Technical Adviser of the Israel Gemological Institute for Precious Stones and Diamonds. The 'carmel' cut, as it is called, is said to give 30 to 50% more brilliance on certain types of stone.

Deviations from recommended angles and proportions

Excluding the emerald, most beryl gems are too pallid to be attractive unless cut in sizes of at least 10 carats and preferably about 15 carats. However, when cut to ideal proportions and angles, the pavilions extend so far down that severe problems arise in mounting them in jewellery. To prevent the bottom of the pavilion from rubbing the skin of the finger in the case of rings, the gem would have to be mounted so high that it tends to topple over or snag on clothing. For this reason, it is customary among lapidaries cutting stones for the jewellery trade to make them somewhat shallower than is theoretically desirable. The result is that considerable light escapes through the bottoms of the gems, creating a dark patch or 'hole'.

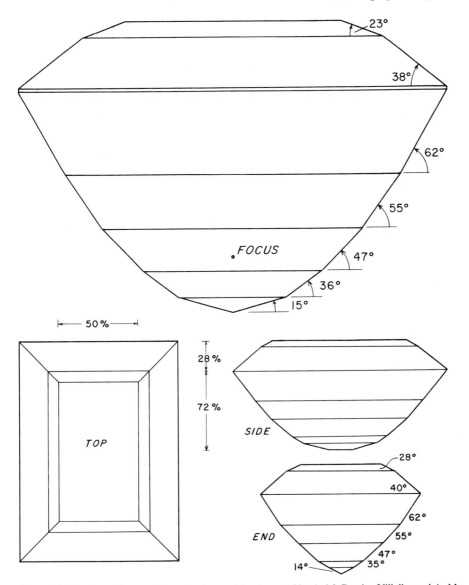

Figure 10.3 Angles and proportions of cut emeralds advocated by A. M. Barriga Villalba and A. M. Barriga des Diestro in *La Esmeralda de Colombia* (Bogota: Colegio Mayor de Nuestro Señora del Rosario, 1973). The pavilion facets closely approximate the curvature of a parabola, the focus of which is shown in the top figure. Slightly different angles are shown in a similar cut below (John Sinkankas)

Polishing laps and agents

Faceting of beryls is simple because the predictable properties of the gemstone cause no difficulties at any stage. The gems may be given their preliminary or 'preform' shape on an ordinary water-fed silicon carbide grinding wheel, or they may be preformed on the dopstick against a diamond-charged metal lap on a faceting machine. The facets are cut on diamond, usually finishing the cuts with the finest-grain diamond lap available.

The laps used for polishing may be pure tin, which is the preferred lap, or an alloy of tin-typemetal, typemetal alone, or plastic. Sharper facets are possible on the metal laps and these should be used in preference to plastic laps. The polishing agents include Linde-A alumina powder, the agent preferred by most cutters, applied to a tin lap, and tin oxide, chrome oxide, and rare earth oxides, the last agents working best on the plastic laps.

References

1 LUCAS, A. *Ancient Egyptian Materials and Industries.* 2nd ed. London: Edward Arnold & Co. 447 pp. (1934)

2 EICHHOLZ, D. E. *Theophrastus De Lapidibus.* Oxford: Clarendon Press. 141 pp. (1965)

3 KING, C. W. *The Natural History, Ancient and Modern, of Precious Stones and Gems, and of the Precious Metals.* London: Bell and Daldy. 442 pp. (1865)

4 BOODT, A. B. de. *Gemmarum et Lapidum Historia.* 3rd ed. Leiden: Joannis Maire. 576 pp. (1647)

5 BLUM, R. *Taschenbuch der Edelsteinkunde.* Stuttgart: C. Hoffmann. 356 pp. (1832)

6 SINKANKAS, J. *Gemstone & Mineral Data Book.* New York: Winchester Press. 352 pp. (1972)

7 KLEIN, F. *Smaragde unter dem Urwald.* Berlin: Oswald Arnold Verlag. 285 pp. (1941)

8 READ, P. G. *Beginner's Guide to Gemmology,* London: 234 pp. Newnes Technical Books (1982)

9 LEIPER, H. How to cut star beryl. *Lapidary Journal* 12:250–4 (1958)

10 SINKANKAS, J. *Gem Cutting, A Lapidary's Manual.* 2nd ed. Princeton: Van Nostrand Co. 297 pp. (1962)

11 QUICK, L. and LEIPER, H. *Gemcraft, How to Cut and Polish Gemstones.* 2nd ed., revised by P. D. Kraus. Radnor, Pa.: Chilton Book Co. 195 pp. (1977)

12 MAIER, W. *Brillanten und Perlen.* Stuttgart: E. Schweizerbart'sche Verlagsbuchhandlung. 188 pp. (1949)

13 EPPLER, W. F. Die Brillanz durchsichtiger Edelsteine. *Fortschritte der Mineralogie* (Stuttgart) 32. 40 pp. (1938)

14 WILLEMS, J. D. *Gem Cutting.* Peoria, Ill.: Charles A. Bennett, 224 pp. (1948)

15 PARSONS, C. J. Charles Schlagel's facet angles. *Gems and Minerals* (Mentone, Ca.) no. 342, pp. 27–9 (1966)

16 HOFFMAN, D. L. *Comprehensive Faceting Instructions.* Spokane, Wash.: Aurora Lapidary Books, 94 pp. (1968)

17 VARGAS, G. and VARGAS, M. *Faceting for Amateurs.* Thermal, Ca.: privately published. 330 pp. (1969)

18 BARRIGA VILLALBA, A. M. and BARRIGA DEL DIESTRO, A. M. *La Esmeralda de Colombia, Descripción y Propiedades.* Bogota: Colegio Mayor de Nuestra Señora del Rosario. 100 pp. (1973)

19 READ, P. G. *Gem Instrument Digest,* No. 5, Vol. 1. pp. 76 (May 1984)

Chapter 11

Beryl deposits and World Sources

Beryllium is one of the rarer elements in the earth's crust. Estimates of its quantity have been made by Goldschmidt[1] (pp. 206–13) and more recently by Beus[2] (pp. 310–22). According to Mason[4] (p. 45), on the average 2.8 grams of beryllium occur per ton of crystal rock, with a little less than one-third of the total concentrated in diabase and about two-thirds in granitic rocks. Among the forty known beryllium minerals, the element itself has been extracted largely from beryl, the most common beryllium species. Furthermore, almost all mined beryl occurs in coarse-grained rocks known as *granitic pegmatites*, in which beryl is sometimes so abundant that bodies of this rock can be mined profitably for the beryl alone.

In addition to a concentration in granitic pegmatites, beryl occurs in substantial to minor quantities in other types of deposits. These are listed according to their genetic type in *Table 11.1*, showing the diversity of the deposits as well as their interrelationships. Beryllium is primarily associated with igneous rocks, and as may be expected, its principal mineral follows the same association, appearing in the rare rhyolite rock occurrences in Utah but more commonly in deposits that originate from granitic magmas or their offshoots. With all of these deposits the role of water is evident, serving primarily as the solvent of mineral matter when occurring in a heated environment, and as the agent largely responsible for the deposition of beryl and other durable minerals in occurrences derived from the weathering of in-place deposits (eluvial and alluvial deposits). The twelve basic types of beryl deposits are listed in *Table 11.1* and are then discussed in detail.

Volcanic

Red beryl in rhyolite

Dark raspberry-red, tabular to short prismatic crystals of beryl occur in unique deposits in two areas in Utah and in one place in New Mexico. The host rocks in all cases are light-coloured rhyolite with the crystals formed in small gas cavities

TABLE 11.1. Genetic types of beryl deposits and beryls

Genetic classification	Deposit type	Hydrothermal activity	Crystal habit	Colours
Volcanic	Gas cavities in rhyolite	Absent	Tabular to short prismatic; euhedral	Pink to dark raspberry red
Early magmatic	Disseminated in granite	Slight	Long to very long prismatic; interlocked and in radiate groups; anhedral	Very pale bluish, greenish, or nearly colourless
	Miarolitic, pegmatitic schlieren in granite	Localized, slight	Short to long prismatic, often striated; slight to severe etching and corrosion	Pale blue, blue green, greenish, yellowish
Late magmatic	Granite pegmatites simple, unzoned	Significant	Short prismatic, poor terminations	Pale greenish, bluish, yellowish, white
	Granitic pegmatites, simple, zoned	Significant	Short prismatic, poor terminations	Same
	Granitic pegmatites, complex, zoned, replaced mucovite-albite and albite	Extensive in inner zones, fracture fillings	Short to medium prismatic, conical, intergrown; fluted faces	Greenish, yellowish, white
	Granitic pegmatites, complex, zoned, replaced spodumene-albite and lepidolite-albite	Extensive in inner zones, fracture fillings	Short prismatic to tabular; also irregular and corroded masses (morganite)	Pink, yellowish, colourless, white
Metamorphic-hydrothermal	Schist type (exomorphic)	Transfer of Be to host rocks	Poorly formed, short to long prismatic, commonly unterminated	Bluish, greenish, green (emerald)
Hydrothermal	Greisens	Intense, local, along fractures	Prismatic; poorly developed when enclosed; fine, euhedral in cavities	Pale blue, greenish, yellowish, and combined colour zones

173

Hydrothermal (continued)	Carbonate veins and tactite bodies	Extensive along fractures	Short prismatic, commonly fine	Colourless, very pale bluish, greenish, also fine green (emerald)
	Alpine clefts	Extensive along fractures	Short to long prismatic to acicular	Colourless, pale blue, greenish; rarely emerald
Sedimentary	Eluvial	Decomposition of deposit	As in the deposit	As in the deposit
	Alluvial	Transported by water	As in the deposit, more or less worn	As in the deposit

Composition	Associated species	Localities	Remarks
Water absent	Quartz, topaz	Thomas Mts., Wah Wah Mts., Utah	Crystals from several mm to ca. 10 mm; small clear areas (Wah Wah Mts.)
Alkali-free; some Fe	Quartz, feldspars, micas	Sawtooth Mts., Idaho	Some clear areas in crystals
Alkali-free; some Fe	Microcline, micas, quartz, albite; also phenakite, topaz, tin and tungsten species; bazzite	Mt. Antero, Colorado; Mongolia; Transbaikalia, USSR	Often splendid crystals, some of gem quality
Alkali-free; some Fe	Quartz, microcline, muscovite, garnet	Colorado	Sometimes abundant and then providing ore
Alkali-poor; some Na may be present	Quartz, microcline (sometimes amazonite), topaz, muscovite, biotite; rarely fergusonite and other Ta–Nb species; allanite, xenotime, monazite	Widely distributed: amazonite-type in Ilmen Mts., USSR; rare earth type Barringer Hill, Tex.; Iveland, Norway	Ore beryl; sometimes fine crystals in vugs
Na_2O ca. 0.5% gas-liquid inclusions abundant	Microcline, quartz, muscovite, albite, schorl, Fe and Mn phosphates; also triphylite, columbite-tantalite, phenakite, chrysoberyl, other Be species	NE Brazil; India; Argentina	Ore beryl; small clear areas in large crystals; rarely fine crystals in vugs

TABLE 11.1. (Continued)

Composition	Associated species	Localities	Remarks
Na and Li, also Cs and Li; Cs greater than 1.0%; Mn often present	Albite, quartz, muscovite, elbaite, spessartine; also lithiphilite, amblygonite, columbite-tantalite, microlite, spodumene, pollucite, lepidolite, petalite, berryllonite, other Be species	Harding mine, New Mex., San Diego, Co.m Calif.; Minas Gerais, Brazil; Madagascar	Fine crystals in vugs and central cavities (morganite)
Aquamarine type; also emerald (Cr)	Quartz, fluorite, apatite, Mg-silicates, micas, sometimes chrysoberyl	Petaca district, New Mex. (aquamarine); emerald; Ural Mts.; Egypt; South Africa	Grading from pale hues, to fine green as in emerald; schist type deposits now important for emerald production.
Alkali-free, some Fe	Quartz, micas, feldspars, also Sn and W species; apatite, fluorite	Transbaikalia, USSR	Fine clear crystals in vugs
Some Fe, Na; Cr in emerald	Emerald: albite, Fe-carbonate, pyrite, parisite, quartz. Tactite: calcite, quartz, calc-silicates, scheelite, magnetite, fluorite, garnet	Colombia (emerald); Kazakhstan, USSR	Classic emerald deposits in Colombia
Some Fe, Na; rarely some Cr	Quartz, feldspars, schorl, monazite, bazzite	European Alps; Hiddenite, North Carolina	Rarely with emerald (North Carolina)
	Durable species of original deposit	Minas Gerais, Brazil; Transbaikalia, USSR	Crystals usually in fine condition
	Durable species of original deposit	Minas Gerais, Brazil; Ceylon	Water-rolled crystals, sometimes with no crystal faces left

Sources: Beus[2]; Vlasov[3]; Buchi[5]; Cameron[6].

(vesicles), in clays derived from alteration of the rock, and in porous phases of the rhyolite. A search of the beryl literature failed to record occurrences of this type elsewhere in the world, thus they are apparently unique to the Western United States.

The absence of water as determined by analyses suggests that the crystals grew at high temperatures, possibly from gas-transported (pneumatolytic) material. Some of the larger and clearer crystals from the Wah Wah Mountains deposit have been cut into very attractive faceted gems which resemble rubies, but they are seldom cuttable over a carat or two in weight.

Early magmatic

Beryl disseminations in granite

In the upper portions of large, upthrust masses of granite (plutons), a coarse-grained texture is sometimes encountered with considerable pore space. Apparently such openings enable beryl and other minerals to be transported, through the agency of water trapped in the granite, more or less uniformly throughout some areas, forming disseminated deposits. The crystals tend to grow as slender individuals in clusters or in masses radiating from a common centre. Because they do not grow in cavities, they are seldom well formed. Deposits of this type are rare and of no commercial significance. They have been identified in Idaho and Utah.

Miarolitic and schlieren beryl deposits

The word *miarolitic* comes from *miarolo*, a term used by Italian quarrymen at Baveno, Italy, to describe a kind of coarse-grained granite in which occur irregular cavities lined with crystals. Bazzite, the scandian analogue of beryl, was first found in the Baveno quarries.

These deposits are strictly of local occurrence and are usually small and irregular in form. Furthermore, they show indistinct contacts with the enclosing rock from which they are derived. The term, *syngenetic*, meaning 'formed at the same time', has also been applied to them. In most examples, the cavities are surrounded by zones containing the regular intergrowth of feldspar-quartz known as *graphic granite*, but this type of rock is not confined to these deposits and is found in other types as well. Characteristically, the grain size rapidly increases as the central portion of the body or the cavity (if one is present) is reached. In cavities, the same minerals as form the walls are present, except now as well-formed crystals, usually of microcline or orthoclase feldspar and quartz, sometimes micas, occasionally the thin-bladed variety of albite feldspar known as cleavelandite, topaz, and rarely beryl or other rare element minerals. Because of growing in such openings, all of the minerals, including the beryl, may be sharply crystallized and often completely transparent.

Since these deposits may not exceed a few decimetres or a metre or two across (less than 12 in to about 6 ft), they seldom produce significant quantities of economically important minerals aside from crystal specimens for collectors and occasionally gemstones. Deposits of this type are common in some areas of New Hampshire (although beryl is rarely found here) and Colorado, but the best-known and the most productive deposits for beryl specimens and gem material occur in Transbaikalia in the southern Asiatic portion of the USSR and in the Ural Mountains of Siberia. Extremely large cavities have been found in the miarolitic bodies of Volhynia, Ukraine. Several types of these deposits and their minerals have been described in detail by Beus[2] (pp. 171 ff.).

Fine crystals of blue aquamarine also occur in small cavities in the granite of the summit of Mt. Antero associated with smoky quartz crystals and the rare beryllium mineral phenakite, which forms small, colourless and inconspicuous crystals in the cavities. In the Volhynian bodies, Beus noted microcline-orthoclase, cleavelandite, colourless and smoky quartz, zinnwaldite, muscovite, lepidolite, schorl and elbaite tourmaline, topaz in several colours, and beryls in various shades of greenish-blue, green, olive-green, blue, golden, pink, and colourless. The beryl crystals in such cavities, often very sharply formed, and highly transparent, may provide important quantities of gem material. However, etching and corrosion sometimes occur, as is notable in the Mt. Antero deposits, and the original crystals may be reduced to masses of slivers which resemble glittering darning needles. None of the crystals tend to be large, ranging from very small up to about 25 cm (10 in) long and 3 to 4 cm (1¼ to 1⅝ in) in diameter. Most crystals, unfortunately, are broken from their matrix points of attachment by natural forces, but occasionally a fine specimen is found with crystals upright on the base rock.

Late magmatic

Granitic pegmatites

The principal sources of beryl crystals are bodies of coarse-grained rock that contain essentially the same minerals as are found in granite, namely, feldspar, quartz and mica, often accompanied by smaller amounts of black tourmaline and rare-element minerals. The size of the grains, or individual crystals, ranges from a millimetre to as much as several metres across, depending on the size of the body and other factors. The dimensions of the bodies range from only several centimetres in thickness and several metres long to those that may be a hundred metres thick and several kilometres long. The name given to them, *pegmatite*, refers to the unusually large grain size and will be used frequently in this chapter.

Pegmatites occur in granites and in the rocks which adjoin granite masses, often as intrusions along fractures. Because they are derived from, and associated with, granites, they are found in many areas of the world, large numbers outcropping in such places as Brazil, United States, Siberia, Madagascar, and India, to name a few. Historically, pegmatites were first exploited for pottery feldspar and mica, the latter once called 'Muscovy glass' in Europe because of its origin in Russian pegmatites. In modern times, they have also proved to be valuable sources of rare elements such as tantalum and niobium, in addition to beryllium. Gemstones derived from the weathering of pegmatites have been collected from stream gravels in Brazil since the 16th century, but it is only in the past century that the bodies themselves have been systematically mined for gemstones, mineral specimens, and rare element minerals.

Accurate geological and mineralogical knowledge of pegmatites is also a recent development, as pointed out by Fersman[7] (vol. 1, p. 11). Studies now show that many pegmatite bodies formed in distinct stages, as reflected in the mineralization of zones within them. For example, the outermost zone, adjacent to the enclosing country rock, is generally fine-grained and mineralogically uninteresting. However, as successive waves of mineralization took place, increasingly larger crystals grew in intermediate zones, and the largest of all in the cores. In the vast majority of bodies, the mineralization is simple; that is, only the basic constituents of feldspar, quartz, and mica are present, with perhaps a little tourmaline, garnet, and beryl. However, other bodies are more complex. They were formed during successive waves of mineralization, often with the introduction of new elements which formed their own distinctive mineral species, or recombined with previously present elements to form additional species. Thus, the complex pegmatites, with their varied minerals, are of greatest interest to geologists, mineralogists, mineral and gemstone collectors, and miners seeking rare element ores.

It sometimes happens that the mineral matter intruded during pegmatite formation fails to fill completely the space available, with the result that openings or vugs, also called 'pockets', are left. Because the minerals lining such openings grew without interference, they provide the finest of all crystals, often beautifully formed, transparent, and colourful. It is from such pockets that gem specimens of tourmaline, quartz, topaz, and beryl are taken, not to mention a considerable variety of other minerals that are eagerly sought after by collectors.

One of the classic works describing the wonderful pocket minerals obtainable from pegmatites, including gem beryls, is that of Lacroix[8], who treats in detail the gem-bearing pegmatites of Madagascar. A summary of the most important features of the internal structures of granitic pegmatites is provided by Cameron *et al.*[6] who studied a large number of pegmatite bodies, especially those occurring in the United States. The geochemistry of pegmatites was treated by Jedwab[9] and Beus[2], the latter being especially valuable for remarks on the internal structures and mineralizations of pegmatites in the USSR.

For the student of pegmatites, a very complete survey of the subject as well as a large bibliography appear in Schneiderhöhn's classic work of 1961[10]. An excellent summary also appears in Booysen[11], a paper written to present essential knowledge in a simple manner for the benefit of prospectors. Although written for South Africans, the information is universally applicable. More recently, Sinkankas[12] provided a simplified explanation of the features of pegmatites for prospectors, placing emphasis on how these could be recognized in the field. Hurlbut's *Minerals and Man*[13] (ch. 5), provides an excellent popular summary of the attractive minerals and gemstones that are found in pegmatites.

In *Table 11.1* pegmatites appear in the Late Magmatic classification, reflecting the fact that they formed after emplacement and solidification of granitic magmas. They consist of the four basic types described in the following pages.

Magmatic

Simple, unzoned pegmatites

These pegmatites are simple in mineralogy, basically containing only feldspar, quartz, and mica with small quantities of other minerals which may include beryl. The latter, if it occurs in them, tends to form uncomplicated hexagonal prisms, often minutely fractured, and seldom providing any clear areas large enough for gemstones. On the other hand, if the beryl is sufficiently abundant, it may be mined as an ore of beryllium.

Simple, zoned pegmatites

As mentioned above, successive waves of mineralization produce zones within pegmatites characterized by differences in mineralization and increasing grain size toward the cores. Chemical reactions produce a larger variety of mineral species, several of which may be economically important.

Simple, zoned pegmatites range in size from mere stringers of several centimetres thick to enormous bodies that may be extremely large. In Maine, for example, pegmatites of this kind, quarried for the sake of pottery feldspar, are often so wide that trucks can be driven into excavations that are entirely within pegmatite. In addition to large crystals of feldspar, such deposits have also provided the world's supply of sheet mica, ore beryl, and tantalum-niobium ores, among others. In respect to beryl, however, most of its crystals are enclosed by other pegmatite minerals such as feldspar and quartz, and only rarely are they found free-standing in pockets. As a result of being solidly enclosed, they are usually shattered internally and seldom yield either good gem material or mineral specimens.

In a few instances, where pockets are found, excellent specimens of colourless and smoky quartz crystals, topaz crystals, and beryl crystals have been recovered. Non-gem beryl crystals, or those 'frozen' in the pegmatite may be as much as one metre (3 ft) in diameter and two metres (6 ft) long.

Most of the beryl is a low-alkali variety, forming crude hexagonal prisms of short to long prismatic habit, seldom well-terminated, and ranging in size from several centimetres in diameter to the giants mentioned above. The colours include pale blue, greenish blue, pale green, yellow, and brownish, with greenish yellow perhaps the most common. For the most part, these hues are so weak that the crystals appear almost colourless and sometimes are mistaken for the ordinary massive quartz which usually accompanies them.

Complex, zoned and replaced bodies

The term *replaced* refers to portions of an original pegmatite body that have been dissolved during late chemical activity and the space reoccupied by new suites of minerals, often of increased variety and complexity. A general feature is the appearance of an inner zone of bladed albite feldspar of the variety known as cleavelandite. This is deposited upon the blocky feldspar-quartz unit and therefore lies between the latter and the core. In addition to cleavelandite, typical species include tourmaline (schorl), iron and manganese phosphates, columbite-tantalite, and other rare-element species. Beryl crystals, commonly of tapered habit (sodium-bearing) and composed of several individual crystals grown together occur mainly in the cleavelandite unit. Cavities containing excellent crystals of beryl and other minerals may occur along the margins of this unit and the quartz core unit.

Additional mineralogical complexity occurs in such bodies where the replacement includes introduction of lithium in the form of the lithium aluminum silicate known as spodumene and the lithium-bearing mica known as lepidolite. Units containing these species occur in inner zones, the lepidolite as masses of fine scaly crystals and the spodumene as lath-like crystals which may or may not protrude into the quartz core. In rare instances, the spodumene crystals may be found in pockets where they are characteristically translucent to transparent, sometimes of fine gem quality and lilac in colour (kunzite).

Beryl found within these units is alkali-rich, generally white, colourless, pink, or peach, and may be grown within small vuggy openings in the a albite-lepidolite units or take the form of well-shaped tabular to short prismatic crystals within larger openings. A common occurrence of these alkali-rich beryl varieties is as crystals perched on a matrix of white, bladed cleavelandite crystals, sometimes with topaz, coloured tourmaline, small crystals of lepidolite, also quartz, and other minerals. Specimens of this kind are highly prized by mineral collectors. As a rule, these beryl crystals rarely exceed several centimetres in diameter, but in some bodies they have been found as tabular to short prismatic crystals as large as 25 cm (10 in) in diameter. In spodumene-albite units these crystals may be pale blue, rarely medium blue, or pale green, colourless, white, or sometimes overgrown with pink zones. In lepidolite-rich units, they tend to be mostly pink to peach or apricot colour.

In addition to gem spodumene and beryl, these pegmatites commonly yield gem tourmaline, topaz, and a number of rare species that are the delight of the mineral collector. Pegmatites of this type are common in New England, California, Madagascar, the Ural Mountains, and Brazil.

Metamorphic-hydrothermal

Schist-type beryl deposits

These deposits receive their name from the fact that beryl crystals, often of the emerald variety, occur solidly imbedded in dark mica schist rocks, from which they must be painstakingly extracted and cleaned of close-adhering mica scales. The schists and associated rocks in which these crystals are found are the product of a chemical interaction between granitic rocks on one side and basic (silica-poor) rocks on the other, such that the materials necessary for the formation of beryl appear to be derived from granitic pegmatites but are transferred through the sides of such bodies into the adjoining basic rocks. This is the process known as *exometamorphism*, or changes induced in an original rock by introduction of outside constituents.

The beryl constituents transferred from the granitic pegmatites, or from the granite bodies themselves, recrystallize in the schists and thus are said to be exomorphic. Much of this beryl resembles the ordinary type found in the pegmatite bodies, but because the schist rocks are formed partly at the expense of the nearby basic rocks, which sometimes contain chromium, small amounts of this element may be incorporated in the beryl crystal structure and impart the typical rich green hue of emerald.

The usually narrow pegmatite veins present in the contact zone between granitic rocks and basic rocks have two names: Beus[2] (pp. 236–44) calls them 'granitic pegmatites of the crossing line' while others refer to them as 'desilicated pegmatites', or pegmatites which have been deprived of silica by virtue of the chemical interchange of constituents.

Classic occurrences of schist-type beryl include the emerald deposits in Egypt, Africa, and Austria. The deposits that have been most extensively studied, however, are those in the Ural Mountains, USSR, which were first discovered in 1831 when emerald crystals were found in outcrop debris. Fersman[14] studied these deposits and in 1929 published his conclusions as to their origin. A more recent study is that of Vlasov and Kutukova[15], published in 1960. Schneiderhöhn[10] (pp. 123–7) also provides a good summary of these deposits in the Urals.

The general features of the Uralian deposits are swarms of narrow pegmatic veins and veinlets associated with metamorphosed basic rocks such as amphibole schists, amphibolites, diorites, and serpentinites, the latter further altered in part to talc, chlorite, actinolite, or tremolite schists. The zones in which these sheet-like bodies occur may be tens of metres across and many hundreds of metres in length along the outcrops. The pegmatite veins usually contain plagioclase feldspar with quartz, sometimes with beryl and other minerals, with the beryl crystals generally being white, pale greenish, or pale yellow in colour.

Although some emerald is found in these veins, it occurs more commonly in the schistose rocks adjacent to the pegmatite veins where it formed through the chemical interactions mentioned above. The crystals are usually small in size, rarely over several centimetres in length, although some have been found in the Uralian mines that weighed several kilograms.

In addition to emerald, the schist type deposit is host to the classic alexandrite variety of chrysoberyl, prized by gem connoisseurs for its colour-change in cut gems and by mineral collectors for its beautiful twin crystals. As may be expected from the metamorphic origin of both emerald and alexandrite in these deposits, internal cracks and inclusions are numerous, and most of the material found is unsuitable for gem purposes.

Schist type emerald deposits are by far the most numerous sources of these gemstones, although in terms of size and quality of crystals they are overshadowed by the Colombian hydrothermal deposits. Many regions are known in which granitic rocks lie adjacent to basic rocks, and it is probable that as these contacts are more fully explored, other schist type emerald deposits will be found.

Hydrothermal

Greisens

The old miners' term, *greisen*, refers to granitic rocks which have been altered along fractures into masses of granular quartz and mica, and often with accessory species as topaz, tourmaline, fluorite, rutile, wolframite and cassiterite, the latter two species providing ores of tungsten and tin respectively. Beryl occurs in some greisen deposits, commonly in sub-prismatic granular aggregates but at other times as fine crystals in openings in the bodies.

Greisens are believed to form by exhalations of gas (*pneumatolysis*) or seepages of heated, mineral-bearing waters from deep-seated igneous rock sources during a process known as *hydrothermal alteration*. The latter is believed to be the more important of the two processes mentioned. Fractures in the host granites provide access to the solutions, and consequently alteration is most complete nearest the original openings, diminishing outward until unaltered granite is met. At times, so much granite is removed by the solutions that cavities lined with crystals appear in thicker portions of the bodies.

Typical minerals found in these openings are quartz, muscovite mica, lithium micas, topaz, tourmaline, cassiterite, wolframite, fluorite, apatite, and sometimes beryl. A famous and mineralogically important greisen deposit is that of the Sherlovaya Gora (mountain) in eastern Transbaikalia, USSR, described in detail by Beus[2] (pp. 263–80). Beryl crystals from these cavities are magnificent and have received worldwide distribution to collections.

Carbonate veins and tactite bodies

Hydrothermal activity also deposits beryl, among other minerals, along fractures in the carbonate (calcite-rich) rocks of the famous deposits of Colombia, noted for centuries for their production of the world's finest emerald crystals. Minerals associated with emerald are calcite and dolomite, derived from the enclosing carbonate rocks, but also albite feldspar, pyrite, quartz, and rarely, parisite, most of the latter species being more typical of granitic sources than the sedimentary rocks in which the veins are emplaced. It is believed that these species have been formed from materials dissolved in hot water issuing from some distant and as yet unrecognized igneous source.

Alpine clefts

In the alpine regions of Europe, splendid mineral crystals, including some beryl, occur in openings along fractures in rock masses that have been folded and distorted by movements of the earth's crust. The rock crystals from such cavities, or *clefts*, as they are called, have been known since Roman times. From the beginning of known history in these regions, mountaineer-collectors, or as they are known today, Strahlers, have climbed the mountains after snows have disappeared to find clefts exposed by weathering and dig out their treasures. The formation of such clefts is due to hydrothermal activity, the heated water dissolving minerals from various points along the network of cracks and depositing them in places where openings existed or were enlarged by dissolution of the country rock.

Typically, clefts occur in gneisses, a fine-grained metamorphic rock formed mostly from compressed and altered sediments. They are characteristically streaked by light-coloured minerals such as feldspar and quartz which more or less correspond to beds in the original sediments that were also rich in these constituents. Unlike carbonate rocks, which are readily dissolved by heated water, gneisses are composed mainly of silicate minerals and are only slowly attacked. For this reason, cavities along the fracture systems are by no means abundant but tend to be narrow and persistent, and only in a few places are they large enough to permit crystals to grow unimpeded and develop terminations.

A large variety of minerals has been found in alpine clefts, and their occurrences and associations in Switzerland are provided in considerable detail by P. Niggli *et al.*[16] and for the alpine regions of Italy by De Michele[17]. In some of the clefts small, long-prismatic aquamarine and other light-coloured beryls have been found, also bazzite, the rare scandian analogue of beryl, which forms very small acicular blue crystals. While emerald has not been reported in European alpine clefts, according to Sinkankas[18], it appears that the emerald crystals found near Hiddenite, North Carolina are an alpine cleft occurrence.

Sedimentary deposits

Important quantities of ore and gem beryl have been found in *eluvial* and *alluvial* sedimentary deposits. The term eluvial refers to deposits formed by the decay of deposit outcrops with little or no movement of the minerals from their place of origin, while alluvial refers to deposits of clay, sand, and gravel containing decay products that have been moved by rainfalls to considerable distances from their places of origin.

Eluvial deposits are usually obvious to the trained eye of the prospector because he can detect sharp, glassy crystals or unabraded pieces of rock resting in the soil or in the surface debris, suggesting that their source is underneath or only a short distance away. By far, the most deposits of beryl have been found merely by examining decayed outcrops (eluvium) and digging beneath the litter to find the original body. Eluvial deposits are characteristic of arid regions where rainfall is insufficient to wash away the evidences of decay, as in northeastern Brazil, southwestern United States, and South West Africa. They are also characteristic of high-altitude regions, such as the Alps, where rocks loosened by cycles of alternate freezing and thawing form slopes covered with rubble where the presence of valuable minerals can be readily detected.

Alluvial deposits are less easy to detect because the heavier and more durable minerals tend to settle to the bottom in beds of sand and gravel, and casual inspection is insufficient to show that they exist. However, they have been found in a number of regions in the world, often as a result of searching gravel beds for gold, as in Brazil, or found in valleys below outcrops of deposits where their presence was suspected. Classic alluvial deposits of beryl and other gemstones are widespread over the island of Ceylon, where they have been mined for centuries, also in Brazil, where many hundreds of pegmatite bodies have been completely decayed and their constituents washed into stream and river gravels. Depending on the distance travelled by such outcrop materials, and the violence of the streams that bore them along, alluvial beryl crystals may be only slightly rounded along their edges or completely smoothed so that no traces of crystal faces remain. Because of the pounding that such crystals receive during their movement, the pebbles that finally result tend to be solid and free of fractures and flaws, hence of gem quality in the case of beryls, topazes, tourmalines, and other gemstones.

References

1 GOLDSCHMIDT, V. *Geochemistry*. Edited by Alex Muir. Oxford: Clarendon Press. 730 pp. (1954)

2 BEUS, A. A. *Geochemistry of Beryllium*. Edited by L. R. Page, translated by F. Lachman. San Francisco: W. H. Freeman, 401 pp. (1966)

3 VLASOV, K. A., Ed. *Geochemistry and Mineralogy of Rare Elements and Genetic Types of Their Deposits*. Vol. 2: *Mineralogy of the Rare Elements*. Translated by Z. Lerman. Jerusalem: Israel Program for Scientific Translations. pp. 67–169 (1966)

4 MASON, B. *Principles of Geochemistry*. 3rd ed. New York: John Wiley & Sons. 329 pp. (1966)

5 BUCHI, S. Studies on the Natural History of Beryl. Ph.D. dissertation, University of Michigan, Ann Arbor. 170 pp. (1962)

6 CAMERON, E. N. *et al. Internal Structure of Granitic Pegmatites*. Economic Geology Publishing Company Monograph No. 2. Urbana, Ill.: Economic Geology Publishing Co. 115 pp. (1949)

7 FERSMAN, A. E. *Les Pegmatites*. 3 vols. Louvain: Librarie Universitaire Uystpruyst (739 pp.) (1961) Original Russian ed. publ. in Leningrad (1931)

8 LACROIX, A. *Minéralogie de Madagascar*. 3 vols. Paris: Augustin Challamel. 624, 694, 450 pp. (1922–23)

9 JEDWAB, J. Étude des Oligo-Eléments dans les Minéraux des Pegmatites. Doctoral dissertation, Free University of Brussels, Belgium. 158 pp. (1953)

10 SCHNEIDERHÖHN, H. *Die Erzlagerstätten der Erde*. Vol. 2: *Die Pegmatite*. Stuttgart: Gustav Fischer Verlag. 720 pp. (1961)

11 BOOYSEN, B. Pegmatites: Hints to Prospectors. *Geological Survey of South Africa Pamphlet No. 6*. 57 pp. (1959)

12 SINKANKAS, J. *Prospecting for Gemstones and Minerals*, New York: Van Nostrand Reinhold Co. 397 pp. (1970)

13 HURLBUT, C. S. *Minerals and Man*. New York: Random House. 304 pp. (1968)

14 FERSMAN, A. E. *Geochemische Migration der Elemente: III. Smaragdgruben im Uralgebirge*. Abhandlungen zur praktischen Geologie und Bergwirtschaftlehre, vol. 18. Halle (Saale): Wilhelm Knapp, pp. 74–116. (1929)

15 VLASOV, K. A. and KUTUKOVA, E. [*Emerald Mines*]. Moscow: Izdatelstvo Akademiya Nauk SSSR. 252 pp. (1960)

16 NIGGLI, P. *et al. Die Mineralien der Schweizeralpen*. 2 vols. Basel: B. Wepf & Co. 661 pp. (1940)

17 DE MICHELE, V. *Guida Mineralogica d'Italia*. 2 vols. Novara: Instituto Geografico De Agostini. 216, 192 pp. (1974)

18 SINKANKAS, J. *Gemstones of North America*. 2 vols. New York: Van Nostrand Reinhold Co. 675, 494 pp. (1976)

WORLD SOURCES

The following are descriptions of sources of gem beryl, arranged alphabetically by country. A list of references follows each country, and sometimes references are given for individual states or provinces.

AFGHANISTAN

Complex granitic pegmatites in Nuristan region recently furnished beautiful crystals of coloured tourmaline; colourless, greenish, pink, and purple spodumene; and various coloured beryls. According to Bariand and Poullen[1], archaeological excavations in Badakhshan indicate early Greek settlement of the region, and the unearthing of 'perfect crystals and gems of Beryl' suggest that these deposits were known many centuries ago. They also mention an occurrence of emerald, possibly in carbonate-skarn, in Pandjshir Valley, but do not give further details.

Geologists of the USSR conducted the first scientific explorations of the pegmatites of Noor and Paich valleys E of Kunar River, and NE of the town of Jalalabad[2]. Much beryl was found, including gem aquamarines of a beautiful, intense blue at Gur-Salak in Kunar Province. However, the splendid tourmalines and spodumenes come from pegmatites which lie along the Alingar River valley in Laghman Province. These are complex bodies of substantial size emplaced in the Nilaw plutonic intrusion[3]. Three mines visited by Bariand and Poullen are at Nilaw and Mawi, N and NE of Dahane Pyar, and Korgal NNW of Nuristan, approximately 80 km (50 miles) N of Jalalabad. All are reached by foot trail only. Both the tourmalines and spodumenes are outstanding, but the latter are unique for their size and perfection. Single spodumene crystals of about 1 m (3 ft) in length have been found, and a clear green prism of 60 cm (24 in) is now in the Sorbonne collection in Paris. The beryls are less important, with gem aquamarines and morganites 'found mainly in the Laghman district, where they occur with the basal pinacoid characteristically well-developed . . . and loose crystals and crystals on matrix have been recovered'[1] (p. 307). Morganites are pink to brownish-pink and reach 6 cm (2.3 in) in diameter.

1 BARIAND, P. and POULLEN, J. F. The pegmatites of Laghman, Nuristan, Afghanistan. *The Mineralogical Record* 9:301–8 (1978)

2 ROSSOVSKIJ, L. N., CHMYREV, V. M. and SALAKH, A. S. Aphanitic dikes with spodumene among lithium pegmatites; conditions of formation. *Doklady Akademiya Nauk SSSR* (Leningrad) 226:1418–21 (1976)

3 FUCHS, G., MATURA, A. and SCHERMAN, O. Vorbericht über geologische und lagerstättenkundliche Untersuchungen in Nurestan, Afghanistan. *Verhandlungen geologische Bundesanstalt Österreich* (Vienna) 1:9–23 (1974)

ALGERIA

The 'emerald' from marble near confluence of Oued-Bouman and Oued-Harrach reported by Ville[1] is green Mg-tourmaline[2].

1 VILLE, L. Notice sur les gîtes d'émeraude de la haute vallée de l'Harrach. *Compte Rendu de l'Academie des Sciences* (Paris) 41:698–701 (1855)

2 LACROIX, A. *Minéralogie de la France et des ses Colonies.* Paris: Librairie Polytechnique. Vol. 1, p. 109 (1893)

ANGOLA

Common beryl has been found in granitic pegmatites mined for mica in Luanda Province[1,2]; a 14-cm (5.5 in) diameter crystal was found in Mussac-Saca mica mine, 22 km (14 miles) E of Sassa.

1 MURDOCK, T. G. The mica deposits and industry of Angola. *U.S. Bureau of Mines Mineral Trade Notes,* Special Supplement to No. 42. 38 pp (1954)

2 BEBIANO, J. B. Jazigos de mica de Angola. *Ministry of Colonies, Memorias, Serie de Geologia Economica,* Lisbon, pp. 11–45 (1946)

ANTARCTICA

Bluish-green, common beryl crystals 2–4.5 cm (0.5–2 in) in quartz veins are found near Commonwealth Bay, Adelie Land[1].

1 MAWSON, D. Antarctic mineral possibilities. *The Mining Journal* (London) 101:522–3 (1913)

ARGENTINA

Ore beryl is a common and commercially important accessory in many granitic pegmatites of Catamarca, La Rioja, San Juan, Cordoba, and San Luis provinces[1,2]. In Sierra San Luis, tabular bodies reach 300 m (330 yd) long[3] and contain greenish-white, yellowish, bluish, and, rarely, medium blue or reddish crystals of simple hexagonal form[1]. Translucent to opaque crystals are the rule, although partly transparent blue crystals were mined from the Santa Ana deposit, San Luis Province, and gem-quality blue and yellow crystals to 8 cm (3 in) were reported from Acjiras, Rio Quarto, Cordoba Province, where they were found in digging a well. Some common beryl crystals were very large, a giant of 1×4 m $(3 \times 12$ ft) was taken from a deposit at Cerro Blanco, 9 km (5.6 miles) E of Tanti, Dept. Punilla, Cordoba Province.

Beryl also occurs in deposits considered by Ahlfeld and Angelelli[1] (p. 201) to be intermediate between granitic pegmatites and hypothermal quartz veins; these typically contain feldspar, biotite, tourmaline, beryl, fluorite, and pyrite at Los Piquillines, El Valle, and Santa Barbara mines near San Martin, San Luis Province.

1 AHLFELD, F. and ANGELELLI, V. *Las especes minerales de la Republica Argentina. Instituto Geologia y Mineria Publ. No.* 458. Jujuy: Universidad Nacional de Tucuman. 304 pp(1948)

2 ANGELELLI, V. El berilo en la República Argentina. *Argentina Comisión Nacional Energía Atomica Informe* 60. 48 pp (1961)

3 HERRERA, A. O. Las Pegmatitas de la Sierra San Luis. *Revista de la Asociación Geológica Argentina* (Buenos Aires) 18, no. 1–2, pp. 43–71 (1963)

AUSTRALIA

Aside from a little emerald and aquamarine, major production has been ore beryl. Between 1939–1964, the total ore beryl production was 4076 long tons, 3605 of which came from Western Australia. With market demands satisfied, there has been very little production since then[1].

Queensland

In Co. Tate, District Cook, large aquamarine crystals were found with cassiterite at O'Brien's Creek, also 'Nine Mile', and Lancewood tin mines 48 km (30 miles) S of Fossilbrook, which is about 155 km (110 miles) SW of Cairns City. Beryl occurs on Quartz Hill, Elizabeth Creek, about 209 km (130 miles) SW of Cairns[2]. Some aquamarine is found in alluvial gold/tin deposits, notably at Brooklands Station, Chillagoe, Co. Lynd, 140 km (75 miles) WSW of Cairns, and at Heberton, Co. Cardwell, 70 km SSW of Cairns[2,3].

Some gem aquamarine is found in alluvial tin deposits at several places in Darling Downs district, Co. Bentinck; associates may include diamond, sapphire, spinel, zircon, garnet, tourmaline, topaz, amethyst, and quartz. Specific localities are Hunt's, Quart Pot, Sugarloaf, Lode, Arbouin's, Cannon, Kettle Swamp Creeks, Severn River, and Dolcoath Creek.

1 KALIX, Z., FRASER, L. M. and RAWSON, R. I. Australian mineral industry: production and trade, 1842–1964. *Department of National Development, Bureau of Mineral Resources , Geology & Geophysics Bulletin* 81. 473 pp (1966)

2 DUNSTAN, B. *Queensland Mineral Index and Guide.* Queensland Geological Survey Publication 241. Brisbane: Queensland Geological Survey. 1014 pp (1913)

3 BARRIE, J. and KALIX, Z. *Gemstones.* Dept. of National Development, Bur. of Min. Res., Geology & Geophysics Summary Report 42. 42 pp (1959)

New South Wales

Scattered occurrences in mountain ranges paralleling the E coast, otherwise only ore beryl in Broken Hill district in the W.

Waterworn prismatic crystals, some of gem aquamarine, in cassiterite gravels of the 'tin belt' extend S from Co. Bentinck in South Queensland to around Tenterfield, Co. Clive, approx. 113 km (70 miles) NW of Grafton, and also farther S into Emmaville district in Co. Gough, approx. 500 km (310 miles) ENE of Sydney. Around Emmaville, gravels yielded waterworn crystals of quartz, sapphire, topaz, and beryl, the last only slightly worn and of yellowish colour. These minerals were derived from weathered cassiterite-bearing greisen veins in the Torrington granite[1]. At Heffernan's Lease, ML 52, 5 km (3 miles) W of Torrington, a vein of feldspar, biotite, wolframite and beryl yielded some good gem crystals of the last, gems of which were placed in the Australian Museum[2]. Another source stated that the museum possesses a yellowish-green faceted gem of 73 carats from Heffernan's. Details on the mineralogy of the deposits appear in Lawrence and Markham[3]. According to Anderson, Torrington beryl crystals measured up to 6×5 cm $(2.3 \times 2$ in); forms c and m only[4]. They were found in soft micaceous vug-fillings associated with feldspar, mica, wolframite, topaz and quartz. Larger crystals contained dark inclusions and others were of 'beautiful colour and transparency'[4]. In 1908, or perhaps somewhat later, Mr. Percy Marks, a Sydney jeweller, obtained a quantity of the better crystals and exhibited them at the 1910 Paris Exposition. The most common colour was bluish-green, but some were nearly colourless, and many were striated and etched. Average RI $o=1.5685$, $e=1.5640$, diff. 0.0045^4.

Emmaville emerald. The district is still remembered for emeralds found at The Glen, formerly known as De Milhou's Reef or Cleary's Lode, 9 km (5.5 miles) NNE of Emmaville and discovered during prospecting for cassiterite. This was the first *in situ* Australian emerald deposit found, although other 'emeralds' found before were later shown to be merely green beryls[5,6]. In 1890, D. A. Porter reported emeralds from an old shaft dump at the locality. In 1891 the newly formed Emerald Proprietary Company sank a shaft of 15 m (50 ft) to follow outcrop indications. At this depth, with the emeraldiferous 'shoot' pitching slightly NE and requiring a short tunnel at the 10 m (33 ft) level to intercept, David reported no emeralds[6]. According to Barrie and Kalix, emeralds occurred as small crystal concentrations solidly embedded in a quartzose vein with cassiterite, topaz, fluorite, arsenopyrite and quartz[7]. Pittman noted that the emeralds were found 'intercrystallized with topaz, frequently penetrating crystals of fluorspar, as delicate prisms' or, 'embedded in kaolinized felspathic rock, occasionally quite surrounded by massive mispickel, rarely encrusted with crystals of tinstone, and in one case traversing plates of mica'[8]. In 1890, the discovery year, 2225 carats were sent to London as a trial shipment and some of the gems were sold for £4.00 per carat. In 1891, 25 000 carats were mined, followed by a like quantity in 1892, but it was reported that 'the hardness of the matrix . . . is still a source of difficulty, as it is almost impossible to break down the rock without injuring and frequently destroying the emeralds'[8]. In 1894, the mine was inoperative; after further unsuccessful explorations in depth, all work ceased in 1898. In 1908, mining was revived and 1000 carats of stones valued £1600–1700 were obtained and sent off to Europe. In 1909, 'the largest cut stone weighed 6 carats'[9]; some 50 stones in another parcel were said to be of 'fair quality' but the general colour was pale[10]. Barrie and Kalix gave a total production of 53 225 carats[7]. The largest crystal may be that described by

David as about 23 carats and 32 × 11 mm (1.25 × 0.3 in) but marred by basal cracks[6]. The largest cut gem reported in 1891 was 2⅛ carats. In this period about 50 carats of cut gems were offered by the company for from £2/- to £2/2/- per carat for the lot. The largest rough crystal weighed 9 carats. The colour was described by Pittman as 'varying from the faint shades of green up to moderately bright emerald green, but never showing a very deep shade of green'[8]. He also noted uneven colouration: 'in places colourless bands appeared . . . running at right angles to the axis'.

1 RAMDOHR, P. Aus meinen mineralogisch-geologischen Reisen. Teil II., Australien. *Der Aufschluss* (Heidelberg) 20, no. 5, pp. 113–26 (1969)

2 SMITH, G. A contribution to the mineralogy of N.S.W. Geological Survey of New South Wales Mineral Resources 34 (Sydney) (1926)

3 LAWRENCE, L. J. and MARKHAM, N. L. The petrology and mineralogy of the pegmatite complex at Bismuth, Torrington, New South Wales. *Journal of the Geological Society of Australia* 10:343–64. (1963)

4 ANDERSON, C. Mineralogical notes, No. X. Beryl, Torrington, N.S. Wales. *Records of the Australian Museum* 13:1–13 (1920)

5 CLARKE, W. B. *Researches in the Southern Gold Fields of New South Wales.* Sydney: Geological Survey New South Wales. 305 pp.; 'Gems, metals and other minerals associated with gold alluvia', App. B., p. 271 (1860)

6 DAVID, T. W. E. Report on the discovery of emeralds in the Vegetable Creek District. *Annual Report of the Department of Mines, N. S. Wales, for 1891* (Sydney) pp. 229–34, 284 (1891)

7 BARRIE, J. and KALIX, Z. Gemstones. *Summary Report of the Australia Bureau of Mineral Resources, Geology & Geophysics* No. 43 (Canberra) 42 pp (1959)

8 PITTMAN, E. F. *The Mineral Resources of New South Wales.* Sydney: Geological Survey of New South Wales. 487 pp (1901)

9 EMERALDS IN NEW SOUTH WALES. *The Mining Journal* (London) 89:405 (1910)

10 ROSE, G. Gemstones. Chapter in *The Mineral Industry of New South Wales.* Sydney: Geological Survey of New South Wales, Dept. of Mines, 20 pp (1960)

Western Australia

Poona emerald. Poona (27°10'Sm 117°25'E) in Murchison Gold Field, lies approx. 64 km (40 miles) NW of town of Cue, the latter approx. 355 km (220 miles) NE of Geraldton. A pegmatite field here is roughly 6.4 km (4 miles) × 3.2 km (2 miles) in size and oriented along a NW–SE line; it contains numerous granitic pegmatites intruded into Archaean greenstones surrounded and invaded by granites. The Poona emerald crystals are commonly well-developed hexagonal prisms, sometimes striated. Only the small crystals were of gem quality. Simpson's analysis found 0.23% Cr_2O_3, very small amounts of Fe, Mn, and Mg, and a substantial quantity of alkali, i.e., 0.48% Na_2O. G = 2.69, o = 1.578, e = 1.573[3,8].

The Poona field was first prospected for cassiterite in 1909 and the first emerald found by Paddy Ryan. A. Montgomery, State Mining Engineer, independently found emerald a few months after Ryan[1]. In 1912, H. P. Woodward, Assistant Government Geologist, examined the field and in 1914 published a report with a map[2]. He found several good crystals and had the best cut in Sydney, obtaining 9 faceted gems weighing from 0.7 to 2.6 carats and some cabochons from 6 to 18 carats. In 1912, J. Pearl, a Perth jeweller, formed a syndicate which proceeded to spend £1000 opening one of the prospects to a depth of 15 m (50 ft), obtaining 'many thousands of carats of emeralds, though of such mediocre quality as to be commercially valueless'. However, two fine crystals among the lot furnished a 5-carats gem sold to the Montana Sapphire Syndicate for £100 and later resold for £170; the second stone was cut into five 'very choice' gems, the largest of 1.25 carats. In 1914, the Montana Sapphire Syndicate prepared to spend £5000 to develop the property, but World War I intervened and put a stop to these plans.

The field remained dormant until 1927 when Star Emerald Syndicate, Ltd., Lewis Marks, engineer and manager, acquired five leases and commenced mining. During that year 5500 carats of rough were sent to London, one parcel containing a 40-carat crystal. One of the better crystals sold in the USA for $750[3]. The latter statistics differ from those provided by Simpson that cover Poona emerald production in carats and value from 1927 until cessation of mining in 1930:

According to contemporary accounts, Star Syndicate acquired ML 79 in 1927, recovering 4700 carats with 8 men at work[4]. In the same year a shaft was sunk to 46 m (150 ft), and at 24 m (79 ft) emeralds were found. Adjoining ground was exploited by Transvaal Financial Trust[5]. By 1928, the Star Syndicate shaft on ML 79 had reached 52 m (171 ft). In 1936, the old workings were reopened and shoots of emerald-bearing biotite schist were encountered at a depth of 50 m (165 ft). In regard to size and quality of crystals, 'the finest stone seen from this field [by Simpson] was obtained by H. Mandestam in 1928' and was a prism of 20 × 6 × 4 mm imbedded in a small quartz veinlet in biotite schist. Furthermore, 'it was of a deep rich green colour, perfectly transparent and possessing very few flaws'[3]. Elsewhere on the Poona field, ore beryl in the amount of 24.53 tons, all from eluvial deposits, was obtained during 1944–1945, with an opinion expressed that direct production from pegmatites probably would be unprofitable[6].

1 Discovery of Emeralds in Western Australia. *Mining Journal* (London) 100:304 (1913)

2 WOODWARD. H. P. A geological reconnaissance of a portion of the Murchison Gold Field. Geological Survey of Western Australia Bulletin 1957 (1914)

3 Emeralds from Australia. *The Jeweler's Circular* 157 (1927)

4 Discovery of Emeralds. *Mining Journal* 157:286, 310 (1927)

5 Western Australia. *The Mining Journal* 158:802 (1927)

AUSTRIA

Salzburg

All beryl occurrences are confined to the N slopes of Hohe Tauern mountain range, which lies E–W approx. 80 km S of Salzburg. References to aquamarine crystals in pegmatite schlieren or in aplite bands within the central gneiss region are numerous[1,2,3,4]. The zone of occurrences is narrow and straight, running from Abichalpe in Untersulzbachtal through Untersulzbachtal ridge, and across Habach Valley, the Habachtal ridge, the downslope partly into Hollersbachtal. The crystals are small and generally frozen in quartz-feldspar. Colours range from pale blue to medium blue.

Habachtal emerald. Habachtal is one of the oldest known and most famous deposits, and may have been known to the Celts and the Romans. The Romans are said to have sent prospecting teams into the Alps where they discovered emerald in the alluvium of the lower Habachtal[5,6,7,8,9]. The emerald site was called 'Mountain of Green Jewels' by the natives, and there is evidence suggesting that the Archbishop of Salzburg caused the deposit to be worked sometime in the Middle Ages. A mining chronicle of 1727 mentioned the deposit as belonging to the Duchy of Bavaria, which controlled the region at the time.

According to Gübelin (p. 342)[6], Empress Maria Theresa (1717–80) owned an inkwell the size of man's fist sculptured from a Habachtal emerald. This may have been the emerald unguent jar, sculptured by Dionysio Miseroni in about 1642 from what is certainly a Colombian crystal, that is now in the treasury in Vienna. Very large emerald crystals from this locality seem to be unheard of, Eberl suggesting that the largest may be a crystal fragment in the Hofmuseum in Vienna that measures only 3.5 cm long and 2 × 3 cm wide, 'which because of its size, far exceeds those found hitherto'[9] (p. 17).

Mineralogical-geological descriptions of the deposit appeared in the 18th century with the first accurate account published in the early 1800s. In 1862, the Viennese jeweller Samuel Goldschmidt (1810–1871) obtained rights to the deposit, and in 1863 he commissioned the mining official M. V. Lipold to investigate. From then on the mine was worked by Goldschmidt in a systematic and profitable manner, using a number of tunnels to follow the emerald-bearing schist,

which by now was recognized as the true matrix of the emerald. A contemporary praised Goldschmidt's campaign and stated that 'he found, among others, a large and beautiful emerald that weighed 42 carats after cutting and today is among the English crown jewels'[9] (p. 19). Upon Goldschmidt's death in 1871, his son-in-law, a Mr. Brandeis, inherited the rights, but having no interest in mining, he allowed the workings to fall into ruin. Shortly thereafter, the mineral collector-guide of Bramberg, Alois Wurnitsch, succeeded in interesting an English company, 'Limited Forster', to work the mine profitably with about 20 to 30 men.

Following this period, another English concern, Emerald Mines, Ltd., secured rights for 1896–1913. Despite a statement that up to 1905 the mines 'were being worked by a few hands by some London diamond cutters, but in a somewhat dilatory fashion', it was also shown that such 'dilatory' work managed to produce 'no less than 68 000 carats . . . turned out by six miners in less than four months, notwithstanding the antiquated mining methods

Figure 11.1 Left: view of the Habachtal emerald mine area, taken from the west slope of the valley and showing the steep, rugged terrain. The black arrow marks the mine itself. Below the small snow patches is the area of debris exploited by collectors seeking emerald, as shown in the righthand photograph. *Courtesy Dr. Heinz Weininger, Leoben, Austria*

employed'[10]. Eberl stated that 32 000 carats of impure and 7000 carats of good stones were sent back to London in 1903, the English then sending the rough to India from whence they returned to the market as 'Indian emeralds' (p. 20)[9]. Mining by this last concern ceased in 1913.

During World War I and for some years after, the deposit was worked sporadically by several small firms but with poor results[9,11]. In 1932, the property was auctioned off at a low price to the newly-organized Schaffhausener Smaragd AG of Zürich, who worked the mine with great energy, driving a gallery of 120 m (110 yd) and accomplishing other profitable improvements. World War II again put a stop to mining temporarily, but it was shortly resumed by the Germans until they were dispossessed after the war and the property was assigned to the Salzburg Government. The latter leased the mine to Colonel Hans Zieger, who, with several assistants, worked it in modest but profitable fashion for several years up to his death[6]. Very little formal mining has been done since, save for occasional clandestine operations. Bölsche notes that many Salzburg families, particularly those in the Pinzgau, own traditional jewellery set with local emeralds and with smoky and clear quartz from the Hohe Tauern. Further details on the history of the deposit, its owners, operators, and productions, as well as much local colour, are to be found in Eberl's work[9].

The deposit is located on the side of Legbach ravine, about 2100 m (6800 ft) above sea level, just below the Legbach Scharte (gap) on the crest of a ridge known as the Habachkamm. The Legbach ravine drops W into the main Habachtal (valley); the latter then descends N to join the valley of the Salzach River at the hamlet of Habach. The nearest town is Bramberg on the Salzach, about 70 km (44 miles) SW of the city of Salzburg. The mine is reached via foot trail to the site of the former Alpenrose shelter (destroyed by avalanche in 1970) and from there via an increasingly steep trail that zig-zags to the mine.

1 ZEPHAROVICH. V. VON. *Mineralogisches Lexicon für das Kaiserthum Österreich*. 3 vols. Vienna: Wilhelm Braumüller I (1859) 627 pp.; II (1873) 436 pp.; III (1893) 478 pp. (1859–1893)

2 HABERLANDT. H. Einige interessante Mineralfunde aus der Hohen Tauern. *Tschermak's min. u. petr. Mitt.* 47: 393–7 (1936)

3 LEITMEIER. H. Das Smaragdvorkommen in Habachtal in Salzburg und seine Mineralien. *Tschermak's min. u. petr. Mitt.* 49:245–368 (beryl pp. 303–32) (1937)

4 BÖLSCHE. R. Neues aus dem Habachtal. *Der Aufschluss* 10:84–7 (1959)

5 GÜBELIN. E. J. Emerald from Habachtal. *Journal of Gemmology* 7:342–61 (1956)

6 GÜBELIN. E. J. The emerald from Habachtal. *Gems & Gemology* 8:295–309 (1956)

7 BAUER. M. *Precious Stones.* Translated by L. J. Spencer. London: Charles Griffin & Co. 627 pp. (1904)

8 BALL. S. H. Historical notes on gem mining. *Economic Geology* (Lancaster, Pa.) 26:681–738 (1931)

9 EBERL. R. *Smaragde – Segen und Fluch.* Vienna: private publ., 105 pp. (1972)

10 THOMPSON. A. Emerald mines of Austria. *The Mining Journal* 78:857 (1906)

11 KUNZ. G. F. Precious Stones. Chapter in *The Mineral Industry, During 1928* Vol. 37. New York: McGraw-Hill Book Co. pp. 512–37 (1929)

BRAZIL

Localities where beryl is found are confined to a series of highlands more or less parallel to the coastline of E Brazil, in a region that is maturely weathered, low in elevation, and heavily vegetated, except in the NE corner where aridity prevails. Granitic pegmatites of all types are abundant and widespread, many so deeply weathered that their feldspars have been altered to clays and the more durable constituents, including gemstones, have been released to the soil. Basement rocks in which the pegmatites are intruded are largely metamorphics of the Precambrian Shield and are associated with numerous granitic plutons.

Bahia

Numerous pegmatites occur in a belt paralleling the Atlantic coastline and extending over a distance of about 600 km (370 miles) from NNE to SSW, then passing over the border into Minas Gerais.

Emerald in Bahia occurs in mica schist on the Fazenda São Thiago, situated on the left bank of the São Francisco River, about halfway between Xique-Xique and Remanso in the municipality of Pilão Arcado, near the town of Salininha[1]. This deposit was known for many years, but positive identification of the emerald was only made in 1962. Many small parties began mining that year, but 'up to the present, only three pits are producing emeralds and inferior beryls. About 15 kilos [33 lb] of largely inferior crystals has yielded

Figure 11.2 The so-called Grota Funda or 'Deep Cavern' at Carnaiba, Bahia, one of the earliest emerald diggings consisting of numerous claims worked by various mining groups. *Courtesy of Walter E. Johansen, Morgan Hill, Calif., who took the picture in 1965*

100 grams of good emeralds[1]. This emerald was spectroscopically examined and contained Cr 0.0003, V 0.15% and numerous other elements in small quantities (US Geological Survey Report, 65-WS-166, Sept. 16, 1965). Vanadium instead of chromium appears to be the colouring ion.

In the Campo Formoso district, the Carnaiba emerald deposits continued production into 1979. The city of Campo Formoso is 77 km (48 miles) N of Jacobina. The emerald deposits are located within an area of several kilometres diameter around the village of Carnaiba, the latter located 27 km (17 miles) SW of Campo Formoso or almost directly S about 9 km (5.6 miles) from the village of Brejão das Grotas[9]. In the same area is the recently discovered (1983) emerald source of Soroto, which, like the Carnaiba mine, consists of a series of pits and underground workings up to 30 m (100 ft) deep in decomposed granitic rocks.

Goiás

This area is noteworthy for occurrences of emerald only. The major deposit is in detritus from weathered mica schist in Serra das Lages, a range of hills 32 km (20 miles) SE of the capital city of Goiânia[4]. Calmbach gives the site as upon the Fazenda das Lages, left bank of Ribeirão do Bugre, a tributary of Rio Urubú, municipality Itaberai, Comarca Rio das Pedras[5].

Minas Gerais (formerly 'Geraes')

The name means 'General Mines' in allusion to its past and present importance as a producer of minerals. It contains one of the world's largest pegmatite provinces. Most deposits are still worked by individual prospector-miners or *garimpeiros* working singly or in small teams. Their winnings are sold on the spot to visitors or taken to the larger cities such as Teófilo Otoni, Governador Valadares, or Conselheiro Pena.

In respect to gem beryls, Minas Gerais is the world's most important producer, surpassing all other countries both in terms of the largest production sustained over several centuries and in quality (with the notable exception of pink beryls, the finest of which stem from the Malagasy Republic).

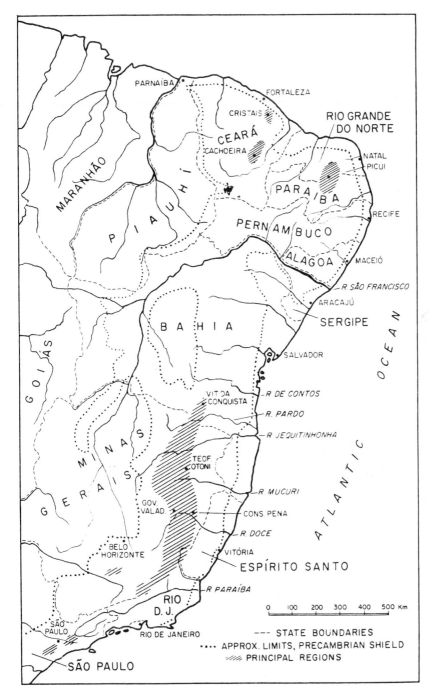

Figure 11.3 Sketch map of Brazil showing extent of the Precambrian Shield (gneisses, schists, granites) and major associated granitic pegmatite regions. Based on a map in G. De Paiva, Provincias pegmatiticas do Brasil, *Divisão do Fomento da Produccão Mineral, Bol. 78 (*Rio, 1946):22 (with additions)

The prime Brazilian beryl is aquamarine, largely obtained from Minas Gerais, and ranging in colour from pure blue of the finest and most valuable tint to various shades of blue-green and yellow-green. Excellent chartreuse, pale green, and golden beryl are also found, as well as pink and colourless beryls. Emerald has been found in two well-documented deposits in Minas Gerais.

At the Maxixe mine in Piaui valley curious blue, gem quality alkali beryl crystals occurred long with pink tourmalines in

Figure 11.4 A splendid, etched, blue aquamarine crystal weighing 19 kg (42 lb) found in Jaqueto, a small town located in the municipality of Miraja, state of Bahia, Brazil, in January 1979. The dimensions are 59 × 38 cm (23 × 15 in). The crystal was purchased by the jewellery and gem firm of H. Stern in Rio de Janeiro and was still in its possession, intact, in late 1980. *Courtesy of Hans Stern, Rio de Janeiro*

gravel deposits. The crystals are deeply corroded with grooves and channels parallel to the *c*-axis. The most striking feature, however, was the strong dichroism in reverse of the normal pattern. That is, the direction parallel to *c*-axis shows a fine blue, but perpendicular to this direction is almost

colourless, or o = cobalt blue, e = near colourless. On exposure for several days to sunlight or after gentle heating, the crystals faded to yellowish[6]. Similar beryls have been found recently elsewhere in Brazil and their behaviour and its explanation described in Chapter 6[7,8].

In Minas Gerais, emeralds are found in schist-type deposits; crystals in decomposed schistose-granitic rocks containing pegmatitic phases; also crystals recovered from detritus. Calmbach vaguely referred to emeralds at São João de Gorotuba, Municipio Grão Mogol, the latter town 270 km (166 miles) NW of Governador Valadares in an area principally noted for alluvial diamonds. Equally vague reports apply to emerald near Sabinópolis, Araçuai and Guanhães, all in pegmatite areas noted for aquamarines, which, in greenish colours, may have been mislabelled 'emerald'.

True emerald was discovered in 1917, 1919, or 1920, on Fazenda Sossego near Sant' Anna dos Ferros, or Esmeraldas dos Ferros as currently shown on maps, in biotite schist in the Serra das Esmeraldas, about 20 km (12.5 miles) SE of Ferros or about 50 km (31 miles) NE of Itabira. In 1919 an emerald was found which weighed 2200 carats, and this and others were exported to Germany[1]. H. V. Walter, British consul in Belo Horizonte, visited the mine in 1940 and reported it was being worked by hand in a series of pits.

Large gem beryls or Minas Gerais. The first well-recorded large aquamarine seems to be a 7 kg (15 lb) stone found in 1811 at São Mateus. [10]. Within the present century, the crystal that garnered greatest publicity was that found either in 1909 or near the end of June, 1910, according to conflicting accounts, at the Papamel alluvial diggings near the village of Marambainha (Marambia), 75 km (46 miles) N of Teófilo Otoni. The somewhat worn, doubly-terminated prism measured 48.5 cm (19 in) long and 38–41 cm (15–16 in) in diameter and weighed 110.5 kg (244 lb). It was virtually flawless and so transparent that newsprint could be read through it from end to end. An outer zone was greenish but the major portion was fine blue. [5, 11, 12, 13, 14, 15]. Several accounts gave David Mussi, a Syrian, as the lucky finder, but a newspaper interview with August Klein, of Idar Oberstein, Germany, supplied by Gerhard Becker, claimed that the find was made by the Syrian brothers Tanuri who dug just one metre below the bottom of an alluvial pit, which had been abandoned in disgust by another miner, and there they found the magnificent aquamarine crystal[15]. According to Oakenfull[16] it was sold locally for 58 contos of reis (£3000) but August Klein, one of the purchasers, claimed that the price given was 73 contos or about 90 000 gold marks[15]. The nearly incredible adventures that befell this stone are described by Hahn[17] and August Klein[15]. Klein was not only co-negotiator for its purchase in the village of Arrasuahy but also the person who actually transported the crystal in a dugout canoe via the Rio Arrasuahy and Rio Jequintinhonha to the seacoast, thence via coastal steamer to the city of Bahia, and finally via the steamer "Westerwald" to Hamburg, Germany. In Hamburg, the large wooden crate holding the crystal was given over to a firm of forwarders to tranship to Idar-Oberstein. After a few days delay in reaching Idar-Oberstein, Klein was shocked to find that the stone had not arrived. Backtracking to Hamburg, he found the crate, unidentified, in a corner of a freight warehouse where the custodian had put it hoping that a claimant would appear to take the parcel off his hands. This time Klein personally escorted the box to Idar-Oberstein. Here the firm of Bohrer-Borges, whose representatives, Viktor Bohrer-Borges was with August Klein in Brazil and apparently supplied the funds for the purchase of the crystal, took possession of the crystal and offered it for sale at a price of one-half million marks. However, no museum or other institution bought the crystal, and it was broken up into pieces that were sold separately. According to Kunz, who gave the original purchase price as $25 000, the crystal was estimated to yield 200 000 carats of finished gems[13]. Oakenfull gave the estimated value of the stone in Germany as £50 000[16].

Another large crystal, according to Oakenfull, was a well-formed prism of 195 kg (430 lb) found at Espera Feliz, 46 km (28 miles) S of Manhuacú, but it "had nothing but a cone [core?] worth cutting"[16]. Calmbach mentions a good blue hexagonal prism of 5 m (16 ft) long and 1 m (3 ft) diameter that was found at Lavra de Ferreira

and weighed 3 000 kg (6 600 lb) but was completely opaque and unfit for gems[5]. In the summer of 1942, an aquamarine crystal of 108 kg (222 lb) was found at Ariranho, Rio Bugre, 30 km (18.5 miles) NW of Governador Valadares; the owners were offered about U.S. $40,000 for the stone[18].

Sometime in 1946, a 25.4 kg (56 lb) rough, hexagonal prism of aquamarine, 28 cm (11 in) long and 25 cm (10 in) in diameter, was found near Respendor, 30 km (18.5 miles) SE of Conselheiro Fena. A syndicate shipped the stone to New York in October, 1946, where it was insured for U.S. $500 000 and claimed to bear a potential of $2 500 000 in cut gems. Title to the stone was badly clouded by four claimants, including the owner of the land on which it was found, and the miners. In November, the stone, valued at $1 000 000 was placed in the vaults of the Manufacturers Safe Deposit Company. Its subsequent fate seems to be unknown.

A splendid deep blue aquamarine crystal of 33 928 kg (74.5 lb) was found in 1954 or 1955 on a farm near Ieófilo Otoni and was estimated as 60% cuttable. This was the specimen later to achieve fame among gem merchants as setting the top standard of colour in aquamarine. It was named the Marta Rocha after Miss Brazil of the time[19, 20].

Schupp described a broken section of an intensely dark blue-green crystal, 37 cm (12.5 in) long and 23 cm (9 in)   found in a "quartz deposit" in the Galvão area near Topazio village, 25 km (15.5 miles) NNE of Teófilo Ontoni[21]. Another large crystal was reported in the December, 1955, issue of the Washington Post from Minas Gerais that weighted 61 kg (134.5 lb) but no further details were provided. However, according to Froés Abreu it was found in gravel at Garajaú, near Governador Valadares, and was named the Lucia[20]. It was estimated to contain 25 kg (55 lb) of cuttable material. In 1964, another 'bomba', the Brazilian colloquialism for an exceedingly fine stone of Marta Rocha quality, was applied to a deep blue to blue-green aquamarine, said to resemble fine tourmaline in colour. It was found by garimpeiro Abelo Ferreira near Padre Paraiso (Agua Vermelha) in the Pedroso alluvial mine, Rio Marambaia valley, 75 km (46 miles) N of Teófilo Otoni.

It weighed 7 kg (15.5 lb) and measured 26 × 11 cm (10.25 × 4.3 in) and was nearly of cylindrical form due to equal development of first and second order prisms. H. Stern, jewellers of Rio de Janeiro, bought the stone and dubbed it the IV Centenario.

Aside from aquamarines and some large golden beryls that have been found from time to time, the gemmy pink or morganite variety, or sometimes a beautiful apricot colour beryl, are found of exceptional size and crystallographic perfection. While they are much larger than the pink beryls of Malagasy Republic, they are not as rich in colour. Some crystals of morganite have been recently obtained that are nearly 30 cm (12 in) in diameter.

Espírito Santo

From the region around Colatina city on Rio Doce, ca. 90 km (56 miles) NNW of the capital city of Vitória, Froes Abreu reported an excellent quality aquamarine crystal of 25.2 kg (55.5 lb) found in alluvium in Vila das Penhas district and valued at one million cruzeiros[9]. Other fine quality aquamarines were recently found in the same area; some have been reported by Froes Abreu from around Leopoldina town, 30 km (18.5 miles) NW of Vitória; others appeared in Municipio Afonso Claudio, 85 km (53 miles) WNW of Vitória[5].

In the S part of the state beryls and aquamarines occur in the Castelo area, which is 95 km (59 miles) SW of Vitória, and extends SSE to Cachoeira de Itapemirim and S to the border along Rio Itapoana: beryls and aquamarines also may be found in the municipality Rio Novo at Rodeio, at Pão Gigante, and along Rio Piuma[5].

Rio de Janeiro

As may be expected, the earliest recorded finds of beryls were made in this small coastline state whose settlement dates to the first colonization of Brazil by the Portuguese. Large crystals from pegmatite at Gamboa near Vallongo, Serra da Providencia, were found in 1814; the largest was 6.5 kg (14 lb) and fetched £1 500; another was 18 × 2.5 cm (7 × 1 in) and sold for £600[5, 16]. Within the city itself, Calmbach recorded beryl occurring at Avenida Atlantica, between Rua Otto Simon and Rua

Rudolpho Dantas, and at Morro da Viuva, Meyer, and Praia das Virtudes[5].

Leonardos gave these localities for beryl: Municipio de Itaboraí near Rio de Ouro Station, 45 km (28 miles) ENE of the city; Municipio Rio Bonito in various pegmitites at Duas Barrios; around Capivari, 90 km (56 miles) ENE of the city; Municipo Glicério at Tira-Teima, 5 km (3.1 miles) S of Glicério (small crystals)[22]. Much beryl was mined from Serra de Glicério, and one large crystal weighed hundreds of kg and was transparent gem material in part. In Valão do Barro, between Santa Maria Madalena and São Fidelis in Municipio S. M. Madalena, beryl occurs in crystals 20–30 cm (8–12 in) long. Some beryl occurs in Municipio Cantagalo, also in Vila Penteha district, and in Municipio Valença area. Calmbach mentioned sources at Petropolis, 45 km (28 miles) N of Rio de Janeiro, at Maricá, 40 km (25 miles) E on the coast, in Municipio Macaé (Macahé), 160 km (100 mi) ENE of Rio de Janeiro on the coast, and at Rio Ouro, Municipio São Gonçalo.

1 DRAPER, T. A new source of emeralds in Brazil. *Gems & Gemology* 11:111–13, 24 (1963)

2 DRAPER, T. The geologic environment for emerald in Brazil. *Lapidary Journal* 23:1488–90, 1492–1502 (1970)

3 COTTON, W. L. A trip to the Carnaiba emerald mines of Brazil. *Lapidary Journal* 23:1360–62 (1970)

4 LEINZ, V. and LEONARDOS, O. H. Notas sobre as esmeraldas da Fazenda das Lages, Itaberahy, Goyaz. *Brasil, Servicio de Fomento da Produção Mineral Avulso* 13 (Rio de Janeiro) 14 pp. (1936)

5 CALMBACH, W. F. v. *Handbuch brasilianischer Edelsteine und ihrer Vorkommen*. Rio de Janeiro: N. Medawar. 220 pp. (1938)

6 SCHLOSSMACHER, K. and KLANG, H. Der Maxixeberyll I. *Zentralblatt für Mineralogie* . . . Abt. A., pp. 37–44 (1935)

7 ROEBLING W. and TROMNAU, H. W. Maxixe Beryll II. *Zentralblatt für Mineralogie* . . ., pp. 134–39 (1935)

8 NASSAU, K. and WOOD, D. L. The nature of the new Maxixe-type beryl. *Lapidary Journal* 27:1032–38, passim, 1052–58 (1973)

9 FRÓES ABREU, S. *Recursos Minerais do Brasil. Minerais não Metálicos*. Vol. 1. 2nd ed. Instituto Brasileiro de Geografia e Estatística, Conselho Nacional de Geografia Publ. No. 20 (Rio de Janeiro), 505 pp. (1965)

10 OAKENFULL, J. C. *Brazil in 1912*. London: Robert Atkinson. 498 pp. (1913)

11 KLEIN. F. *Smaragde unter dem Urwald*. Berline: Oszald Arnold. 285 pp. (1941)

12 KUNZ. G. F. [On x-ray coloration of beryl]. *American Journal of Science* 31:45. (1911)

13 ——. Precious stones. Chapter in *The Mineral Industry during 1910*. Vol. 19. New York: McGraw-Hill Book Co. 27 pp. (1911)

14 DREHER, O. Grosser Aquamarinkrystall aus Brasilien. *Centralblatt für Mineralogie . . . etc.*, 1912, no. 11, p. 338. (1912)

15 BECKER, G. Personal communication, 26 August 1980

16 OAKENFULL, J. C. *"Brazil" A Centenary of Independence. 1822–1922.* Freidberg, I. B.: C. A. Wagner, 826 pp. (1972)

17 HAHN, M. Edelsteine und Perlen. In *Schmuck und Edelsteine* by E. Schondorff. Munich: Droemersche Verlagsanstalt. 237 pp. (1955)

18 BALL, S. H. Gem stones. Chapter in *U.S. Bureau of Mines Minerals Yearbook 1942*, pp. 1509–20. (1943)

19 BASTOS, F. M. A 15.4 pound Brazilian aquamarine. *Gems & Gemology* 11:239–41. (1964)

20 FRÓES ABREU, S. *Recursos Minerais do Brasil. Minerals não Metálicos. Vol. 1. 2nd ed.* Instituto Brasileiro de Geografia e Estatística, Conselho Nacional de Geografia Publ. No. 20 (Rio de Janeiro), 505 pp. (1965)

21 SCHUPP, K. Vierunddreissig Kilo Schwere Aquamarin. *Zeitschrift der deutsche Gesellschaft für Edelstein kunde* (Idar-Oberstein) 11:23. (1955)

22 LEONARDOS, O. H. Um Jazida de beryllio, mica, columbita, annerodita e monazite, em Sabinopolis, Minas Gerais. *Mineração e Metalurgia* 1:15–16. (1936)

COLOMBIA

Colombia stands supreme in respect to emerald, for nowhere else are they found in such consistently high quality and quantity. The deposits were exploited by the natives long before the appearance of Europeans in the 16th century and have been worked more or less continuously since then. Nevertheless, the formations in which they occur are so widespread that new deposits have been found in modern times and the probability is great that still others will be discovered in the future. There will be no shortage of emeralds in our lifetime; indeed, the problem may be one of regulating production to insure that no glut on the market drives down the price. However, as with so many other precious stones, Colombian emeralds must be won arduously and at high cost.

Geology of Colombian emerald deposits

Three prongs of the northern end of the Andes form the western portion of Colombia. The mountain cores are igneous and metamorphic rocks, overlain on their flanks by folded and faulted sedimentary rocks of Cretaceous age. The emerald-bearing formations lie along the flanks of the east prong, or the Cordillera Oriental, and occur mainly in the provinces of Boyacá, Cundinimarca, and Santander, or generally N–NE of Bogotá. All deposits are in steep, rugged terrain, solidly covered with lush and largely impenetratable tropical rain forest with dense underbrush. Mine altitudes range from 600 m (2000 ft) to 1200 m (4000 ft) above sea level. The terrain reflects weathering and erosion of a series of strongly folded anticlines and synclines of sedimentary rocks, especially limestones.

Muzo–Coscuez mines. The mines are located about 105 km (65 miles) N of Bogotá. The Muzo mines are in a deep ravine of the SE-flowing Rio Itoco, which joins the N-flowing Rio Minero. The Coscuez mines are about 10 km (6.2 miles) N of the Muzo mines along the margin of the Rio Desaguadero ravine which empties into the ravine of Rio la Caca, the latter flowing W into Rio Minero. The land is national property under control of Banco de la Republica (ECOMINAS).

Chivor mine. Due to similar topography, formations, supply of water, etc., mining at Chivor generally follows the patterns established at Muzo[5,6]. At the time of Johnson's visit in about 1960, the mine was being worked by benching, tunnelling and bulldozing, with major effort concentrated on benching[5]. Only one tunnelling project was underway and that was scheduled to cease in the near future. Bulldozers were used to strip away overburden but were also employed to follow emerald-vein leads. Recovered stones at Chivor, according to Colombian law, must be kept in storage at mine headquarters until a government official from Bogotá comes to inspect, weigh, and seal production lots. These are then shipped under seal to the capital. In Bogotá the seals are examined by government officials and the contents of the parcels verified and their value appraised. The parcels are then re-sealed, export licenses granted, and the stones allowed to leave the country if such is desired. For a recent account of mining, see Keller[7].

Beryl elsewhere in Colombia. Beryl is reported from mica pegmatites in Norte de Santander Province near the Venezuelan border. Aquamarine occurs in calcite/ dolomite veins near Guatequé, Boyaca; the

Figure 11.5 Views taken in the Chivor emerald mine about 1920, showing clearing of overburden (top photos) and development of the 'step' or 'benching' method to systematically excavate the emerald-bearing ground. From L. J. Canova, *Chivor-Somondoco Emerald Mines of Colombia* (New York, 1921)

occurrences seem related to the emerald-bearing veins of Somondoco–Chivor–Almeida[8].

1 HINTZE, J. Die Smaragdlagerstätten Kolumbiens. *Der Aufschluss* (Heidelberg) 30:83–92 (1979)

2 GANSSER, A. Quarzkristalle aus der kolumbischen Anden (Südamerika). *Schweizerische mineralogische und petrographische Mitteilungen* (Zurich) 43:91–103 (1963)

3 LATHAM, E. B. The newly discovered emerald mines of 'Somondoco'. *Columbia School of Mines Quarterly* 32:210–14 (1911)

4 KLEIN, F. *Smaragde unter dem Urwald.* Berlin: Oswald Arnold. 285 pp. (1941)

5 JOHNSON, P. W. The Chivor emerald mine. *Journal of Gemmology* 8:126–52 (1961)

6 RAINIER, P. W. The Chivor–Somondoco emerald mines of Colombia. *Transactions of the American Institute of Min. & Met. Eng.* 96:204–23 (1931)

7 KELLER, P. C. Emeralds of Colombia. *Gems & Gemology* 17:80–92 (1981)

8 WOKITTEL, R. *Recursos minerales de Colombia.* Bogota: Editorial Lumbre. 393 pp. (1960)

INDIA

Mentions of an Indian source of emerald, variously given as 'Cangagem' or 'Canjargum' (probably a corruption of Kangayam, a town in Coimbatore, Madras), most likely refer to aquamarines of greenish colour, which have been found, in modern times at least, at Padyur[1]. It is only since 1943 that true emeralds were found in several deposits in Rajasthan[2].

Aside from emerald occurrences in India, virtually all gem and common beryl is presently mined from granitic pegmatites.

Kashmir

The famous sapphire area of Soomjam (Sumsam) is also noted for fine blue gem-quality aquamarines, the locality lying in the Padar area of Zanskar-Udhampur, 33°25′ N, 76°25′ E[3,4,5,6,7]. The mines are 4 km (2.5 miles) W 30° N of Soomjam, the highest village on the S side of the range dividing Zanskar from Chanab and at an altitude of 4440–4850 m (14 800–14 950 ft). They were discovered in 1881 ot 1882, and the then unrecognized sapphires were sent to F. R. Mallet of the Geological Survey of India for identification. Gem beryls were found not only in the pegmatite bodies but also as loose crystals in detritus below the outcrops.

Tamil Nadu

The most important occurrences of gem beryl are in Coimbatore district, 425 km (265 miles) SW of Madras and were first exploited in the early part of the 19th century. Productive pegmatites were mined near Pattalai (or Padiyur), 11°3.5′ N, 77°30′ E; during 1819–20 they yielded 2196 stones weighing 10 kg (22 lb) valued at £1210. For Indian pegmatites, it was unusual that the crystals occurred in vugs associated with 'interlacing crystals of cleavelandite' and were sea-green to blue in colour. Some experts classed them better in quality than comparable Siberian aquamarines[4,5,7,8].

Emerald in India

The modern history of emerald in India began with the discovery in 1943 of green crystals near Kaliguman, a small village between Amet and the old fortress of Kumalgarh in south Rajasthan. The crystals were identified as emerald by H. Crookshank of the Geological Survey of India[9]. Kaliguman was granted to Sir Bhagchand Soni and mining began in 1944. Shortly thereafter, probably in 1945, the Bubani and Rajgarh deposits were located at points about 32 km (20 miles) apart on the same strike of rocks but farther NE toward Ajmer city. In 1945 the Tekhi deposits N of Kaliguman were found, again the same rock belt. New finds in the belt occurred at Gum Gurha, 36.8 km (23 miles) SSW of Kaliguman during 1950–1951. In 1955 the Kaliguman mine was converted from underground workings to an opencut. By 1955 other mines were known at Kabra, Bagmara, and Malpura[2,3,9,10,11].

All known occurrences lie within a narrow and remarkably straight belt of rocks in which the emerald-bearing schists are included. They strike NE–SW over a distance of 200 km (125 miles)[11].

Emerald crystals are simple hexagonal prisms as well as angular grains and broken crystal fragments, and sometimes occur in aggregates of crystals. Many are brittle and easily crumbled. Sizes range from several mm to about 12.5 cm (5 in) long but those over 2.5 cm (1 in) are scarce. Typically, there are numerous flaws and inclusions such as layers of talc or biotite[9]. The best emeralds came from Rajgarh deposits and fetched better prices than those from Kaliguman because of being larger on the average, better in colour, softer in lustre and more transparent. In the best, the colour is velvety emerald green and compares favourably to that of Muzo emerald[12].

Mining was accomplished mainly by open-cut and benching using hand tools to loosen the rock. Roy reported that the emerald ore was taken to sheds and there crushed to extract the crystals[11]. Brown and Dey stated that the stones were then placed in locked boxes and later emptied into bags that were sealed under strict supervision[7]. Further processing involved removal of rock remnants and cleaning of crystals by boiling in both alkaline and acid solutions and finally coating with thin oil.

Bubani mines. These are on small low hills between Bubani and Muhami villages, 26°31′ N, 74°48′ E. A number of small workings occur around Gudas. The southernmost mine is the most important, the opencut at the time measuring 107 m (250 ft) × 15 m (50 ft) and in places sunk to 12 m (40 ft) in depth; some underground workings were driven also.

Rajgarh mines. These are located about 1.6 km (1 mile) SE of Rajgarh village, 26°17.5′ N, 74°38′ E. The main opencut is on a low ridge of highly folded and contorted biotite schists intruded by a beryl-bearing pegmatite which formed the top of the ridge. Another pegmatite here contains inclusions of emerald-bearing biotite schist. Mining began here in 1947 and the total value of emeralds sold until November 1951 was nearly Rs 250 000[2,7].

Kaliguman mines. Located near Kaliguman village, about 25°20′ N, 73°50′ E, or about 89 km (55 miles) NNE of Udaipur city. They are the oldest mines, having been worked since 1944, at first by underground methods, then later converted to opencut. In 1959, the main pit was 137 m (450 ft) × 4.5–22 m (15–70 ft) and 14 m (45 ft) deep. The country rock is hornblende schist with emerald crystals irregularly distributed within veinlike bodies of soft talcose biotite schists ranging from 0.5–1.5 m (1.5–5 ft) thick and emplaced between hornblende schist and an altered peridotitic rock. Up to the end of 1951 production stood at 2567 lb or about 1165 kg of mine-run material, while sales of stones up to November 1951 totalled

Rs 778 261[7]. Other mines in this district are the Kabra, a small opencut, the Bagmara mine, an opencut of 31 m (100 ft) square and 9 m (30 ft) deep, and the Malpaira mine, an opencut in which crystals occur in actinolite schists[2].

Gum Gurha mines. These are the southermost workings in the emerald belt and are found at 25° N, 73°39′ E. About six pits are on the flanks of a hill composed of altered peridotite, pegmatites, and actinolite, talc and biotite schists. A good quality emerald was produced from the talcose biotite schists.

1 BROWN, J. C. Emeralds in India. *The Gemmologist* 22:133–6, 165–8 (1953)

2 ROY, B. C. *The economic geology and mineral resources of Rajasthan and Ajmer.* Memoirs of the Geological Survey of India, Vol. 86. Calcutta. 356 pp. (1959)

3 LA TOUCHE, T. H. D. The sapphire mines of Kashmir. *Records of the Geological Survey of India.* Vol. 23, pt. 2 (1890)

4 LA TOUCHE, T. H. D. *A Bibliography of Indian Geology and Physical Geography with an Annotated Index of Minerals of Economic Value.* Part II: *An Annotated Index of Minerals of Economic Value.* London: K. Paul, Trench, Trübner & Co. 490 pp. (1918)

5 MIDDLEMISS, C. S. Precious and semi-precious gemstones of Jammu and Kashmir. *Jammu and Kashmir Mineral Survey Reports,* no. 9. (Jammu) 58 pp. (1931)

6 IYER, L. A. N. *A Handbook of Precious Stones.* Calcutta: Baptist Mission Press. 188 pp. (1948)

7 IYER, L. A. N. and THIAGARAJAN, R. Indian precious stones. *Geological Survey of India Bulletin* 18. 105 pp. (1961)

8 KRISHNAN, M. S. *Mineral resources of Madras.* Memoirs of the Geological Society of India, vol. 80 (Calcutta), 299 pp. (1951)

9 CROOKSHANK, H. Emeralds in Mewar. *Geological Survey of India. Indian Minerals,* Vol. 1: pp. 28–30 (1947)

10 GEOLOGICAL SURVEY OF INDIA. Investigations for emeralds in Udaipur. *Indian Minerals.* V. 5 (Calcutta) pp. 148–50 (1951)

11 ROY, B. C. Emerald deposits in Mewar and Ajmer Merwara. *Records of the Geological Survey of India* 86:377–401 (1955)

12 GÜBELIN, E. J. Some additional data on Indian emeralds. *Gems & Gemology* 7:13–22 (1951)

MALAGASY REPUBLIC

The Malagasy Republic (formerly Madagascar) is the fourth largest island in the world. Two major groups of rocks cover the island: ancient Precambrian basement rocks and younger sediments. The basement rocks, which cover most of the area, consist mainly of gneisses and schists overlain over wide areas by crystalline limestones, cipolins in part, and schist-quartzites. Numerous granite intrusions contributed pegmatite mineralization which is commonly complex and affords a large variety of minerals, including those suitable for gems and mineral specimens. Both common and gem beryl occur in many bodies[1].

Despite the relatively small quantities of gem beryl, the quality of beryls tends to be much higher than that from other countries. Especially prized are the pink beryls, of a unique magenta tint that suggests the colour of high quality kunzite. Of equal merit are the blue varieties, some of which were described by Lacroix as 'sky-blue', as from Ampangabe, or of 'a very special dark blue, with a black tint', as from Tongafeno, Fefena, etc. Murdock and other writers extolled the beauty of the blue beryls of Marijao[1].

Cut pink beryls from the Malagasy Republic appear in almost every important public and private collection. The American Museum of Natural History in New York owns several splendid gems of 98.5 and 75.25 carats[2], and a remarkable Chinese carving in pink beryl that measures 15 cm (5 in) tall and is said to be the finest such carving in pink beryl in existence. An astonishingly large and fine, rich-pink, cut, beryl gem from the Malagasy Republic is displayed in the Mineral Hall, British Museum (Natural History) London; it is a flawless, square cushion-brilliant weighing 598.7 carats (see Plate 10). Large beryl gems are also in the US National Museum, Washington, D.C., and include a 133-carat faceted yellow gem and a 44-carat golden-yellow cat's-eye cut from a Sahanivotry crystal.

Lacroix summarizes colour varieties and type sources for beryl as follows (vol. 2, pp. 91–2)[3]. *Colourless:* Ampangabe, Anjanabonoina. *Yellow,* pale to golden: Ampangabe, Sahanivotry, Ankazobe. *Sky-blue or pure blue:* Ankazobe, Ampangabe, Ambotolampy, Masompenoarivo, Ikalamovony, Betsiriry, etc. *Deep blue,* with tint of black: Tongafeno especially, seldom cuttable over 9 carats; similar but not identical from Antaboaka, Fefena, the last providing stones zoned in blue with a touch of green. *Blue green,* ordinary aquamarine colour: Ampangabe, Jaiky, Ifempina, Betsiriry, Ankazobe. *Asparagus green:* Sahanivotry,

Antaboaka, Ifempina. *Green,* with a touch of olive (like kornerupine): W of Laondany where it is common. *Emerald green:* not found; an exterior zone of blue Tongafeno crystals is reminiscent of emerald. *Rose:* Tsilaizina, Ampangabe, Vohidahy, Tsaravovonana, Marahitra, Anjanabonoina, finer than those from San Diego County, California.

1 MURDOCK, T. G. Mineral resources of the Malagasy Republic. *U.S. Bureau of Mines Information Circular* 8196. 147 pp. (1963)
2 KUNZ, G. F. Precious stones. Chapter in *The Mineral Industry during 1910.* Vol. 19. New York: McGraw-Hill Book Co. 27 pp. (1911)
3 LACROIX, A. *Mineralogie de Madagascar,* 3 vols, Paris: Augustine Chalamel, 624, 694, 450 pp. (1922–23)

MEXICO

Baja California

The same batholith that in Southern California contains so many mineralogically interesting granitic pegmatites crosses southward across the border into this state and continues in this direction for many hundreds of kilometres. The paucity of known pegmatite occurrences is due not so much to absence of favourably mineralized bodies as it is to lack of access and exploration. During 1960–1970, a number of complex pegmatites were found and exploited in Baja California Norte, largely by teams of mineral collectors from the United States.

The earliest reference to beryl is a vague one by Flores and Gonzalez in 1912[1], followed by one by Wittich[2], who in 1914 stated that this species had been found in the Sierra de San Pedro Mártir, the highest range of mountains in the peninsular. In the early 1960s a swarm of small pegmatites of vein-like form were found just N of Route 2 at a place called La Jollita, about 40 km (25 mi) E of Tecate and very close to the border of the United States. Small amounts of blue topaz, smoky quartz crystals, apatite, green tourmaline, and golden beryl, the latter in much corroded crystals, were found.

Sinkankas reported other occurrences: gemmy aquamarine and golden beryl in small prismatic crystals from small vugs in a granitic pegmatite near El Mesquite village, about 27 km (17 mi) S of El Condor turnoff from Highway 2 (El Condor is ca. 49 km [30.6 mi] E of Tecate)[3]. The pegmatite occurs between Jasay and El Topo and is mineralogically simple, consisting largely of feldspar with some quartz, schorl, mica, rare purplish apatite, albite, and euhedral prisms of pale greenish yellow to pale golden-yellow beryl, ranging from acicular to some about 7 mm (0.5 in) in diameter and to 77 mm (3 in) long. Some are smooth-faced, others etched and tapered like the crystal depicted in fig. 9–7. Most contain abundant inclusions of extremely small size which render the bases opaque or only translucent but in a sharp transition; these disappear toward the terminations, the latter then being transparent. A similar body yielding the same type of crystals was found in barren hills immediately S of Jacumba, a town in the United States close to the Mexican border. Some beryl also occurs in complex pegmatites, which yielded coloured tourmaline, topaz, and quartz in the Alamo-Rancho Viejo area as described by Sinkankas (p. 18 ff)[3].

Sonora

Crystals in pegmatite dikes on Sierra de Oposura, Municipio de Moctezuma, range up to 10 × 5 cm (4 × 2) in size; the bodies consist largely of feldspar with much schorl, some biotite, scheelite and little beryl[4,5].

San Luis Potosí

Beryl was reported from a ravine branching from Arroyo de Los Arcosin, Guadalcazar district as blue green prisms to 1 cm (0.4 in) in pegmatite[6]. Jones reported small terminated aquamarine crystals not over 1 cm (0.5 in) in thin granitic pegmatite veins in the granite stock known as Cerro de San Cristobal, just S of Rancho Realejo near Guadalcazar; the locality is ca. 95 km (60 mi) NE of the city[7]. Pegmatite veins with beryl are also mentioned by Foshag and Fries[8].

Oaxaca

Granite pegmatites, some beryl-bearing, occur near Santa Ana, Municipio de San Francisco Telixtlahuaca, about 39 km (24.5 mi) from Oaxaca city[9]. The bodies are largely feldspar and quartz with accessory beryl, tourmaline, spodumene, ilmenite, allanite, and several rare species.

1 FLORES. T.. and GONZALEZ. P. 1912. Las erupciones y diques pegmatíticos de la Sierra de San Pedro Mártir. Sociedad Geologica Mexicana, B. C. Acta de la Asemblea General 19 Enero, Mexico D.F.
2 WITTICH. E. 1914. [Occurrence of precious stones in the peninsula of Lower California]. Centralblatt für Mineralogie (Stuttgart) pp. 449–56.
3 SINKANKAS. J. 1976. Gemstones of North America. Vol. 1. New York: Van Nostrand Reinhold Co. 494 pp.
4 SANTILLAN. M. 1933. Berilo y berilio en Mexico. International Geological Congress, 16th Annual Meeting, Washington, D.C., abstracts, pp. 65–6.
5 REYNA. J. G. 1956. Riqueza minera y yacimientos minerales de Mexico. Congreso Geológico Internacional, XX Sesióon, Mexico 1956, 3rd ed. pp. 331–2.
6 WITTICH. E.. and KRATZERT. J. 1922. Cenizas volcanicas de vidrio y de cuarzo en los placeres de Guadalcazar, S.L.P. Memorias y Revistas de la Sociedad Cientifica 'Antonio Alzate' (Mexico) pp. 655–61.
7 JONES. W. 1962. The Guadalcazar-Realejo collecting area. Lapidary Journal 16:283–3.
8 FOSHAG. W. F.. and FRIES. C. 1942. Tin deposits of the Republic of Mexico. U.S. Geological Survey Bulletin 935–C, pp. 107–17.
9 REYNA. J. G. 1960. Las pegmatitas graníticas de Santa Ana, Telixtlahuaca, Oaxaca, México. International Geological Congress, Reports of 21st Session, Norden 1960. Part 17: Proceedings, pp. 63–76.

NAMIBIA

A very large region of granitic pegmatites covers much of the central and extreme southern portions of this country. A few bodies, such as those at Rössing and Spitzkopje, are famous for golden beryl and gem aquamarine. Ball recorded a production of gem beryl from this area of 7240 gm from 1937–39, of which 4550 gm were exported[1].

Beryl in pegmatites had been known since 1893, but early interest attached to cassiterite, and only later, when the gem pegmatites at Rössing were opened in 1910 for quartz, tourmaline and topaz as well as beryl, did interest in such bodies result in explorations for the sake of gemstones alone. In cassiterite-rich bodies, miarolitic cavities are common and from these were obtained superb crystals of beryl, topaz, quartz and other species, which have found their way into collections all over the world.

Kleine Spitzkopje. Both Kleine Spitzkopje (1580 m) and Grosse Spitzkopje (1750 m) rise steeply from the Namib Plain about 110 km (69 miles) NE of Swakopmund.

Many pegmatitic schlieren bodies with cavities occur along the edges of the granite of Kleine Spitzkopje, notably along the SE base of the mountain, and it is this area that is famous throughout the world for its production of splendid crystallized specimens.

Golden beryl colours range from deep golden yellow to pale to yellow green, the latter at times reminiscent of peridot, and also into colours that are nearly pure blue.

Rössing. This classic mineral locality was first brought to the attention of the world when E. Reuning, in 1910, discovered a series of remarkable, complexly mineralized granitic pegmatites about 5 km (3.3 miles) N of Rössing railway station, at a point about 35 km (22 miles) ENE of Swakopmund. The deposits were worked on a small scale prior to World War I and produced gem aquamarine and golden beryl, the latter partly of the heliodor variety, as well as excellent, rich-hued, rose quartz and numbers of splendid mineral specimens[3].

Those crystals that occur in vugs and hence are smaller, but gemmy are fine, sharp, aquamarine and golden beryl varieties. The aquamarines in particular, afford the largest clear areas suitable for faceted gems and range in colour from nearly colourless, very pale blue, to bluish green and yellowish green.

1 BALL. S. H. Gem stones. Chapter in *U.S. Bureau of Mines Minerals Yearbook for 1940*. 13 pp. (1940)
2 GÜRICH, G. Geologisch-mineralogische Mitteilungen aus Südwestafrika. 1. Mineralien aus dem deutschen Schutzgebiete in Südwest Afrika. *Zeitschrift für Kristallographie*. 21:150–1 (1893)
3 KAISER. E. Ein neues Beryll (Aquamarin) Vorkommen in Deutsch Südwestafrika. *Centralblatt für Mineralogie* (Stuttgart) 13:385–90 (1912)

PAKISTAN (WEST)

Granitic pegmatites are abundant in the foothills and flanks of the extreme N portion of the Himalaya Mountains.

Baltistan

Splendid aquamarine crystals and common beryl are found near Daso village, 35°43′ N, 75°31′ E, on the right bank of the Braldu River, several miles above the junction with Shigar River at an altitude of 2500 m (8300 ft). The finest crystals come from vugs with some beryl crystals observed penetrating into open spaces from cavity walls. Crystals are bluish green and range from transparent to cloudy, flawed. Another aquamarine mine exists at Nirjit village. Heron[1] regarded these deposits as promising for future exploitation.

North-West Frontier Province

Beryl occurs in Chitral, ca. 170 km (108 miles) NNE of Rawalpindi, as very beautiful, water clear aquamarine crystals with remarkable dark banding parallel to basal plane, they are believed to be from a granitic pegmatite field along the right bank of Sirink Gold River, 34 km (20 miles) upstream from Mogh. Beryl is also reported from Latkoh and Gabar-O-Bach districts, the last noted for large aquamarine and topaz crystals from pegmatite[1].

In the Swat region, Shams reported inky blue beryl displaying strong biaxiality and with RI of 1.599 ± 0.001 and 1.607[2]. Far better known are the emeralds which were reported in 1962 by Davies who gave the locality as Mingaora[3]. In October, 1973 during Carbonnel's visit, the mine was being worked opencut by about 50 miners and 'the mine is thought to have produced in 13 years about 400 000 carats'.

Mingaora emeralds were examined by Gübelin who remarked that the quality of the finest cut gems is 'good to outstanding' in respect to liveliness, transparency and saturated green colour, which compares them favourably to Muzo stones[5].

1 HERON. A. M. Directory of economic minerals of Pakistan. *Records of the Geological Survey of Pakistan* (Karachi) vol. 7, no. 2. beryl pp. 10–11 (1954)
2 SHAMS. F. A. An inky blue beryl from Swat State. *Punjab University Geology Bulletin* no. 3 (Lahore) p. 31 (1963)
3 DAVIES, R. G. A green beryl (emerald) near Mingaora, Swat State. *University Geology Bulletin* no. 2, pp. 51–2 (1962)
4 CARBONNEL. J. P. A visit to the Mingaora emerald mine, Swat, Pakistan. *Lapidary Journal* 30:1236–8 (1976)
5 GÜBELIN. E. J. Gemmologische Beobachtungen am neuer Smaragd aus Pakistan. In *Edelsteine*, Sonderheft 18 of *Der Augschluss* (Heidelberg) pp. 111–6 (1968)

REPUBLIC OF SOUTH AFRICA

Transvaal

The important schist-type emerald deposits of Leysdorp, or more accurately, the

Gravelotte district in NE Transvaal, were discovered sometime late in 1927, but, as so often happens, the identity of the discoverer is controversial. According to an early account, the crystals, lying loose on the surface, were found by S. A. Van Lingen and correctly identified by W. E. Bleloch[1]. However, Van Eeden *et al.* credit the discovery, locally at least, to a certain Jack Tarr, who was prospecting in the vicinity of what is now known as the Somerset Mine, and 'his discovery led to the flotation of the Beryl Mining Company which commenced operations at the Somerset mine on the Farm Barbara in 1927'[2]. Very shortly thereafter, claims were staked by R. Reeves-Moore and acquired by the Beryl Mining Company, Ltd., which registered a capital of £20000 in 200000 shares at 2 shillings each.

Only a few companies survived the initial boom-and-bust period, among them the Beryl Mining Co., Ltd., and Cobra Emeralds, Ltd. The deposit on Somerset Hill belonging to the Beryl Mining Co. proved to be the most prolific producer for a time and was blessed with rich ore bodies amenable to large-scale mining and recovery treatment.

In 1929, the Somerset mine was supplied with a mechanical treatment plant capable of processing 200 tons of schist per day to reduce costs of hand work by native labour and reduce thefts. The ore was fed to a tube mill and trommel supplied with water from the Selati River for the purpose of softening the rock and aiding removal of most of the biotite mica that adhered to crystals. The concentrates, rich in crystals, were discharged into locked bins to await sorting.

In early years of exploitation the Beryl Mining Co., Ltd. enlarged their opencut to 30.5 m (100 ft) in width and reached a depth of 12 m (40 ft). By 1930, tunnels had been driven at the 24.5 m (80 ft) and 91.5 m (300 ft) levels, still in emerald-bearing schist[3]. At about the same time, Cobra Emeralds worked their mine vigorously but were forced to shut down about 1939 because of a depressed market and decreasing quality in the stones mined[4]. Some work was resumed in 1945, principally at the Somerset mine. In 1946, the total production was 11 533 carats with exports of 6492 carats valued at £3101; in 1947, 7753 carats were produced[5]. A news item in 1956 stated that the Cobra mine was reopened in January of

that year under ownership and management of the African Gem Co. of Johannesburg, and that the mine's highest output was 154 081 carats in 1937.

Recent mining practice

Wollin reported that in 1967 only two mines were operating, the Gravelotte Emerald Mine and the BVB, the latter reputed to have produced some exceptionally large crystals, one of 400 carats found recently was valued at 417 000 Rand or US $584 000[6]. At the Gravelotte mine the emerald-bearing schist forms a low hill that was being mined systematically at the rate of 250 tons per day with the rock taken to an adjacent plant for crushing and recovery of crystals. A total of 560 native labourers and other personnel were employed and required to reside at the mine for security reasons. Of this force, 138 were employed as sorters at the Gravelotte mine and 46 at the BVB. A useful innovation was a white-surfaced conveyor belt upon which the crushing plant output is discharged and from which the sorters pick out crystals and lumps of rock in which emerald crystals remained imbedded. Production commonly achieved 15 ounces of gemstones per day, along with 30 ounces of cabochon-quality rough. The lots were sold abroad, principally in Europe, and none of the rough stayed in South Africa.

Since 1957 Gravelotte Emeralds (Proprietary) Ltd. (known as GEMS), has owned the various emerald-bearing sites, of which the main zones currently being worked are Cobra, Nine Reef, Discovery and Selati. The BVB area, 14 kilometres to the ENE of the Gravelotte Mine is not being mined at the moment, but is expected to be worked again by GEM in the near future.

1 TRANSVAAL EMERALDS. *South African Mining and Engineering Journal. Yearbook*, pp. 585–8 (1928)
2 VAN EEDEN. O. R., PARTRIDGE. F. C., KENT. L. E. and BRANDT. J. W. The mineral deposits of the Murchison Range, east of Leysdorp. *Memoirs of the Geol. Survey of S. Africa*, no. 36 (Pretoria), 163 pp. (1939)
3 THE POSITION OF THE BERYL MINING COMPANY. *South African Min. and Eng. Journal* 41:470–1 (1930)
4 BALL. S. H. Gem stones. Chapter in *U.S. Bureau of Mines Minerals Yearbook for 1940*. 13 pp. (1940)
5 BALL. S. H. and JOSEPHSON. G. W. Gem stones. Chapter in *U.S. Bureau of Mines Minerals Yearbook for 1948*. 12 pp. (1949)
6 WOLLIN. J. C. A rockhound visits Southern Africa. Part 3. *The Lapidary Journal* 22:756–65 (1968)

SRI LANKA

Gem aquamarine pebbles have been found for centuries in the gem gravels, but only a few in situ deposits are known and these offer virtually no gem material. According to Wadia, common beryl is found in large prisms in pegmatite veins, especially those that have been worked for mica[1]. Most are bluish or greenish and may weigh up to 1.8 kg (4 lb). Such crystals have been noted in mica pegmatite at Gannoruwa near Peradeniya, Central Province, as sharp crystals of fine bluish green colour. They are transparent in part and more than 15 cm (6 in) long but so flawed that only small areas could be cut into gems. Beryl occurs also in pegmatite at Kaiawela, Matale district, Central Province. Yellowish crystals come from Talatu-oya near Kandy and from mica pegmatites at Akuressa.

In the gem gravels, some beautiful stones of pale blue colour have been found which weigh as much as 200–300 carats[1]. The firm of Macan Markar, jewellers of Colombo, possess a 271-carat gem which came from a pit near Ratnapura[2]. Another in the American Museum of Natural History, New York, is a cushion-cut gem of 355 carats. Coates concluded that such beryls weathered from pegmatites[3].

1 WADIA, D. N. and FERNANDO, L. J. D. Gems and semi-precious stones of Ceylon. *Ceylon, Records of the Department of Mineralogy, Professional Paper* 2 (Colombo) 44 pp. (1945)
2 GÜBELIN, E. J. *Die Edelsteine der Insel Ceylon.* Luzern: privately published. 152 pp. (1968)
3 COATES, J. S. The geology of Ceylon. *Spolia Zeylanica, Ceylon Journal of Science* (Colombo) Sect. B., vol. 19, pp. 101–87 (1935)

TANZANIA

Lake Manyara Emerald. In 1969, the first emerald crystals from this deposit, then in possession of a Mr. Khanji of the town of Moshi, were seen by H. P. Kristen, a prospector, who ultimately found the deposit on February 17, 1970[1,2,3]. The property is located about 2.4 km ((1.5 miles) W of the shore of Lake Manyara, just S of Moji Moto Hot Springs.

Workings are opencuts exposing biotite mica in which occur the emerald crystals and from which rock they are easily separated. During its early days, the mine produced

231 877 gm of rough from July 1970–April 1972. It was nationalized by the government in February 1973, and the original exploiter, H. P. Kristen, relegated to the position of manager[3].

1 THURM, R. E. The Lake-Manyara-emeralds of Tanzania. *Journal of Gemmology* 13:98–9 (1972)
2 THURM, R. E. Smaragde vom Lake Manyara in Tansania. *Zeitschrift der deutschen gemmologischen Gesellschaft* (Idar-Oberstein) 21:9–12 (1972)
3 GÜBELIN, E. J. The emerald deposit at Lake Manyara. *Lapidary Journal* 28:338–44, 346, 347, 359, 360 (1974)

USSR

As may be expected from the vast extent of this union, deposits containing beryl are plentiful but scattered among widely-separated regions in Asia and Europe. Three major regions, notably the Chita subdivision of southern central Siberia (Transbaikalia), the Ural Mountains, and more recently, the Ukraine, have provided excellent gem material and mineral specimens.

Chita Subdivision (Transbaikalia)

Known anciently by the name of Dauria, it is the opinion of some authorities that beryl gemstones have been mined here since antiquity[1].

This view is reasonable because of the fact that it has been populated for many centuries; in regard to the gemstone deposits, some of which are superficial, as at Adun Chilon, these would have yielded their treasures to anyone caring to take them away. More certain is the exploitation of these deposits in modern times: Koksharov, for example, quoted Kulibin's remarks as follows: 'the famous locality for coloured stones in the Adun-Chilon was, as one must presume, discovered in 1723 by the Nerchinsk inhabitant Gurkov, as published in a ukase of the Berg-Collegium of 22 December 1724 which awarded him a gratuity of 5 roubles for his discovery.' Furthermore, 'the most fruitful production of coloured stones occurred in 1796 when in this year alone more than 5 puds [80 kg or 180 lb] of pure and workable aquamarine were found.' (vol. 1, 164)[2].

Brückmann, the indefatigable chronicler of gemstone news during the 18th century, remarked that he first obtained beryl crystals from this locality in 1780 (p. 83),[3] while Macquart, in 1789, described a number of

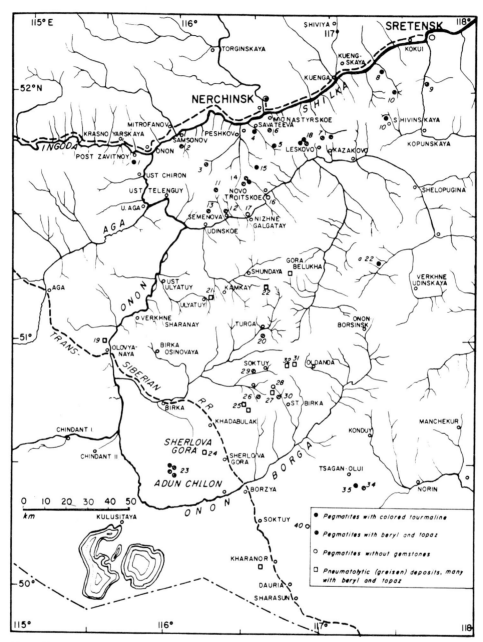

Figure 11.6 The famous gemstone-bearing pegmatite districts in the Chita (Transbaikalia) region of the USSR. Perhaps the finest beryl specimens of all were found in the deposits shown in the lower portion of the map, namely Sherlova Gora (Schorl Mountain) and Adun Chilon. Mines: 1. Zavitnaya, 2. Boetz, 3. Urulga, 4.–6. Urulgaya (Savateeva), 7. Borshchovka, 8. Kurkura, 9.–10. Kurenga, 11. Zolotaya Gora, 12. Tulun, 13. Dushnaya, 14.–15. Kibirevskie Kopi, 16. Kokui (amazon.), 17. Kokui (moonstone), 18. Leskovoi, 19. Olovyannye Rudnik, 20. Turga, 21. Ulyatui, 22. Bukuka, 22a. Alengui, 23. Adun Chilon, 24. Sherlova Gora, 25. Antan, 26.–29. Soktui mines, 30. Birka, 31. Oldonda, 32. Antonova, 34. Altangan, 35. Kadaya, 40. Kliuchevskoi Karer. After A. E. Fersman, *Dragotsennye i Tsvetnye Kamnii, SSSR* 2 (Leningrad, 1925)

typical Adun Chilon crystals,[4] thus showing that by the latter part of the 18th century, aquamarines from this area were already well-distributed throughout Europe. It is not known if these deposits are being worked now, but the absence of specimens on the world market, aside from those redistributed from old collections, suggests that they lie dormant.

The largely mountainous region under consideration is located immediately N of the junction of the borders of the Mongolian Republic, Inner Mongolia, and Siberia, and generally lies E of Lake Baikal. The city of Nerchinsk, on the Shilka River, is at the N end of a series of ranges that are studded with granitic pegmatities and related beryl-bearing deposits. For practical purposes, the area is enclosed between 50°15′–52° N and 115°30′–118°E (see *Figure 11.6*).

Alabashka–Mursinka–Shaytansk Region. This region is enclosed between 57°45′–15′ N, straddling the 61° E meridian, and is centered about 70 km (44 mi) NNE of Sverklovsk. It is by far the best known and justifiably famous of the granitic pegmatite regions in all of the USSR, being particularly noted for superb crystals of topaz, beryl, and coloured tourmaline. A chronology of events, from discovery into modern times, was provided by Fersman who noted that 'the first deposits of precious beryl and topaz in Russia . . . [were] discovered by the miner Michael Tumashev in the Mursinki area in the Central Urals in 1668' (p. 65).[1] The emerald deposits, to be considered later, were found in the early part of the last century. In the region, the northernmost group of mines lies around Alabashka village, as shown in *Figure 11.7*. Other mines are found southward to Mursinka village, thence to the villages of Kornilova, Lipovska, Sarapulka, and Shaytansk, the last known since 1815 for fine pink beryls. The first useful account of the deposits is by Rose, who visited them early in the last century as a member of Humboldt's famous exploring expedition (vol. 1, pp. 439 ff).[5] At Mursinka he found and described various pegmatite minerals, including yellow, transparent beryl crystals, and at Shaytansk, pale rose-red beryls perched on ball-like aggregates of albite. Even at this time, he noted that the mines had been long unworked.

All deposits are in low, wooded, and well-watered terrain, with mining conducted in winter for the reasons mentioned before. Photographs of the mines taken in the early part of the present century show rude cabins for miners next to open-cuts with crude log cribbings and shaft linings, and primitive but effective hoisting arrangements. Mezhetsky visited the mines sometime before 1886 when many were in operation and found three groups of workings around Mursinka, 44 pits around Mursinka itself, 23 around Alabashka, and 8 around Sarapulka along the Ambarka River.[6] However, by 1886, only 9 remained working, mostly for amethyst, while a mine on Krivaya brook was being worked for beryl and topaz. The average annual production was 63.5 kg (140 lb) of amethyst, 6.8 kg (15 lb) of topaz and beryl, and 455 kg (1 000 lb) of quartz. On the other hand, Kalugin visited the area several years later and located 75 mines, of which 65 produced quartz and amethyst, with 54 of the latter number exclusively devoted to these gemstones and 9 mines to topaz, of which 4 also produced gem tourmaline and beryl.[7]

The pegmatite bodies are variable in size and shape but those around Mursinka are typically lenticular and composed largely of yellowish white or greyish white feldspar, with much graphic granite, minor quartz and still less greyish-white mica. Vugs were numerous and ordinarily filled with brown clay in which many of the crystals occurred loosely. According to Koksharov, the beryl crystals from these mines were the finest in all the Urals and were usually wine-yellow to greenish yellow, but also yellowish green, blueish green and less commonly pale blue (vol. 1, pp. 147 ff).[2] A large number were transparent, very regularly formed, and ranged in size from individuals that were only a few millimetres long to some that were several decimetres. A multiple crystal group, found in the Starzevsky mine near Mursinka in November 1828, and placed in the Mining Museum in St. Petersburg, measured 27 cm (10.6 in) long and 31 cm (12.2 in) in circumference. Its value was placed at 42 830 roubles. Another large crystal of the time was in the collection of Grand Duke Nicolai von Leuchtenberg and described as a specimen 'distinguished by transparency, beauty and pleasing yellowish

206

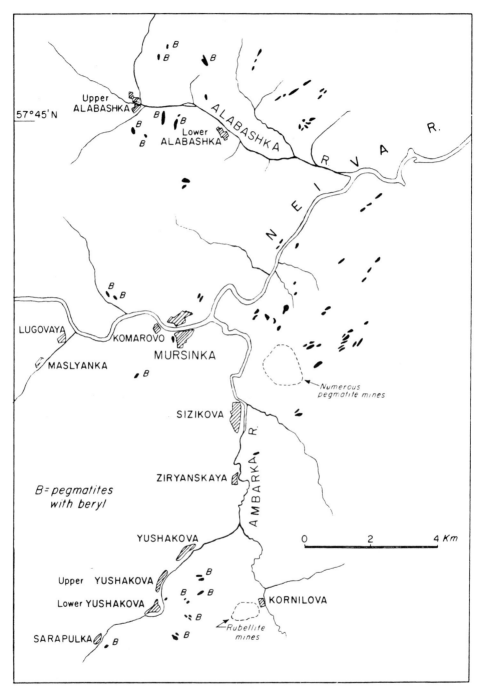

Figure 11.7 Detailed map of the Alabashka-Mursinka beryl-producing pegmatites, east flank of the Ural Mountains, USSR. After A. E. Fersman, *Dragotsennye i Tsvetnye Kamnii, SSSR* 2 (Leningrad, 1925)

green (asparagus green) colour and also by size.' Presumably this crystal was also from around Mursinka and measured 65 cm (25.8 in) in height and 26 cm (10.2 in) in diameter (vol. 6, pp. 94–7).[2]

Ural mountains

In years past, most pegmatite mining, specifically for gemstones and mineral specimens, was administered by local entrepreneurs who hired local workers as needed and operated under authority granted from the Director, Imperial Lapidary Works, Ekaterinburg. The heyday of gem mining came to an abrupt halt with World War I, and mining was thereafter forbidden by the Revolutionary Government in order to shift workers to occupations considered more helpful to the economy. Even today, if the current market is any indication, no gemstones or specimens identifiable as coming from these mines are available and suggest that the deposits are not being worked. However, some recently-mined materials such as nephrite, charoite, etc., have come from the USSR and offer some hope that these mines, as well as those in Transbaikalia, will be reopened and work resumed.

Emerald deposits of the Urals. Uralian emeralds were probably discovered in the early part of the last century, but it has been suggested by various writers that these deposits may have been the source of the Scythian emeralds mentioned by Pliny in his *Natural History*, and hence known long before. The Scythians inhabited some vaguely-defined region N of the Black Sea and it is conceivable that they were in communication with tribes living in the Urals. Greek and Roman writers spoke of fabulous precious stones from the mysterious Rhipaei Montes, which mountains, according to the *Oxford Classical Dictionary*, lie between 57°30′ and 63°21′ N but are not further identified. However romantic these speculations may be, there is no firm evidence that emeralds were found earlier than the modern era. What is certain is that the first *in situ* crystals were found in 1830 or 1831 near the small brook called the Takovaya in an area lying about 45 km (28 mi) NE of Sverdlovsk.

Mining began in 1831; the first few years' work produced outstanding crystals, one of

which was presented to the Tsarina, who had it cut into a 101.25 carat pear-shaped gem valued at 6075 roubles in 1832. Upon invitation of Count L. Perovsky, Minister of Appanages in St. Petersburg, Grevingk conducted the first systematic investigation of these deposits, and in 1853, he published the first geologic map of the mine district[8]. By this time, a series of pits had been sunk upon the N–S outcrop of the emerald-bearing schist, and the mines had been named as follows: (from N to S) the Marinsky and nearby Krestovik; the Troitsky or Starsky; and Lubinskaya or Takovskaya (the original find); the Stretensky; and a branching belt of similar schists farther to the S contained the Ostrovsky. Krasnovolotsky and Chitny mines.

Apparently some emerald crystals from the outcrops found their way into nearby gravel beds, for it was reported in 1842 that a rounded crystal of 3/4 solotnik (approx. 5 gm) was found in the Pokrovsk-Danilovsk alluvial gold mines on Schemeika brook, which lies N of the emerald deposits not far from the Marinsky mines (vol. 1. p. 180)[2]. This stone was completely clear and of beautiful colour. Small emerald crystals were subsequently found in stream gravels elsewhere in the district.

Opencut mining. carried on until about mid-19th century, was abandoned in some of the deposits in favour of shafts and tunnels with mechanization of ore-crushing and sorting. Steady production was maintained toward the latter part of the century when costs, sporadic finds, and other factors, forced closure of most of the mines (pp. 128 ff)[1]. Considerable work was done in 1898, but little emerald was recovered[9]. In 1900, the mines were leased to 'The New Emeralds Company,' at which time they were examined by Zemyatshensky, who furnished some mineralogical notes on the deposits[10]. After World War I, the mines were taken over by the Soviet Government, who formed a 'Precious Stones Trust' in 1923 to administer these and other gemstone deposits[11].

1 FERSMAN, A. E. Dragotsennye i Tsvetnye Kamni SSSR. *Izdavaemye Kommissiy po Izucheniu Estestvennykh Proizvoditelnikh sil SSSR, Akademiya Nauk, Leningrad, Monografiya* 3. Vol. 2: Mestorozhdeniya. 386 pp. (1925)
2 KOKSHAROV. N. *Materialien zur Mineralogie Russlands.* 11 vols., atlas. St. Petersburg: Carl Kray. (1853–1891)

3 BRÜCKMANN, U. F. B. *Gesammlete und eigene Beyträge zu seiner Abhandlung von Edelstein*. Zwote Fortsetzung. Braunschweig: Fürstl. Waisenhaus Buchhandlung. 250 pp., beryl p. 83. (1783)

4 MACQUART, L. C. H. *Essai ou Recueil de Mémoires sur plusiers Points de Miñealogie*. Paris: Chez Cuchet. 580 pp. (1789)

5 ROSE, G. *Mineralogisch-geognostische Reise nach dem Ural, dem Altai und dem Kaspischen Meere*. 2 vols. Berlin: Sanderschen Buchhand. 641, 606 pp. (1837)

6 MEZHETSKY. Ueber die uralischen Gruben 'farbiger Steine'. *Zeits. für Krist* . . . 11:393. (1886)

7 KALUGIN, P. Die Edelsteingruben von Mursinka und Alabaschka. *Zeits. für Krist* . . . 15:550. *(1889)*

8 GREVINCK, D. Die Smaragd-Gruben des Ural und ihre Umgebung. *Verhandl. der Russ.-kaiserl. min. Gessellschaft zu St. Petersburg* 1854:206–33. (1854)

9 KUNZ, G. F. Precious stones. Chapter in *Mineral Resources of the United States for 1898. Part IV*. 20th Annual Report. Director of the U.S. Geological Survey. (Washington, D.C.) pp. 557–600. (1899)

10 ZEMYATCHENSKY, P. A. Izumrud i berill Uralskikh izumrudnykh kopei. *Trudy Imperatorskogo telei, Sankt-Petersburgskago Obshchestra Estestuoispyta* (geol. min. sect.), vol. 29, no. 5, pp. 1–21. (1900)

11 KUNZ, G. F. Precious stones. Chapter in *The Mineral Industry During 1923*. vol. 32. New York: McGraw-Hill Book Co. p. 578. (1924)

UNITED ARAB REPUBLIC (Egypt)

Egypt's emerald deposits supplied this treasured gemstone to the rest of the civilized world for centuries, but while the exact date of the discovery of the deposits remains unknown, tools found in some of the older workings were dated to the reign of Sesortis II in the 12th Dynasty or about 1925 BC[1,2]. Schneider believes that the earliest mining began by at least 1500 BC[3]. It is known that mining was continued by the Greeks during the time of Alexander the Great (356–323 BC) and by the Romans, as shown in the numerous extracts from their writings as cited by Ball[1,2,4] and Schneider[3]. After the Romans, further exploitation was carried on by Arabs.

In succeeding centuries, emerald mining was also undertaken by the Turks, but all mining ceased by about 1740, at which time the mines lapsed so completely into obscurity that their very existence came to be doubted, with some authorities even venturing opinions that the emeralds of antiquity actually had come fromr Siberia or Far Eastern sources no longer identifiable. The controversy was laid to rest, however, with their relocation by the Nantes goldsmith-adventurer Frédéric Cailliaud (1787–1869)

who undertook two trips to the site[5]. Cailliaud's first journey in 1816 was exploratory in nature, but the second, in the following year, was a serious attempt to mine emeralds, and Cailliaud was placed in charge of a large expedition financed by the viceroy. While mining proved uneconomical, much of value was learned about the geography of the region and the nature of the deposits. A good summary of Cailliaud's work appeared in Schneider[3].

After many commercially unsuccessful attempts over the ensuing century to mine the deposits, in 1927 a group of Parisian jewellers decided to reopen the mines despite discouraging advice given by Max Ismalun[6]. Nevertheless, an expedition was dispatched under French geologist Arsandeaux during the winter months of 1927–28, but as predicted, without financial success. Ismalun reviewed the history of the mines, especially in modern times, and concluded that the deposits 'were not susceptible to remunerative exploitation for gem emeralds'. He also candidly stated that Egyptian emeralds are generally 'mediocre' in quality, a conclusion that is confirmed by products of recent mining and by specimens still available for examination in museum collections. An excellent historical summary of emerald mining and descriptions of the deposits and the emeralds themselves is contained in Hume[7].

The deposits are centred on Gebel [mountain] Sikait, approximately 24°40′ N, 34°48′ E, or 285 km (180 miles) slightly SE of Idfu, a city on the Nile River.

1 BALL. S. H. Egyptian gem stones of the pre-Ptolomaic days. *Jewelers' Circular* (New York) Feb. 23, pp. 147–57, *passim.* (1928)

2 BALL. S. H. *A Roman Book on Precious Stones*. Los Angeles: Gemological Institute of America. 338 pp. (1950)

3 SCHNEIDER. O. Der ägyptische Smaragd. *Zeitschrift für Ethnologie*, (Berlin) 24:41–100; mineralogy/petrography by Arzuni, pp. 91–100 (1892)

4 BALL. S. H. Historical notes on gem mining. *Economic Geology* (Lancaster, Pa.) 26:681–738 (1931)

5 CAILLIAUD. F. *Voyage à l'Oasis de Thèbes . . . Pendant les Années 1815–1816, 1817–1818*. Paris: Imprimerie Royale. pp. 60–63, 81 (1821)

6 ISMALUN. M. Émeraudes et béryls. *Bulletin de la Société Royale Géographique de Égypte* (Cairo) 21:51–60 (1943)

7 HUME. W. F. *Geology of Egypt*. Vol. 2, part 1: *The Metamorphic Rocks*. Cairo: Government Press. 300m 124 pp. (1934)

UNITED STATES OF AMERICA

It is not known when the first beryl was found, but the place of discovery probably was in New England. By 1825, Samuel Robinson had published his *Catalogue of American Minerals with Their Localities*[1], in which he included 21 beryl localities in New England, 10 in the Middle Atlantic states, and one in Maryland. In the following years, beryl was also discovered in other pegmatite deposits of Maryland, Virginia, and additional southeastern states. Localities in the Rocky Mountains and California were found much later, indeed many of them only in this century.

Up until World War II, beryl was saved at pegmatite mines only if it afforded attractive mineral or gem specimens; by far the largest quantity was sent over the dumps as economically useless. A useful summary of pegmatite districts is provided by Landes for all of the country[2], while the most important papers on regional groups of pegmatites are those of Cameron *et al.*[3], Jahns *et al.*[4], and Page *et al.*[5] Reserves of beryl in New England are recorded in Barton and Goldsmith, while occurrences of gem beryls are described by Sinkankas, whose work includes an extensive bibliography on North American gemstones in its second volume.

1 ROBINSON. S. *A Catalogue of American Minerals with their Localities*. Boston: Cummings, Hilliard, & Co. 316 pp. (1825)

2 LANDES. K. K. Age and distribution of pegmatites, *American Mineralogist* 20:81–105, 153–175 (1935)

3 CAMERON. E. N. *et al.* Pegmatite investigations 1942–45 New England. *U.S. Geological Survey Professional Paper 255*, 352 pp. (1954)

4 JAHNS. R. H. *et al.* Mica deposits of the Southeastern Piedmont. *U.S. Survey Prof. Paper 248 A-G* (1952–3)

5 PAGE. L. R. *et al.* Pegmatite investigations 1942–1945 Black Hills, South Dakota. *U.S. Geol. Survey Prof. Paper 247.* 228 pp. (1953)

6 BARTON. W. R. and GOLDSMITH. C. E. New England beryllium investigations. *U.S. Bureau of Mines Report of Investigations 7070.* 177 pp. (1968)

7 SINKANKAS. J. *Gemstones of North America.* 2 vols. New York: Van Nostrand Reinhold Co. 675, 494 pp. (1976)

ZAMBIA

Miku Emerald Deposit. This deposit is SSW of Kitwe, 13°04′01″ E and named after the nearby Miku River, a tributary of the Kufubu, the latter a tributary of the Kafue River. It was discovered in 1931 by G. J. Baker but no work was done until some time after 1962[1,2]. The deposit was examined by Hickman and by 1973 some emeralds had been produced. Most are small but others reach 20 cm (8 in) long; in all crystals, clear areas are not large so that cut gems of satisfactory jewellery grade seldom exceed one-half carat.

In about 1978, according to Kanis[4], 'vast' quantities of emeralds were being produced from the nearby Kafubu field which lies just to the SW of Miku. Not only are the emerald crystals abundant, they have been found to as much as 130 carats (Kamakanga) and quite clear. Emeralds also are reported from alluvial occurrences. The large production of substantial high-quality stones has made 'Zambia the world's largest producer of fine quality emeralds during the last few years' and 'therefore, the emerald potential of this large area appears to be enormous'[4].

1 BANK. H. Ein neues Smaragdvorkommen in Zambia (Miku-Deposit). *Zeitschrift der deutschen gemmologischen Gesellschaft* (Idar-Oberstein) 2, no. 2, p. 60 (1973)

2 BANK. H. The emerald occurrence of Miku, Zambia. *Journal of Gemmology* 14:8–15 (1974)

3 HICKMAN. A. C. J. The Miku emerald deposit. *Republic of Zambia Geological Survey Department Economic Report 27* (1972)

4 KANIS. J. Gemstone news from Southern Africa. *Zeits. der deutsch. gemmol. Ges.* 29, no. 1/2, pp. 55–7 (1980)

ZIMBABWE

Beryl-bearing pegmatites occur in a number of areas and have been mined for ore. For example, in the twelve-year period ended 1962, nearly 10 000 tonnes were produced[1]. Much of the beryl was recovered from dumps of mines previously worked for cassiterite, tantalite, and mica. Recently, however, emerald deposits of considerable importance have been found.

Mayfield farm emerald. Anderson described a new occurrence on this farm in 1976[2]. The claims are located in the NW corner of the tract, about 12 km (7.5 miles) NE of Fort Victoria and were first staked in 1970 but are now owned and operated by Callock (Pvt.) Ltd. The crystals occur in a 'glassy quartz reef that is comformable with the country rocks [schists]' and exposed in an opencut and several trenches[11].

Victoria field emerald. Among other prospects this area includes the well-known deposits of the Novello prospect and the abandoned Twin Star mine, both located about 17 km (10.6 miles) NW of Fort Victoria[3]. Emeralds and chrysoberyls were discovered here in 1960 by Mrs. C. Girdlestone, with the deposit becoming primarily famous for twinned chrysoberyl crystals of very dark colour, providing excellent mineral specimens[4].

Belingwe-Sandawana field. Of greatest interest is the most important emerald deposit of Zimbabwe, located near Sandawana or about 120 km (75 miles) SW of Fort Victoria. Gem quality crystals of small size but beautiful intense green were found here in 1956 by prospectors L. J. Contat and C. J. Oosthuizen[4,5]. When the importance of the find became obvious, Sandawana Emeralds, S.A., a Geneva corporation, was formed to exploit the deposit and market the stones[5]. Samples sent to the United States for evaluation comprised an initial shipment of 1.27 ounces. By 1959, ownership of the property, now called the Zeus claims, passed to Rio Tinto (Rhodesia) Ltd., who formed Sandawana Mines (Pvt.) Ltd. to take over mining and distribution of the stones[4].

1 BRANSCOMBE. K. C. Beryl in Southern Rhodesia. *Chamber of Mines Journal* (Salisbury) 4, no. 7, pp. 32–7 (1962)

2 ANDERSON. A. A note on the occurrence of emerald at Mayfield Farm, Fort Victoria, Rhodesia. *Journal of Gemmology* 15:80–2 (1976)

3 METSON. N. A. and TAYLOR. A. M. Observations on some Rhodesian emerald occurrences. *Journal of Gemmology* 15:422–34 (1977)

4 MARTIN. H. J. Some observations on Southern Rhodesian emeralds and chrysoberyl. *Chamber of Mines Journal* 4, no. 10, pp. 34–8 (1962)

5 MAYERS. D. E. The Sandawana emerald discovery. *The Gemmologist* 27, no. 320, pp. 39–40 (1958)

Appendix: Beryl names and terms

To save space, some related terms are placed together. Quotation marks indicate false or misleading terms.

Abruki – 'Shade of smoke', in emerald, India[11] (vol. 2, p. 901)

Acquamarine – Aquamarine, Ital.; **'a. crisolide'** – peridot; **'a. del orientale'** – sapphire; **'a. de Siam'** – blue zircon; **a. Siberiana** – greenish-blue aquamarine from the Urals[12].

Aeroid (Czech.), **Aeroide** (Span.), **Aeroides** (Engl., Ger., Ital., Port.) – Sky-blue aquamarine, from Pliny[4,13].

'African Emerald', 'Afrikasmaragd', or **'Afrikanischer Smaragd'** (Ger.) – Green fluorite.

Agmarine – Aquamarine, O.Fr[14].

Aguamarina – Aquamarine, Span.; **'a. de Siam'** – zircon; **'a. orientale'** – greenish-blue topaz[13,15].

Agua-marinha – Aquamarine, Port.; **'a. de Sião'** – zircon[13].

Aigue Marine – Aquamarine, Fr.; **'a. chrysolithe'** – peridot; **'a. de Siam'** – zircon; **'a. orientale'** – sapphire[13].

Aku Vamarin or **Ekmarin** – Aquamarine, Turk[15a].

Amarantsteen – Seldom used Dutch term for emerald[5].

Amaraud – Emerald, O.Fr[14].

American Emerald – Colombian emerald; briefly used in Europe ca. 1770[1].

'Amethyst Basaltine' (Engl.), **'Amethiste B.'** (Fr.), **'Amethyst Basaltin'** (Ger.) – Pale violet var. beryl, probably applied originally to apatite crystals mistaken for beryl[16,18].

Apanica – Emerald, Sanskr[5].

Aquamarijn – Aquamarine, Dutch[13].

Aquamarin – Aquamarine, Ger.; **'a. chrysolith'** – peridot; **'a. achter'** – topaz[18] (citing Mohs); **'Aquamarin'** – apatite[18] (citing Brunnich); also rarely used to indicate pale blue topaz.

'Aquamarine Emerald' – Rarely used trade term for triplet of genuine emerald and aquamarine; **'a. topaz'** – greenish topaz[16].

'Aquamarinfluss' (Ger.) – Apatite, fluorite[19]; **'Aquamarinschörl'** – gem beryl[19].

Aque Marine – var. sp. Fr[14].

Arabijj – Emerald from Arabia of very light colour[5] (p. 43).

Asmagarba, Asmagarbhajam, Asmagarbham, Amajoni – Emerald, Sanskr[11]. (vol. 2, p. 1021) and in Keferstein[5].

Asmer. Smer – Name of clear green stone of Egypt, suggested as root of Greek word for emerald, *smaragdos*.

'Augites' – Mentioned by Pliny, sometimes thought to mean a variety of beryl.

Bahani – Natural flaw in emerald, cleverly hidden by gem cutters and setters, India[11] (vol. 2, p. 901).

Bahia Emerald, B. Smaragd (Ger.) – Genuine emerald from State of Bahia, Brazil.

Bajhur – 'A stone of green colour mixed with black . . . sometimes mistaken for the Zuburzud', with the latter mistaken for the emerald, Egypt[11] (vol. 2, pp. 952–3).

Ballur, Billaur, Bulur – Arabic and Persian names for beryl, but also for rock crystal[5,8]; **Belur, Belura** – Hebrew, Pahlevi, Syriac[8].

Bapabolam, Baprabalam – Emerald, Sanskr[11] (vol. 2, p. 1021).

Baraket, Baraketh, Barekat, Bareketh, Barkat, Barket – Possible beryl in Bible, Hebr[5,6,20].

Barbara Beryl – Beryl from Barbara mine, South Africa.

Barille – Beryl, Mid. High Ger[21].

Barkta, Barkan – Emerald, Chaldaic[5].

Barragtu, Barraktu – Emerald, Egypt. Assyr.[6,66]; **Berakta** – Chald[5].

'Basaltes Spatosus' – Possible emerald, mentioned by A. F. Cronstedt in his *Mineralogie*, 2nd ed. (Stockholm, 1758).

'Basaltin Ametystovy' (Czech.), **'Basaltina'** (Span.), **'B. Ametista'** (Ital., Port.), **'Basaltine Amethyste'** (Fr.) – Pale violet beryl[13].

'Bastard Emerald' – Quartz coloured to resemble emerald[1]; also any green stone resembling emerald; rarely peridot as **'Bastard-Smaragd'** (Ger.)[22].

Bazzite – Scandian analog of beryl with Sc substituting for Be.

Berala – Beryl, early Ger.[8]; **Berall** – beryl, early Ger[14].

Berel – Beryl, Ethiopic[5].

Bericle – Beryl, O. Fr.[22]; possibly derived from *besicles*, O. Fr. 'eyeglasses'.

'Berigem' – Peridot-coloured synthetic spinel[23].

'Beril Azul – Kyanite[15]; **'b. de oro'** (Span.) – golden beryl; **'b. de Saxe'** (Fr.) – apatite of Saxony, also called 'agustit' or 'agoustite'[24]; **'b. feuillete'** (Fr.) – kyanite[18] (citing B. G. Sage).

Berilio – Beryl, Port.[13]; **b. amarelo** – golden beryl; **b. olho de gato** – cat's-eye beryl; **b. rosa** – rose beryl or morganite[13].

Berill, Beriillis, Berial, Beril, Berille, Berillus, Berolus, Berre, Berulus, Beryall, Birillus, Birrall, Byral, Byrrall, Byralle, Byrillus, Bureall – Various spellings used in Europe.

Berillo – Berul, Ital.[42]; **b. aureo** – golden beryl; **b. azzurro** – aquamarine; **b. giallo** – yellow beryl; **b. occhio di gatto** – cat's-eye beryl; **b. rosa** – rose beryl or morganite[12,13].

Berillos (Gr.), **Berillus** (L.), **Beryllos** (Ger.), **Beryllus** (L.) – Beryl.

Berillus Misnicus – Beryl[25].

Berilo – Berul, Span.; **b. amarillo** – golden beryl; **b. ojo de gato** – cat's-eye beryl; **b. rosado** – rose beryl or morganite[13].

'Berilo' – Falsely applied to apatite; **'b. alterado'** – pseudo-emerald or pseudosmaragadite[15].

Beruj – Beryl, India, of a colour much lighter than emerald[11] (vol. 2, p. 901).

Berula, Berulo – Beryl, Syriac[5]; **Berulin** – Arab[66].

'Beryl' – Misapplied, according to King[9] (p. 134), 'to every variety of the Sard in which yellow predominated'. 'A term that designates amongst lapidaries and virtuosi a very rich deep brown diaphanous carnelian; it is frequently engraved into intaglios'[26] (vol. 3, p. 1037).

Béryl de Barbara (Fr.) – Beryl from Barbara mine, South Africa; **Béryl jaune** – yellow beryl; **Béryl rose** – rose beryl or morganite. **Beryl Růž̌ovy** (Czech.) – rose beryl[13]. **Béryl pierreux** – common beryl, Fr.

'Beryl Schorlacé', 'B. Schorliforme' – In part true beryl, according to T. Bergman and A. G. Werner, but usually misnomer for topaz, variety pycnite[18] (pp. 175, 192).

Berylite – Variety of beryl[27]; **'Berylite'** – trade name for synthetic rose spinel[28].

'Beryll' – Cornelian or apatite[19]; **Beryll, Unächtiger'** – rock crystal, fluorite[19]; **Beryllcarneol'** – cornelian[19]; **'Beryllfluss'** – fluorite[19]; **'Beryllkristall'** – rock crystal[19]; **'Beryllschorl'** – schorlartiger Berul[19].

Beryllion – Beryl, Coptic[5].

Beryllium – Beryl, rare[19,20]; **Beryllium diadochus** – aquamarine; **b. omphax, b. scorillodes** – aquamarine[19].

Berylloid – In crystallography, 'the dihexagonal pyramid is often called a berylloid because a common form with the species beryl' (Dana-Ford, *Textbook of Mineralogy*, 4th ed. [New York: John Wiley, 1932] p. 114).

'Beryllus Chitim' – Chrysolite[19]; **b. hexagonus** – rare name for beryl generally (J. D. Dana, *System of Mineralogy* [New Haven, 1837], p. 324); **b. oleaginus** – oil-coloured beryl of Pliny.

Besady – Beryl, Persian[5].

Bilaur (Arab.), **Birla, Birula** (Chaldaic), **Biurey** (Armenian) – Beryl[5].

Billurin – Beryl, Aramaic[66].

Bixbite – Raspberry-red beryl, Utah, named by A. Eppler[29] but rarely used.

'Bloagrün Topaz' – Beryl, Swedish[18] (citing A. F. Cronstedt).

'Bohemian Emerald' – Fluorite.

Borko – Emerald, Syriac[5,6].

Brahmin Emerald – Emerald the colour of sirish flower (*Albizzia procera*), India[30].

'Brasilianischer Aquamarin' (Ger.) – Pale blue Brazilian topaz; **'Brasilsmaragd'** – green tourmaline, sometimes a misleading name for Brazilian beryl[23]; **'Brazil Emerald', 'Brazilian E.'** – green tourmaline.

'Brighton Emerald' – Green glass beach pebble, England.

Brille – Beryl, Mid. High Ger[21].

Brulo – Beryl, Syriac[5].

Budharatnam – Emerald, Sanskr[11]. (vol. 2, p. 1021).

Burallu – Beryl, Assyrian[66].

Büregh (Armenian), **Burl, Burla** (Chaldaic); **Burlo** (Syriac) – Beryl[5,8].

Byvrili, Byvrilioni – Beryl, Georgian[31].

'Carneolberyll' – Cornelian[19].

Cäsiumberyll (Ger.), **Caesium Beryl** – Beryl containing Cs, usually colourless or pink.

Canary Beryl – Bright, pale yellow beryl.

Canutillos – Colombian emerald miner's term for very thin and small prismatic crystals of high quality emerald.

'Cape Emerald', 'Capscher Smaragd' (Ger.) – Prehnite from Cape of Good Hope, South Africa[19].

Catel – A beryl of 'obscure chrystal Colour'[32].

Ccomer Rumi – Emerald, meaning literally a 'green stone', Quichua of Peru[33].

Cerinus – Beryl, 'similar in colour to wax'[34]; perhaps same as *cervinus* of C. Leonardus[32], i.e., a beryl of 'tawny colour'.

'Chatham Emerald', 'Chatham Cultured E.', 'Chatham Created E.', 'Chatham Zuchtsmaragd' (Ger.) – Synthetic emerald made by C. F. Chatham, San Francisco[23].

Chir – Streaks in emerald, India[11] (vol. 2, p. 901).

Chispas – Literally 'sparks' in Span., used by Colombian emerald miners to designate gemmy bits of emerald too small to cut.

Choaspites – A variation of *chrysoberyllus* or golden beryl; from Choaspes River in Persia[34].

Chrysoberyllus – Golden beryl[34] from Pliny's *Natural History*; adopted by A. G. Werner for present chrysoberyl; rarely used as misnomer for greenish-yellow beryl from U.S.A.[23]

'Chrysolite der Alten' (Ger.) – Topaz or emerald[19].

'Chrysolite du Brésil' – Beryl from Brazil[18] (citing Romé de L'Isle).

Chrysolith, Blaulichgrüner (Ger.) – Beryl[18].

Chrysolithus – Golden beryl[23].

Chrysopilon – Pale golden beryl[32].

Chrysoprasius – Used by Pliny, possibly for beryl; Ball[4] suggests it is chrysoprase quartz; the colour is like 'gold and the juice of a leek'[34] (citing Agricola).

Colam – A kind of emerald used by Arabians to decorate their edifices[10].

'Congo Emerald', 'Copper E.' – Dioptase.

Crisoberillus – Variety of beryl; **Crisopassus** – beryl of golden colour mixed with purple [*sic*]; **Crisopilon** – variety of beryl[32].

'Cristallinus' – Misleading name for beryl, 'because it is colourless'[34].

'Cultured Emerald' – 'False name for synthetic emerald'[23] (p. 49).

Ču-mu-la – Emerald, 14th-century China[6].

Dabbhani – Vivid green emeralds, like colour of *Cantharides* insects, Arab[5].

Dánbhá – Surface marks on emerald, 'somewhat like a spider's web', India[11] (vol. 2, p. 901).

Davidsonit (Czech., Ger.), **Davidsonita** (Span.), **Davidsonite** (Engl.) – Greenish-yellow beryl from vicinity of Aberdeen, Scotland, named after Dr. Davidson, discoverer, by T. Thomson (*Outlines of Mineralogy, Geology and Mineral Analysis*, vol. 1, 1836, p. 247); see also Oelschagel[13] and Bristow[35] (p. 105).

Dhání – Emeralds tinged with yellow, India[11] (vol. 2, p. 901).

Diacodas, Diacodus, Diadochis, Diadochus – 'Is similar to, if not actually the same as, *beryllus* since the writers who describe this stone do not say in what way it differs from the latter'[34] (p. 127); 'like beryl in colour'[32] (p. 95).

Dsobab – Equivalent to *dabbhani* (which see).

Edelberyll (Ger.) – Superfluous name for precious beryl[23].

Ekmarin – Aquamarine, Turk[15a].

Eliodoro – Heliodor, golden beryl, Ital[12].

Ellipomacrostyla – Beryl crystal name[36] (citing Dr. Hiller).

'Emerada' – Trade name, yellow-green synthetic spinel[28]; **'Emeralda'** – same[23].

Emeral – Emerald, J. G. Wallerius in his *Mineralogia, eller Mineralriket irdelt och Beskrifvet* (Stockholm, 1747).

Emerald, Émeraude – Commonly used in 18th and early 19th centuries as species name for beryl, forcing use of adjectives to distinguish emerald from other varieties.

Emerald, Emeraude, Emraud, Emerauld, Emeroyde, Emmorant, Emerant, Emerode, Emrade, Esmeralde, Esmeraldus, Esmeraude, Esmeraulde, Esmeragd, Esmeragde, Emeraud, Hemerauld, and others – Variants used in Europe and England[14,22].

'Emerald Copper' – Dioptase[18] (citing R. Jameson).

'E. Malachite' – Dioptase[18].

Emerald Matrix – Compact rock of albite, black tourmaline, mica, and emerald crystals, capable of being cut into cabochons.

'Emerald Matrix' – Also known as 'mother-of-emerald', reflecting belief of the ancients that certain greenish stones, if allowed to 'ripen', would turn eventually into emeralds, or the latter would be nourished by such matrix and grow from same; applied mostly to green varieties of jasper, prase, fluorite, etc.

'Emerald Nickel' – Zaratite[18] (citing B. Silliman).

'Emerald Schörl, Shirl, Shorl' – 'Mother-of-emerald' according to Hill[37], (p. 140–1), but his description clearly fits true Egyptian emerald.

'Emerald Spodumene' – Hiddenite.

'Emeraldin' (Ger.), **'Emeraldine'** (Engl.) – Green-dyed chalcedony[38]; also trade name for pale green synthetic spinel[23].

'Emeraldit' (Ger.), **'Emeraldite'** (Engl.) – Green tourmaline[23].

'Emeralite' – Pale green tourmaline, Ware mine, San Diego Co., Calif., sometimes spelled 'emeraldite'[28].

'Emerandine' – Dioptase[16].

Émeraude – Emerald, modern French; **'Emeraude batarde'** (Fr.) – peridot; **'é. cuivre'** – dioptase; **'é. d'Afrique'** – green fluorite, rarely green tourmaline; **'e. de lithion'** – hiddenite; **'é. de nickel'** – zaratite; **'é. de nuit'** – peridot; **'é. d'Oural'** – demantoid garnet; **'é. de Sibérie'** – dioptase[18]; **'é. du Brésil'** – green tourmaline; **'é. du cap'** – prehnite; **'é. de Perou'** – emerald from Colombia; **'é. électrique'** – green glass; **'é. Espagnole'** – green glass; **'é. ferrer'** – green glass[23]; **'é. miellée'** – very pale honey-yellow beryl[39]; **'é. morillon'** – green fluorite[40]; **'é. orientale'** – green sapphire; **'é. soudée** – doublet gem made of two pieces cemented together with green central layer[23]; **'é. tecla'** – emerald imitation.

Émeraude de Bahia – Genuine emerald, State of Bahia, Brazil.

Émeraude de Colombie – Emerald from Colombia.

Émeraude Vert – Used by R. J. Haüy (*Traité de Mineralogie 1801*) to designate emerald as distinguished from other beryls.

'Émeraudine' – Dioptase[18] (citing J. C. Delametherie).

'Émeraudite' – Diallage[40] (citing L. J. Daubenton); or pyroxene[18].

'Emerita', 'Emerita-Smaragd' – Trade name, Lechleitner synthetic emerald[23].

'Emerita-Stein' – Core of beryl overcoated with emerald[23].

Equemarine – Aquamarine, O. Fr.

Esmeragda (Old Catalonian), **Esmeragdo, Esmeraldo** (Port.) – Emerald[5].

'Esmeragdita' – Diallage, Span[15].

Esmeralda – Emerald, mod. Span and Port.; **'esmeralda'** – sometimes falsely applied to green tourmaline[23]; **'e. de Cartagena'** – green fluorite[15]; **Esmeralda Falsa** – 'false emerald', usually green fluorite[15].

'Esmeralda Cobre' (Span., Port.) – Dioptase; **e. de Colombia** (Span.) – Colombian emerald; **e. da Colombia** (Port) – same; **e.**

de Bahia (Span.) – Emerald, State of Bahia, Brazil; **e. da Bahia** (Port.) – same; **'e. del Brasil'** (Span.) and **'e. do Brasil'** (Port.) – green tourmaline; **'e. litio'** (Span.) – hiddenite; **'e. soldada'** (Span.) – doublet gem of two pieces with coloured layer between[13].
Esmeraldas Meridionales – Emeralds, probably Egyptian; **'e. viejas'** – green sapphires[41].
Esmeroud – Emerald, Old Dutch[5].
'European Emerald' – Beryls of Europe[1].
'Evening Emerald' – Peridot.

False Emerald, Fausse Émeraude (Fr.) – Fluorite, sometimes malachite.
Faz, Fozz, Fozzon – Grains of emerald washed from sand, Arabic[5].
'Ferrer-Smaragd' (Ger.) – Emerald-green glass[23].
Feruza, Ferruzegi, Feruzegi, Firuza, Peruzegi – Turquoise (Persian), sometimes misapplied to emerald[42,43].
'Foliated Beryl' – Pycnite variety of topaz[18].
Fortaleza Aquamarine – Finest blue aquamarine from Brazil[23].
Fustafi – Emerald in which green is mixed with black, from the name of the pistachio nut, Arabic[11] (vol. 2, pp. 876–7)

Galactites, Galactitis – Possible smaragdus in Pliny, described as 'a smaragdus surrounded with veins of white'[44] (p. 449).
Gánjha – Loss of clarity in emerald due to inclusions, India[11] (vol. 2, p. 901).
Garalárih – Emerald, meaning 'enemy of poison', in allusion to reputation as antidote for all poisons and venoms, Sanskrit[11,45].
Garamantica – 'Is like the Emerald, and has a cross white line; it is of great use in the Magic Art'[32] (p. 109).
Garden or Jardin (Fr.) – Host of filamentous inclusions in emerald resembling moss.
Garuda – Denotes very precious stone in Sanskrit, but also the 'bird and vehicle of Vishnu'; Wilson's *Dictionary* defines it as emerald[5]. Derived terms: **Garudmata, Garudodgara** (literally 'vomit of Garuda'[46]), **Garudottirna, Garudaçmen, Garuram, Garurankitam, Garurodgirnam, Garurottirnam, Garutmatam** – Emerald, Sanskrit[4,11].
Gemelo – Segmented emerald crystal of Colombia, originally thought to be a

trilling by Bertrand (1879), but now called *trapiche* (which see).
Geschenite – Apple green beryl, rich in sodium[47].
Gilson Emerald, Gilson Synthetischer Smaragd (Ger.) – Synthetic emerald made by Pierre Gilson, France[23].
Glatter Smaragd (Ger.) – Emerald[18] (citing D. L. G. Karsten).
Goldberyll (Ger.), **Golden Beryl** – Yellow beryl[23].
'Golden Emerald' – Golden beryl[14].
Gosenita (Span.), **Goshenit** (Ger.), **Goshenite** (Engl., Fr.) – Colourless beryl named after deposit at Gosehn, Massachusetts by C. U. Shepard (*A Treatise on Mineralogy*, 2nd ed. [New Haven, 1844], vol. 1, p. 143).
Gota de Aceite (Span.) – 'Drop of oil', referring to rich colour and clarity of fine emerald crystals of Colombia[28].
Gyou – Emerald, Tibetan[55].

'Halbanita Aquamarine' – Intense blue Maxixe-type beryl, named ca. 1973 after the Halba-Comércio e Industria de Pedras Preciosas, S.A., Belo Horizonte, Brazil.
Harinmani, Harinmanih, Haritasman – Emerald, Sanskrit[5,11].
'Hartglas-Smaragd' (Ger.) – Rapidly cooled, hardened emerald-colour glass[23].
Heliodor, Heliodoro (Span.) – Golden beryl, SW Africa (Namibia), named by Lucas von Cranach[48]; suggested as general term all yellow beryls[47]; said to be 'somewhat opalescent'[23]. See also Oelschlagel[13] and Pough *et al.*[28]
Hemerauld – Emerald, O. Fr[14].
Heroides – Variation of *aereoides*[32].
Hesperus, Hesphorus, Vesperugo – The 'Bohemian emerald', i.e. green fluorite[49].
Hughes Emerald – Synthetic made in Hughes Research Laboratory, Calif[23].
Huzrul Haiya – Emerald, Egypt[11].
Hyacinthozontes, Hyacintozontes (Ger.) – Deep blue beryl of Pliny[4]; 'similar in colour to the hyacinthus'[34] (p. 127); 'like Emeralds'[32]; (p. 76); 'superfluous name for light sapphire-blue beryl in the USA'[23] (p. 79).

Iaschpech, Iaschpeh, Iaspeh, Yashpheh – Beryl in the Bible, Hebrew[20] (f.24 v.); aquamarine[10]; jasper[53].

'**Igmerald**' – Synthetic emerald produced by I. G. Farbenindustrie, Germany[23,28].

'**Indian Emerald**', '**Indischer Smaragd**' (Ger.) – Crackled and dyed quartz[23,28].

'**Inkasmaragd**' (Ger.) – Emerald supposedly from Ecuador[23].

Ismaragda, Ismaragdan, Ismaragdon, Ismoradh – Emerald, Chaldaic[5,11,50].

Isoumrode (Polish) – Emerald[5].

Isumrud, Izoumrud, Izurud (Russ.) – Emerald, the last is current.

Jahaji – Emerald variety, India[11] (vol. 2, p. 901).

Jardin –See *Garden*.

Junjari (Arabic), **Jungari** (Persian) – Emeralds the colour of pepper[11] (vol. 2, pp. 876–7).

Káhí – Emeralds of a black tinge, India[11] (vol. 2, p. 901).

Kai-sui-shoku-ritoku-giyoku – 'Green gem of the colour of the sea', i.e. aquamarine, Japanese[17].

'**Kapsmaragd**' (Ger.) – Prehnite from Cape of Good Hope[23].

Kashatriya Emerald – A variety of deep green colour, India[30].

Kazab – Crystals of emerald in matrix, Arabic[5].

Kerásí – Emeralds the colour of the *keras* vegetable, Arabic[11] (vol. 2, pp. 876–7).

'**Kongo Emerald**', '**Kongosmaragd**' (Ger.) – Dioptase[23].

'**Kupfersmaragd**' – Dioptase[18,23].

Lapis Mulieris, Lapis Virgineus – Emerald, the 'stone of women', because conferring special protection to[51].

'**Lapis Smaragdinus**' – Serpentine[52].

Lechleitner Emerald, Lechleitner Smaragd (Ger.) – Synthetic emerald coating over aquamarine core, made by Lechleitner in Austria[23].

Lieu-pau-shih – 'Valuable or precious stones of green colour', possible emerald, Chinese[17].

Limoniates, Limoniatus – 'Would appear to be the same as smaragdus'[44]; an emerald, like 'a mist green pasture'[34] (p. 124); 'is a green stone in the similitude of an Emerald, but not so much Greenness and Transparency'[32] (p. 118); S. H. Ball classes it as emerald.

Linde Emerald, Linde Smaragd (Ger.) – Synthetic emerald made on aquamarine wafer seed by Linde Air Products Co. of U.S.A.[23,38].

'**Lithia Emerald**', '**Lithionsmaragd**' (Ger.) – Hiddenite.

Lithium Beryl, Lithiumberyll (Ger.) – Beryl containing Li[23].

Liu Lu – Beryl, Chinese.

Lomasarara – Emerald, Sanskrit[5].

Lou-soung-chi – Emerald, Chinese[55].

Luk-syak, Luksyák – Emerald, Cantonese[11,53].

Madagascar Aquamarine – Trade designation of fine blue beryl[28,38].

Mafek, Mafek-en-ma, Mafek-ma – Emerald, Egypt; Kunz believed the name denoted primarily malachite but could have meant emerald also[53].

Mahá Marakata – An emerald, which when placed on the palm and exposed to the sun, scattered light all around; the term literally means 'great emerald' (vol. 1, p. 391).

Maragda (Prakrit), **Maragd** (Ethiopic), **Maragde** Provençal Fr.), **Maragdos** (Gr.), **Maragdus** (Lat.), **Marakata** (Sanskrit, Bengali), **Marakatam, Markat** (Sanskrit)[5,43] – Emerald; according to Garbe[45] (p. 76), the root 'marakata' is possibly derived from açmagarbhaya, or 'sprung from the rock', perhaps alluding to crystals found embedded in schist or protruding from cavity walls.

Mar-gad – Emerald, Tibetan[6].

'**Mascot Emerald**' – Trade name for a triplet gem made from three pieces of genuine beryl[28].

'**Mass-aqua**' – Hard glass imitation of beryl[23].

Maxixe Aquamarin (Ger.), **Maxixe Aquamarine, Maxixeberyll** (Ger.), **Maxixe Beryl** – Deep blue aquamarine from Maxixe mine, Brazil[23,28].

'**Medina Emerald**', '**Medina Smaragd**' (Ger.) – Emerald-green glass[23,28].

Miya – Emerald, Burmese[11] (vol. 2, p. 941).

Modravec – Aquamarine, Czech; also given as *Akvamarin*[13].

Mo-lo-k'ie-to – Emerald, Chinese[6].

Morallas – Translucent to opaque beryls, which may or may not be emerald colour, of the emerald mines of Colombia; Webster[38] (p. 71) gives spelling as *Moral-*

lons; Oelschlagel[13] as Morallión. See also Pough *et al.*[28]

Morganiet (Dutch), **Morganit** (Ger.), **Morganita** (Span.), **Morganite** (Engl., Fr., Port.)[13] – Name given to pink beryl by G. F. Kunz to honour J. P. Morgan in 1910.

'Mother-of-Emerald' – Prase or green jasper, rarely green fluorite; "the Jasper is often the Matrix of the Prasius, and that of the Emerald'[1] (pp. 120–1).

Mujá – Emerald, Burmese[53].

Murguj, Murgujká – Variety of emerald, India[11] (vol. 2, p. 901).

Muzo Emerald – Trade designation of top quality emerald, after the deposit in Colombia.

Nayá – Variety of emerald, India[11] (vol. 2, p. 901).

Neronian Emerald – An emerald improved in colour by dyeing according to an ancient recipe[54].

'Nertschinsk-Aquamarin' (Ger.) – False name for topaz[23].

New Granada Emerald – Term used for locality of Colombian emeralds soon after discovery.

'Nickel Emerald', ' Nickel Emeraude' (Fr.) – Zaratite[18].

'Night Emerald' – Peridot[28].

Nophech, Nophek – Possible Biblical emerald[50].

Occidental Emerald – Term used to distinguish true emerald from green sapphire or 'oriental emerald'.

Oleagenus – Beryl 'similar [in colour] to that of oil'[34] (p. 127).

Omphax – Possibly identical to Pliny's Beryllus oleaginus[1].

'Oriental Aquamarine', 'Orientalischer Aquamarin' (Ger.) – Pale blue sapphire; the designation 'oriental' was used as early as 1667 by Pierre de Rosnel in his *Mercure Indien*.

'Oriental Emerald', 'Orientalischer Smaragd' (Ger.) – Green sapphire.

Oukiou (Mongolian), **Ouyou** (Manchu) – Emerald[55].

Pacha (Peruvian Indian, Persian, Asiatic Indian), **Pachae** (Persian, Indian), **Pachee** (Hindi, Persian Indian), **Pachel** (Peruvian Indian, Hindi) – Emerald[1,5,10,42].

Pánná – Emerald, Hindustani[11] (vol. 2, p. 876).

Pantaura, Pantaure – Emerald, Old Fr., according to Cornelius Agrippa[56] (p. 96), and so named because its figure resembles that of a panther; also called **'Pierre Solaire'**. *Pantaure*, meaning emerald, used by Jean De Taille de Bondaroy in 16th century[57].

Param Puchche – Emerald, Singhalese[11] (vol. 2, pp. 960–1).

Páriva dra – Aquamarine, Sanskrit[11] (vol. 2, p. 509).

Paryll – Variant of beryl[8].

'Peruanischer Smaragd' (Ger.) – Apatite[19].

'Peruvian Emerald' – Misnomer for Colombian emerald, used when exact source unknown.

Peruza, Peruzegi, Feruzegi – Emerald, Arabic[42]. See **Feruza.**

Peyáleká – Emerald variety, India[11] (vol. 2, p. 901).

Pinga – Emerald, Brazilian Portuguese[5].

'Piro-esmeralda' (Span., Port.), **'Piro-smeralda'** (Ital.) – Fluorite.

'Plasma di Smeraldo' – Prase, Ital[52].

'Prasine Domiciane', 'Prasine Neomane', 'Prasino Domiziano', 'Praisino Neroniano', 'Prasinus' – Emerald[58]; a kind of emerald improved in colour by dyeing[42]; the terms Domitian and Neronian were first used by Epiphanius[20,31] and repeated by de Boodt[10].

'Prassius' – Equivalent to **'mother-of-emerald'** (which see); 'they say that the *Prassius* is the House of the Emerald . . . and has all the virtues of the Emerald tho diminutively'[32] (p. 218).

'Praxini' – Term used for emeralds in inventory of Papal jewels in 1295[59].

'Prime d'Émeraude', 'Prisme d'Émeraude' (Fr.), **'Prime of Emerald'** – Fluorite or other green stone and equivalent to **'mother-of-emerald'** (which see); King[54] believed the term was derived from 'prasius'.

'Prismatic Emerald' – Euclase[18] (citing Mohs).

'Prismatic Emerald Malachite' – Euchroite[18] (citing Mohs).

'Pseudosmaragd')Ger.), **'Pseudosmaragdus'** – Applied to materials resembling emerald in colour, e.g., green fluorite, jasper.

Puchche, Puchche Marakatam, Pudu Puch-che – Emerald, emerald-like green stone, and 'new' emerald respectively, Singhalese[11] (vol. 2, pp. 960–1).

Puraní – Variety of emerald, India[11] (vol. 2, p. 901).

'Pyro-Emerald', 'Pyro Émeraude' (Fr.), **'Pyrosmaragdus'** – Chlorophane variety of fluorite[18].

Quetzalitzi – 'Stone of the quetzal', Mexican Indian, green jadeite sometimes mistaken for emerald[60].

Ra-e-háni – Emerald coloured like the flower of the same name, India[11] (vol. 2, pp. 876–7).

Raichanijj, Rihani – Emerald of basil-green colour, Arabic, Persian[5].

Rájanílam, Rauhenayam – Emerald, Sanskrit[11] (vol. 2, p. 1021); **Rajavaral** – 'king beryl', Gujarati[8].

Rekha – Streaks in emerald, India[11] (vol. 2, p. 901).

Riyoku-giyoku, Riyoku-ho-seki, Riyoku-giyoku-seki – 'Green gem' or 'green gemstone', commonly applied to emerald, also **So-giyoku**, Japanese[17].

'Root-of-emerald' – 'Mother-of-emerald' (which see).

Rosaberyll (Ger.), **Rose Beryl** (Engl.), **Rozeberil** (Dutch) – Rose or morganite beryl[13].

Rosterit (Ger.), **Rosterita** (Ital.), **Rosterite** – Slightly altered beryl from Elba named after G. Roster by A. Grattarola in 1880.

Sabardschah – Emerald, Arabic[5].

Sábouní, Sabuni, Zabunijj – Emerald of a mixture of white and green, Persian, Arabic[11] (vol. 2, pp. 876–77).

'Sächsischer Beryll' (Ger.) – Apatite[18] (citing Trommsdorf).

Salaki, Saluki – Emerald, Arabic[5].

Samarrud (Pers.), **Samurat** (Turk.), **Samurod** (Arab.) – Emerald[5].

'Sandwich Smaragd' (Ger.) – Layered synthetic emerald of Lechleitner[23].

Saupurnam – Emerald, Sanskrit[11] (vol. 2, p. 1021).

Sayadi – An emerald that when gazed upon shows the image of a man with eyes shut[11] (vol. 2, pp. 876–7).

Sbaragd – Emerald, variant of smaragd, Arabic[5].

Schmaragd – Emerald, Old Ger.

'Schmaragd Spath' (Ger.) – Smaragdite (which see).

'Schmelzflusssmaragd' (Ger.) – Synthetic melt-process emerald[23].

Schohan, Schoham – Beryl, Hebrew[5].

'Schorlartiger Beryll' (Ger.) – Pycnite variety of topaz[18] (citing A. G. Werner).

'Schorl Agua Marina' (Span.), **'Schorl Aigue-Marine'** (Fr.) – Epidote[14,18].

'Schorlous Beryl' – Pycnite variety of topaz[18].

'Scientific Emerald' – Fused green beryl glass[28]; also sometimes applied to green synthetic corundum or spinel, or green glass paste.

Scythian Emerald – Emerald from Scythia, according to Pliny[4].

Seberdsched – Stone of green and yellow colour, possibly emerald, Persian, Turkish[5].

Semargad (Chaldaic), **Semerid** (Arab.), **Semerrud, Smerud** (Pers.) – Emerald[5]. See also *Samarrud*.

Shudra – Emerald of dark green colour, Hindi[30].

'Siam Aquamarine' – Blue zircon or greenish spinel[28].

Siberget – Possibly emerald[5].

Siberian Aquamarine – Trade name for pale greenish-blue aquamarine from Russia[28].

'Siberischer Smaragd' (Ger.) – Green tourmaline[23].

Silikijj, Selongi – Leaf-green emerald, Arabic[5].

'Sinaraydoprase' – A variety of emerald[58].

'Sklo Berylové' – Green glass, Czech[13].

'Skythischer Smaragd' (Ger.) – Apparently dioptase and not the Scythian emerald of Pliny[23].

Smarag (Scot. Gaelic), **Smaragd** (Ger., Bohemian, Czech, Magyar, Swed., Dan., Dutch), **Smaragdes** (O. Ger.), **Smaragdo** (Pers.), **Smaragdos** (Gr., Coptic), **Smaragdu** (Wallachian), **Smaragdus** (L., O. High Ger.), **Smarakata** (Sanskrit), **Smaraldus** (O. Swed., O. Ger.), **Smarall** (Ger., 16th c.), **Smarat** (Mid. High Ger.), **Smareit** (Mid. High Ger.), **Smargdo** (Syriac), **Smerald** (Dalmatian, Wendic), **Smeraldo** (Span., Ital.), **Smiraldus** (Europe, Middle Ages), **Smrucht** (Armenian) – Emerald[5,21,42,61].

Smaragd Bahjský – Emerald, State of Bahia, Brazil; **s. Brasilský** – Brazilian emerald; **s.**

Kolumbijský – Colombian emerald; **'s. lithový'** – hiddenite; **'s. medený'** – dioptase; **'s. soudé'** – doublet emerald; **s. synthetický** – synthetic emerald, all Czech designations[13].

'Smaragdine' – Green chlorophane variety of fluorite[49].

'Smaragdite' – Greenish massive amphibole[16]; actinolite pseudo after hornblende, also foliated hornblende or emerald-green diallage, or jadeite-like zoisite, or beryl glass imitation which is chemically analogous to beryl[23].

'Smaragdfluss' (Ger.) – Rock crystal, fluorite; **'Smaragdkrystall'** – rock crystal[19]; **'Smaragdmatrix'**, **'Smaragdmutter'** – fluorite, also a green stone actually the matrix of emerald[21]; matrix of emerald crystals consisting of feldspar and quartz, but also a false name for prase[23]; **'Smaragdochalcit, 'Smaragdochalzite'** – atacamite or dioptase[18]. **'Smaragdolin'** – fused beryl glass[23,28]; **'Smaragdoprasem'** – prase, plasma[19]; **'Smaragdo-Prase', 'S.-Prasus'** – various green stones, usually some green massive variety of quartz, but none emerald[40]; **'Smaragdospath'** – feldspar[19]. All German terms.

'Smaragdus Calcedonius' – Amazonite[52]; **'S. Cyprius'** – 'mother-of-emerald'[52] (which see); **'S. medicus'** – malachite[28]; **S. Scythicus** – Scythian emerald of Pliny[4], but King[54] (p. 311) deems it 'green ruby', i.e., green sapphire.

'Smaryll (Ger.) – Composite gem of two layers of pale emerald or beryl cemented with coloured plastic layer[23,28].

Smeraldo – emerald; **'s. Africano'** – green fluorite; **'s. degli Urali'** – demantoid garnet; **s. di Bahia** – emerald, State of Bahia, Brazil; **'s. del Brasile'** – green tourmaline; **'s. del Capo'** – prehnite; **s. di Colombia** – Colombian emerald; **'s. di litio'** – hiddenite; **'s. lition'** – hiddenite; **'s. matrice'** – green fluorite; **'s. orientale'** – green sapphire; **'s. di rame'** – dioptase; **'s. ricostituto'** – green glass; **'s. saldato'** – composite gem; **s. syntetico** – synthetic emerald, sometimes applied to green glass. All Italian terms[13].

So-bo-riyoku – 'Sea-green gem', aquamarine, Chinese.

So-ko – Emerald, Japanese[17].

'Soldered Emerald' – See *Soudé Emerald.*

Sommorod, Somorods, Sümrud – Emerald, Arab[5].

'Soudé Emerald', 'Soudé Émeraude' (Fr.), **'Soudé Smaragd'** (Ger.) – Composite gem made from two pieces of quartz with emerald-coloured layer of plastic between[23,38].

'Spanish Emerald' – Green glass; in older periods sometimes designating finest quality Colombian emerald[28].

Star Beryl, Sternberyll (Ger.) – Brown or black beryl from Brazil displaying six-legged star[23]; **Sternaquamarine** (Ger.) – same, ilmenite inclusions[23].

Sulkí – Emerald partaking of colour of *Chekundur*, the Persian curry[11] (vol. 2, pp. 876–7).

'Symerald' – Name given to later Lechleitner synthetic emerald[23].

'Synthetic Aquamarine', 'Synthetic Aquamarin' (Ger.) – Blue synthetic corundum or spinel.

Synthetic Emerald – Artificially grown equivalent of natural emerald.

'Synthetic Rosaberyll' (Ger.) – Synthetic rose spinel[23].

Szmaragd – Emerald, Polish[5].

S'zmulu – Oriental name for emerald derived from the name of Island of Sumatra according to Pumpelly, cited in Geerts[17].

Tabarget – Emerald, Arabic[10].

Taperzeta – A stone sometimes given as equivalent to emerald in Middle Ages literature[5].

Tap-y-acar – 'Green stone', used by Muzo Indians of Colombia to designate emerald[62].

Tarkshya – Emerald, Sanskrit[30].

Tarshish – Biblical name for possible beryl, Hebrew[28,53].

'Tecla Emerald', 'Teclasmaragd' (Ger.) – Three-layered emerald imitation made from quartz or glass with green central layer[23].

Thalassus Marinus (Gr.) – Aquamarine, probably coined in Middle Ages[63].

To-hi-sui – Emerald, Japanese[17].

Torá – Beryl tinged with yellow[11].

Toréka – Variant of emerald[11] (vol. 2, p. 901).

Trapiche Emerald, Trapiche Smaragd (Ger.) – Emerald crystal containing radial inclusions or growth sectors of pale colour, somewhat resembling the cogs of the Spanish *trapiche* gear used in crushing sugar cane[23].

'Tripletin')Ger.) – Emerald-green triplet imitation gem[23].

Tsu-mu-lu, Tsie-mu-lu – Emerald, 17th-century China[6].

Tsung-yu (Chin.) – 'Valuable or precious stone of green colour', sometimes applied to the emerald[17].

Tsuni (Bengali) – Emerald[5].

Umiña – Emerald, Quichua of Peru[33].

Vaidhurya, Vaidurya (Sanskrit, Hindi, Canarese), Vaidugra (Marathi), Vayaja (Canarese), Veluriya (Pali), Veruliyam (Prakrit), Weluriya (Singhalese) – Beryl, also identified with lapiz-lazuli in some Sanskrit dictionaries[8]; *vaidurya* identified as emerald by Ball[64] (p. 719–20), and the word may be of Dravidian origin[21] (p. 189).

Vaishya Emerald – Yellowish-green variety, Hindustani[30].

Vetro di Berillo (Ital.), Vidrio de Berilo (Span.), Vidro de Berilium (Port.) – Glass[13].

Vorobeyevite, Vorobyevite, Vorobievite (Engl.), Worobieffit, Worobiewit (Ger.) – Caesium beryl, white or pink, named after mineral collector V. I. Vorobyev, who first exhibited specimens from Lipovka, Urals[65] (citing Vernadsky).

'White Emerald' – Goshenite.

Yashpeh, Yashpheh – See *iaschpech*.

Yemerarudo – Emerald in cursive Japanese[17].

Ysoberillus – 'A species of the Beril'[32].

Zabargad (Arab.), Zabargat (Pers.), Zabergad (Hindi), Zeberjed, Sabardschad (Arab.) – Emerald[4,5,6]; one or more of these terms may also apply to the peridot of St. Johns Island or Zebirget, in the Red Sea, and Keferstein[5] claims that this is the case most of the time.

Záhábí – Emeralds that have the 'colour of gold'[11] (vol. 2, pp. 876–7).

Zamargad (Ethiopic), Zamardun (Europe)[43], Zamarut, Zamarrute, Zamorat (Arab.), Zamrud (Malayan) – Emerald[1,5,10,11,42].

Zemeroud Mesri (Persian) – Egyptian emerald[5]; zemerud (Turk., Malay.), zemrukht, zemruxt (Armenian) – emerald[5,6].

Zerfass Emerald, Zerfass Smaragd (Ger.) – Hydrothermal synthetic emerald made by W. Zerfass of Germany[23,38].

Zmeroud (Polish, Persian), Zmeroud Misrai (Egypt. = 'first class emeralds'), Zmerud (Persian), Zmroukt, Zmrukht, Zmrroud (Armenian), Zmuri (Georgian) – Emerald[5,31].

Zobabi – Vivid green emeralds, like *Cantharides* flies in colour, Arabic[5].

Zubara Emerald – Egyptian emerald[28].

Zuburzud – 'A stone sometimes mistaken for the emerald', Egypt[11] (vol. 2, pp. 952–3).

Zucht-Smaragd (Ger.) – Synthetic emerald[23].

Zumarrud (Arab., Persian), Zumurud (Egypt., Arab.), Zumurrud (Arab., Persian, Syriac), Zumurid, Zumird, Zümrüt, Zimbrut (Turk.) – Emerald[5–7,11,15a,53].

References

1 HILL. J. *Theophrastus's History of Stones*. 2nd ed. London. 342 pp. (1774)

2 KING. C. W. *Antique Gems. Their Origin, Uses and Value*. 2nd ed. London: J. Murray. 498 pp. (1866)

3 *EDINBURGH REVIEW*. vol. 124, no. 253, pp. 228–60 (1866)

4 BALL. S. H. *A Roman Book on Precious Stones*. Los Angeles: Gemological Institute of America. 338 pp. (1950)

5 KEFERSTEIN. C. *Mineralogia polyglotta*. Halle: Eduard Anton. 248 pp. (1849)

6 LAUFER. B. *Sino-Iranica, Chinese contributions to the history of civilization in ancient Iran*. Field Museum of Natural History Publication 201, Anthropological Series vol. 15, no. 3. Chicago: Field Museum of Natural History. pp. 185–630 (1919)

7 HASCHMI. M. Y. Der ägyptische Smaragd. *Der Aufschluss* (Heidelberg) 7:100–2 (1956)

8 WIENER. L. *Contributions Toward a History of Arabico-Gothic Culture*. Vol. 4: *Physiologus Studies*. New York: Neale Publishing Co. 388 pp. (1921)

9 KING. C. W. *The Natural History of Gems or Decorative Stones*. London: Bell & Daldy. 377 pp. (1867)

10 BOODT. A. B. DE. *Gemmarum et Lapidum Historia*. Hanover: Typis Wechelianis. 294 pp. (1609)

11 TAGORE. S. M. *Máni-Málá, or a Treatise on Gems*. 2 vols. Calcutta: Stanhope Press. 1046 pp. (1879)

12 ALOISI. P. and BALDASSERONI. V. *Trattato sulle Pietre Preziose con un' Appendice sulle Perle e sui Coralli di Vicenzo Baldasseroni*. Florence: Felice Le Monnier. 405 pp. (1932)

13 OELSCHLAGEL. H. *Dictionnaire Technique des Métaux Précieux, des Pierres Fines* The Hague: Mouton & Co. 836 pp. (1939)

14 KOZMINSKY. I. *The Magic and Science of Jewels and Stones*. New York and London: G. P. Putnam's Sons. 434 pp. (1922)

15 APOLINAR MARIA. H. Apuntes sobre las esmeraldas. *Academia Colombiana de Ciencias Exactas Fisicas Naturales Revista* (Bogota) 7:324–7 (1947)

15a SAYAR, M. *Mineraloji v. jeoloji*. Istanbul: Teknik U. Matbaasi. 762 pp. (1955)

16 SCHALLER, W. T. Gems and precious stones. Chapter in *U.S. Geological Survey Mineral Resources of the United States for 1917*, pp. 145–68 (1918)

17 GEERTS, A. J. C. *Les Produits de la Nature Japonaise et Chinoise*. 2 pts. Yokohama: C. Lévy. 662 pp. (1878–83)

18 EGLESTON, T. Catalogue of minerals and synonyms. *U.S. National Museum Bulletin* 33 (Washington, D.C.). 198 pp. (1889)

19 REUSS. F. A. *Neues mineralogisches Wörterbuch*. Hof: G. A. Grau. 503 pp. (1798)

20 EPIPHANIUS. *De XII. Gemmis*. Zürich: Conrad Gesner. 56 pp. (1565)

21 LÜSCHEN. H. *Die Namen der Steine*. Thun & Munich: Ott Verlag. 384 pp. (1968)

22 PANNIER, L. C. A. *Les Lapidaires français du Moyen Âge*. Paris: F. Vieweg. 340 pp. (1882)

23 CHUDOBA. K. F. and GÜBELIN. E. J. *Edelsteinkundliches Handbuch*, 3rd ed. Bonn: Wilhelm Stollfuss. 408 pp. (1974)

24 GALLITZIN, D. *De Recueil de Noms . . . en Minérologie*. Brunsvik: Orphelins. 320 pp. (1801)

25 SPENER. J. J. *De Gemmis Errores Vulgaris*. Leipzig: Typis Christophori Fleischeri. 40 pp. (1687)

26 HOLTZAPFFEL. C. *Turning and Mechanical Manipulation*. Vol. 3. London: Holtzapffel & Co. pp. 1026–1477 (1850)

27 CHESTER. A. H. *A Catalogue of Minerals. Alphabetically Arranged*. New York: John Wiley. 52 pp. (1886)

28 POUGH. F. H., BOWMAN. J. J. and HOKE. C. M. *The Jewelers' Dictionary*. 2nd ed. New York: 230 pp. (1950)

29 EPPLER. A. *Die Schmuck- und Edelsteine*. Stuttgart: P. Krais. 464 pp. (1912)

30 TANK, R. R. CA. *Indian Gemmology*. Jaipur; Dulichand Tank. 171 pp. (1968)

31 BLAKE. R. P. and DE VIS. H. *Epiphanius De Gemmis, The Old Georgian Version*. London: Christophers. 335 pp.

32 LEONARDUS CAMILLUS. *The Mirror of Stones*. London: Printed for J. Freeman. 240 pp. (1750)

33 OLDEN. C. Emeralds: their mode of occurrence and methods of mining and extraction in Colombia. *Transactions of the Institution of Mining and Metallurgy* (London) 21:194–203 (1911)

34 BANDY. M. C. and BANDY. J. A. TRANS. 1955. *De natura fossilum (Textbook of Mineralogy)*, by Georgius Agricola. Geological Society of America Special Paper 63. New York: Geological Society of America. 240 pp.

35 BRISTOW. H. W. *A Glossary of Mineralogy*. London: Longman, Green, Longman, and Roberts. 420 pp. (1861)

36 HARRIS. T. M. *A Dictionary of the Natural History of the Bible*. Rev. ed. London: T. T. and J. Tegg. 350 pp. (1833)

37 HILL. J. *Fossils Arranged according to their Obvious Characters*. London: Printed for R. Baldwin. 420 pp. (1771)

38 WEBSTER. R. *The Gemmologists' Compendium*. 5th ed. London: Wehman. 235 pp. (1970)

39 MANGIN. A. *Earth and Its Treasures*. Translated by W. H. D. Adams. London: T. Nelson and Sons. 405 pp. (1875)

40 LANDRIN. *Dictionnaire de Minéralogie*. Paris: Firmin Didot Frères. 506 pp. (1852)

41 ARPHE DE VILLAFAÑE, J. *Quilatador de la Plata, Oro y Piedras*. Valladolid: privately published. ca. 142 pp. (1572)

42 GIMMA, G. *Della Storia Naturale delle Gemme*. 2 vols. Naples: Gennaro Muzio. 551, 603 pp. (1730)

43 LAET, J. DE. *De Gemmis et Lapidibus . . . Theophrasti Liber de Lapidibus*. Lugduni Batavorum. Also Leiden: J. Maire. 210 pp. (1647)

44 BOSTOCK, J. and RILEY, H. T. *The Natural History of Pliny*. Vol. 6. London: Henry G. Bohn. 529 pp. (1855–7)

45 GARBE, R. *Die indischen Mineralien*. Leipzig: Verlag von S. Hirzel. 104 pp. (1882)

46 RAY, P. C. *A History of Hindu Chemistry*. 2nd ed. 2 vols. Calcutta: Chuckervertty, Chatterjee & Co. 312, 70 pp.; 290, 152 pp. (1904)

47 VLASOV, K. A. *Geochemistry and Mineralogy of Rare Elements and Genetic Types of their Deposits*. Vol. 2.: *Mineralogy of the Rare Elements*. Jerusalem: Israel Program for Scientific Translations. pp. 67–169 (1966)

48 EPPLER, A. Der Heliodor. *Die Umschau* 24, no. 33, pp. 497–500 (1920)

49 BECKMANN, J. *A History of Inventions*. 4th ed. 2 vols. London: Henry G. Bohn. 519, 548 pp. (1846)

50 CLAPTON, E. *The Precious Stones of the Bible*. 2nd ed. London: Simpkin, Marshall, Hamilton, Kent & Co. 231 pp. (1899)

51 NEUHAUSER, W. E. *Coronae Gemma Nobilisima*. Frankfurt ? privately published. 164 pp. (1621)

52 CORSI, F. *Delle Pietre Antiche*. 3rd ed. Rome: Gaetano Puccinelli. 448 pp. (1845)

53 KUNZ, G. F. *The Curious Lore of Precious Stones*. Philadelphia and London: J. B. Lippincott. 406 pp. (1913)

54 KING, C. W. *The Natural History, Ancient and Modern, of Precious Stones and Gems*. London: Bell and Daldy. 442 pp. (1865)

55 ABEL-RÉMUSAT, J. P. *Histoire de la Ville de Khotan*. Paris: Imprimerie De Doublet. 239 pp. (1820)

56 SANTINI DE RIOLS. E. N. *Les Pierres Magiques*. Paris: Bibliothèque Chacornac. 173 pp. (1905)

57 TAILLE DE BONDAROY, J. DE LA. *La Geomance . . . Ensemble le Blason des Pierres Precieuses*. Paris: Lucas Breyer. 68 pp. (1574)

58 D. M.D.L.S.D. *Le Denombrement, Facultez et Origine des Pierres Precieuses*. Paris: Chez André Boutonné, 71 pp. (1667)

59 TWINING. LORD. *A History of the Crown Jewels of Europe*. London: B. T. Batsford. 707 pp. (1960)

60 KUNZ. G. F. *The Magic of Jewels and Charms*. Philadelphia and London: J. B. Lippincott. 422 pp. (1915)

61 FELDHAUS. F. M. Imitation emerald problems in the 16th century. *The Gemmologist* (London) 23:174–6 (1954)

62 MORELLO. T. The gem of Colombia. *Américas* 8, no. 10, pp. 21–4 (1956)

63 BRÜCKMANN, U. F. B. *Abhandlung von Edelsteinen . . .* Braunschweig: Waysenhausbuchhandlung. 143 pp. (1757)

64 BALL. S. H. Historical notes on gem mining. *Economic Geology* 26:681–738 (1931)

65 VERNADSKY. V. I. O vorob'evite. *Trudy Geologicheske Museya Akademiya Nauk* (St. Petersburg) 2, no. 5, pp. 81–102 (1908)

66 THOMPSON, R. CAMPBELL. *A Dictionary of Assyrian Chemistry and Geology*. Oxford: Clarendon Press. 266 pp. (1936)

Index

Index

How-to™
buildabrand
www.howtobuildabrand.org

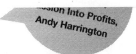
...sion Into Profits,
Andy Harrington

THE 7 Reasons Why Customers
DON'T CHOOSE YOU!

And How **You** Can Change That ✓

- 👀 **Enhance** Your Personal & Business Profile
- 👀 **Gain** Greater Credibility & Respect In Your Industry
- 👀 **Build** Trust With Your Dream Customers
- 👀 **Increase** Your Word Of Mouth Referrals
- 👀 **Save** Wasting Your Time On Ineffective Marketing
- 👀 **Reduce** Your Branding & Marketing Costs
- 👀 **Boost** Your Profits Significantly Over The Next 12 Months

WRITTEN BY SAMMY BLINDELL & MILES FRYER

FOREWORD

Do you know what your personal mission is in life? If you're like most of the business owners I meet whilst travelling the world to motivate millions, you may know what it is, but perhaps you aren't truly living it yet.

There are activities you love doing and you want to do more of them, if only you had the time. Maybe you have some experiences in mind, some goals you want to achieve or dreams you want to fulfill, if only you had the energy. Potentially you want to buy your dream home, have your dream car sat on your driveway or put your children through university, if only you had the money. Maybe you want to travel the world and see new places or perhaps you just want more free time to spend with the people you love, if only you had the time freedom. One thing's for sure... if you don't know what your mission in life is, you won't attract the customers willing to pay for your products and services so it becomes possible.

As an internationally acclaimed speaker, trainer and coach, I travel the world motivating people every year to share their message through public speaking. I have had the pleasure of speaking on some of the largest international stages with the world's best-known speakers, such as Sir Richard Branson, Les Brown, Bill Clinton, Robert Kiyosaki, Tony Robbins, Donald Trump and Nick Vujicic. My work also impacts on hundreds of thousands more people through my students at the Professional Speakers Academy, who go out into the world and make a difference doing what they love using my Jet Set Speaker System.

Yes I am living my life mission and purpose now, but it wasn't always this way. At age 28, I was working for Churchill Insurance making £1,500 a month and addicted to class A drugs. I hit rock bottom. It wasn't until I invested in the opportunity to work one to one with Anthony Robbins, one of the best coaches in the world, at his UPW event in America that the light bulb switched on. I began teaching and inspiring others to reach their full potential and over time I've gotten closer to reaching my own.

Motivating, empowering and inspiring people is a mission in my life, and building my brand with Sammy and Miles has played a huge part in creating exposure to my brand on a worldwide scale. I mentioned investing in coaching with the best coach in the world... Well you are about to be coached by two world-class branding and marketing experts right here in this book!

I get to meet a lot of people on my travels, but you'll be hard pushed to meet two more dedicated, motivated, loyal, passionate, knowledgeable and inspiring branding experts than Sammy and Miles. They really do go the extra mile to help people transform their businesses and build credibility around their brand.

When you surround yourself with great people, great things happen and the same is true of this book. By reading each chapter, playing full out and committing to take part in all the activities they have laid out for you within the exercises, your business and therefore your life could transform. With their help I hope you'll become the obvious leader of choice in your industry and build a brand with an incredible amount of trust associated to it. Great branding will add a huge amount of credibility and value to your label, enabling you to charge premium prices. Make this book your branding companion and if you get the chance to work with Sammy and Miles on the B.R.A.N.D. Accelerator Programme, I believe your business could truly fly.

I wish you great joy and success on your journey!

Andy Harrington,

The Jet Set Speaker

Creator of The Events: Power To Achieve, Public Speakers University and Mentors Academy.

Founder of: Professional Speakers Academy

Author of: Passion Into Profits.

In this book, we show you how to achieve in just a few months what it takes the average businessperson a lifetime to achieve. If you have the ambition, passion, and mindset to radically transform your future and build a successful business, then this book is perfect for you.

Having spent in excess of 60,000 hours in the commercial world studying, developing and implementing branding techniques that have helped thousands of business owners like you, we share some of the most successful strategies in this book that get us in front of over 10,000 new potential customers every month. You hold in your hands the seven most effective techniques that really work, to build your brand strategy in a way you can learn quickly, and implement NOW. Oh, and there are three bonus chapters for you in here too!

By picking up this book, you are working your way up to the top 1% of ACTION TAKING entrepreneurs and business owners, who are among the wealthiest and most successful people on the planet. You are also stepping away from the 1 in 3 businesses that fail every year. Are you ready for huge paydays and lots of fun?

Are you ready to make your mark on the world?

Get started NOW!

> *"If you're stuck in determining your message, or how to deliver it, and you feel like you've tried everything, talk to Miles & Sammy because they will show you the things you never dreamed of that are spot on for your business."*

Lisa Pattendon,
Women's Legacy Creator

> *"Sammy and Miles make a genuine difference to the businesses they support. When you hit a wall that you can't break through, these guys will help you to smash through it."*

Kris Florek,
Entrepreneur, Trainer & Public Speaker

> *"I thought that marketing was a cost and not a driver of sales. It was only when I met Miles and Sammy that I understood the true value of branding, which is the expression and value of my business. People see my brand, know who I am and now want to do business with me long before we talk about money."*

Sue Copeman,
Lifestyle, Wedding & Portrait Photographer

Images bought from www.istock-photo.com, www.bigstockphoto.com and www.sxc.hu

ISBN: 9781512311228

First published in 2014 by How2become Ltd

To order additional copies, please contact How2become Ltd, Suite 3, 50 Churchill Square Business Centre, Kings Hill, Kent, ME19 4YU. You can also order via the email address info@how2become.co.uk

CONTENTS

BONUS CHAPTERS...

ACKNOWLEDGEMENTS...

To our families, we thank you from the bottom of our hearts for your relentless support, and consistent encouragement. We cannot express enough how much we value what you have done for us throughout our lives that have led us to this point. To Bonnee & Bob Blindell, Gillian & Martin Cossins, Greg Garrity, Lee Cossins & Crystal Lang, Kieran Cossins & Katie Hughes, Lewis & Marie Tyrrell, Elsie & Syd Succamore, Derrick & Mary Fryer, Paul & Monique Fryer and Kim Fryer, thank you so much. You are loved and valued more than you will ever know.

To Andy Harrington, Simon Coulson and Daniel Priestley, who taught us: "If you're not living the life you want, you aren't helping enough people yet". Your continued support and faith in us to become the best we can be in our industry has been astonishing. It is this support from you and our fellow members at the Professional Speakers Academy, The ACE Team, Power To Achieve, Internet Business School and KPI, that has helped us to build a business that positively impacts on thousands of lives around the world every day. For this we are eternally grateful.

To our team at The Brand Brains, we are most humbled that you accepted us into your lives, and continue to give so much of yourselves to our customers. We are truly proud to work with the best of the best in this industry to support small businesses. Together we will continue to make a valuable contribution and difference to the lives and businesses we touch. Thank you to all of you who have helped to make our online publication such a great success: Kym Ciftci, Andrea Sangster, Ben Brophy, Chris Coney, Geoff Alexander, Matt Hodkinson, Matthew Dixon, Nicholas Robus, Rick McMunn, Sharon Callix, Penny Power, Tim Bradley, Andrew Whitfield, Jane Malyon and Tosin Ogunnusi.

To those who inspired, motivated, challenged and transformed our thinking to become better people, we thank you and hope that one day we get to thank you in person: Sir Richard Branson, Richard Wilkins, Lyndon Ogden, Richard Reed, Michelle Mone, Shaa Wasmund, Anthony Robbins, Dan Bradbury, James Lavers, Chris Cardell, Dan Kennedy, Brendon Burchard, Frank Kern and Raymond Aaron.

A heartfelt thank you to you all.

About The Authors...

As business owners since 1999 who have built seven of their own companies and helped over 1200 businesses across five different continents to design and build successful brands, Sammy Blindell and Miles Fryer now advise thousands of business owners across the world every day through their small business marketing resources: *www.howtobuildabrand.org* and *www.thebrandbrains.com.*

They pride themselves on the quality of their work, delivering brand strategies and branding to companies who are serious about building a brand that attracts the right customers from the very beginning.

Business owners worldwide have worked with Sammy and Miles directly via their B.R.A.N.D. Accelerator Programme over the last seven years, achieving tangible and measurable results that have greatly increased the value, visibility, credibility and profitability of the businesses they work with. It is the pain that these customers faced, before working with Sammy and Miles that inspired the dynamic duo to write this book.

Sammy and Miles see beyond the norm in terms of strategic and tactical techniques that will help you to build your brand and develop client-focused communications, using clever, simple, low-cost and no cost marketing techniques that will position YOU as the brand LEADER in your industry.

They brought their strategic and tactical experience together in 2007, having been introduced at a business-networking event two years previous, and started to refer business to one another. Eventually they became known as a powerful marketing team and built a strong word of mouth marketing strategy on their reputation. In 2007 they launched their first company together and have since built five other businesses, selling their last business in 2013 after launching How To Build A Brand.

There is no doubt that this marriage of skill, creativity, technical expertise, strategic excellence and innovative thinking created a very powerful team that takes building your business and brand to a whole new level when you work with them.

With a staggering amount of written and video testimonials, plus word of mouth referrals, Sammy and Miles are passionate about helping you to align your brand strategy and marketing communications to attract the quality customers and clients you want to do business with. So much so, after eighteen years in the branding industry watching small business owners plough their hard earned money into Marketers to tell them what to do (leaving no money to spend on what actually needed doing), Sammy and Miles got increasingly frustrated.

The reason they got so frustrated is because as a small business owner, you know you need to create a professional image for your business and start marketing yourself, but you don't know the best place to start, right? If this is a similar challenge for you, don't worry, you are not alone. So what happens when you don't know what to do first? You ask an expert, such as a Marketing Manager or Marketing Consultant to help you create a plan. This will cost you money that you don't have; yet there is an even greater challenge than this...

You know that the best way to fast track your results is to hire a Marketing Manager or Consultant. Asking an expert is a clever thing to do, as they will help you to move forward much faster than you can on your own. BUT, as a small business, any money you spend on them will eat most, if not your entire budget for the activity your Marketer has suggested.

At this point the plan (that you've paid them for) goes in the drawer and you go into what we call 'Doing Syndrome'. This is where you end up 'doing' random marketing activities by yourself to feel like you are doing something, because doing something is better than doing nothing, right? Wrong! It's better to have nothing out there than to have the wrong thing damaging your brand and reputation. Why? Because...

Once you put it out there, you cannot take it back.

Sammy and Miles became so frustrated watching this process of failure and demoralisation happen time and again that they spent two years pouring their 36 years' worth of knowledge and experience into developing resources that will help small business owners, like you, to focus your money and time on the important activities that WILL grow your business.

They have, in effect, removed the need for you to spend your money on a Marketing Manager or Consultant, by giving you the tools you need to create your plan yourself. You now have a proven system in your hands that gives you control and puts you firmly in the driving seat of your business.

This book has been created to give you an insight into the greater B.R.A.N.D. system and give you access to some of the valuable knowledge, techniques and strategic skills that Sammy and Miles use with their clients to help them become THE market leaders in their industry.

Now it's your turn to step up and show the world what a true leader in your industry really looks like.

Enjoy the journey!

"Branding isn't about picking a logo. It's telling the world what you stand for in business, and demonstrating that in everything you say and do. Miles and Sammy are the best team I know for helping companies without a brand define the right one, and refine it until it's perfect. They are a world class act."

Andrea Hook, Award Winning Copywriter

"Sammy and Miles give people like me the support and confidence they need to bring their dream to the market easily and profitably."

Viv Lambert, Feng Shui Specialist

"Sammy and Miles are like business pimps... They pimp up your business and make it attractive to the people who you most want to spend money with you."

Rob Zappone, Internet Marketing Coach

"Sammy and Miles share their wealth of knowledge and experience in a fun, practical and engaging way that really makes it so easy to learn from them."

Debbie Kinghorn, NLP Kids Coach & Author

PREFACE...

Hello, valued friend.

It's nice to finally meet you. You may not know us personally, but we feel like we have known you for a long time already. How could this be? Because there are lots of things we already know about you.

For example, we know you want to do greater things with your life because you picked up this book. We know you want to be greater, achieve greater and become greater than most people settle for in life. So let us start by asking you a couple of questions...

★ Would you like more money?

★ Would you like to have more time to enjoy your money?

★ Do you desire the financial freedom that comes with having a profitable brand that effortlessly attracts new customers?

★ And do you have aspirations to do something more significant?

If you answered yes to one or more of these questions, you have definitely picked up the right book. If you aren't already making the kind of money or living the kind of lifestyle that comes from being a magnetic and profitable brand, then quite frankly, you haven't touched the lives or businesses of enough people yet.

We are alike you know. We are achievers. Most average people, who prefer to stick with the herd are afraid of the concepts we share with you in this book. They would love to **be more**, but are unwilling to do what is takes. They would love to **do more**, but are unwilling to do what is takes. They would love to **have more**, but are unwilling to do what is takes. Can you see a pattern forming?

Have you ever heard someone mention the success of a really simple idea and say "I could have done that myself?" Yes they probably could have, but they didn't did they? These are the kind of people who complain about everything, but they are afraid of having the big goals that make them stand out from the comfort of mediocrity. In fact, they have no problem putting the successes of others down. Maybe you know someone like this, but it's not YOU is it? YOU are different. We know this because YOU are the one we designed our system for.

By choosing to leave the herd and participate in this seven-step customer attraction program we have created for you, you have separated yourself from everyone else and decided to stand out. To become **THE** market leader. 97% of the population either doesn't know how to do what it takes to live the life they want, or they simply can't be bothered. Not you though. Here you are among the top 3% of achievers and you are truly living out of your comfort zone. In fact this is your opportunity to spend far more time out of your comfort zone, i.e. the 'Oh Shit' zone of opportunity, as our good friend and business mentor Simon Drury would say.

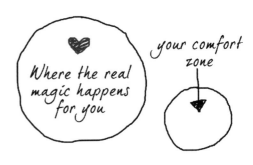

Congratulations! What a pleasure it is that you have invited us to join you on your journey.

In this book, we will show you how to achieve in just a few months, what it takes the average business person in a lifetime. Quite a bold statement we know, but far too many business owners leap straight into starting and growing a business without first thinking about the core principles that we are going to stare with you in this book. Principles that when ignored at any stage in your business (as most business owners do), will fail to attract the customers you really dream of doing business with.

You see, fundamentally your customers are looking for 7 key things when they first come into contact with your business that will give them the first, last and lasting impression of your business. If any one of these things is missing from your strategy, your business will limp along, draining your personal life and relationships with it.

This may sound overly dramatic, but give it a few years' worth of hard graft, learning how NOT to attract customers, and you'll know exactly what we mean… if you don't already! If however, you have got the ambition, passion, determination and mindset to radically transform your future using what we are going to share with you in this book, **AND** you commit to taking action on it, you will create an outstandingly successful business, a far reaching reputation and a financially certain future. Sound good to you? Fantastic, lets continue together then :)

We have a combined 36 years of branding, marketing and strategic online experience, with over 60,000 hours of delivering marketing activities to our customers. Couple this with seventeen years of rolling up our sleeves to gain our commercial business knowledge the hard way (and the seriously challenging lessons we learned whilst building our main six figure business), and you can rest assured that you will learn a thing or two from our successes, and our mistakes.

In fact, to make it simple for you to learn in several hours what it took us years to find out the hard way, we have broken down the most effective and consistently profitable strategies into 7 easy steps that will help you successfully achieve the following:

★ Create a strategic profile of your ideal customers and clients so they will find you faster, easier and more effectively

★ Give your customers and clients at least seven solid reasons why they should do business with YOU over and above anyone else

★ Develop over 100 key messages about your business that you can actively use to promote yourself immediately across all marketing channels, both online and offline

★ Create a brand growth strategy to give to your brand designer, website designer and marketing manager so they GET IT RIGHT for you FIRST TIME

It really would take you years to learn everything that we have learned the hard way, not to mention the thousands of pounds worth of investment we have individually and collectively made to find out what works and what doesn't. So we thought we would help you by highlighting the top seven things your customers want to see, hear, and feel from you in order to make that all important decision to start a relationship with you.

The seven brand strategy exercises you are going to go through in this book have consistently worked for business owners just like you and we use them in our own business at least every six months to ensure we are still on track with our customers. These exercises will help you start to build your brand strategy in a way you can learn quickly, and implement immediately.

Yes there are thousands more incredibly effective marketing activities you can do, many of which we teach in our intensive B.R.A.N.D. Accelerator Programme, where we help our students to become the most highly positioned, greatly valued, exceptionally sought after and abundantly paid leaders in their industry.

Perhaps, like many others, you will get halfway through this book and become so excited about the potential of your business, that you book onto the course to progress even further and faster with our hands-on support. However, for now we want to help you get started by using part of our proven program for achieving

BIG BUSINESS GOALS.

Does that sound good to you? Great, well let's get started straight away.

INTRODUCTION...

Have you ever wondered how to use your knowledge and expertise, to position yourself in such a way that you attract more customers and become the obvious leader of choice in your industry? And not only that, but you also build a brand that enables you to work when you want, with whom you want, and earn what you want. Because that's what you want, isn't it?

Your business should provide you with the life you deserve – Yes or No?

Well when you position your brand in the right way; whether it's a personal brand or a company brand that represents your products and services, you will attract the customers you want, who will pay what you are worth, so YOU can live the life you deserve.

If you have already completed our FREE online 6 Step Brand L.E.A.D.E.R. System, this book is the perfect next step in helping you build your brand growth strategy. If you haven't yet completed it, don't worry. You can either work on it before you start reading this book, at the same time, or once you have completed it. The great thing is, they complement each other perfectly and the 6 Step Brand L.E.A.D.E.R. System is absolutely FREE, so you get the very best of both worlds by completing them both.

By picking up this book you are positioning yourself amongst the top 1% of entrepreneurs and business owners who are the wealthiest and most successful people on the planet. You are also stepping away from the 1 in 3 businesses that fail every year. Yes, you read that correctly, and it's worth repeating so you know the risks other business owners are taking right now because they aren't doing what you are doing to build a solid foundation for their business.

1 in 3 businesses fail every year... PERIOD.

One of the biggest reasons for this is because they inadvertently plan to fail in business because they fail to plan. At a guess, you are here because you already understand the power branding can have for you. Now you just need to know how to apply that knowledge to a strategy that attracts, converts and engages more people into a lifetime customer relationship with your business, right?

As part of our business growth journey, we have committed ourselves to studying and developing branding & marketing techniques that have helped thousands of business owners, like you, on a worldwide scale to achieve outstanding results, increased sales, and remarkable customer retention. These are the same techniques we have tested in our own businesses to get us in front of over 10,000 new potential customers every single month. Perhaps you would like to find out how you can do the same. Are you ready for huge paydays and lots of fun while you make money?

Are you ready to put your mark on the world?

Standing out against a mass of competition is a challenge for every shape, size and type of business. Your competitors are seeking more influential and effective ways to impact upon your prospects and customers to build their reputation over yours. On an average day your prospects are exposed to in excess of 60,000 brands, from the moment they wake up to the moment they go to sleep.

So how can you make enough of an impact on them to ensure your brand is the No.1 on their mind when they need your type of service?

How your brand is positioned will determine whether <u>YOU</u> or <u>YOUR COMPETITOR</u> wins the sale. SIMPLE!

The best way to ensure you have the leading edge on your competitors, is to strengthen your brand position by creating a solid brand growth strategy; a 'Brand

Bible' for your business, as such, which you and your team can consistently refer to as you grow and build a business that attracts the kind of customers who will pay for the lifestyle you want to live. *"**So what exactly is a brand growth strategy?**"* we hear you ask.

That's a brilliant question because it's greatly misunderstood and not as 'fluffy' as you might think. In fact, a brand growth strategy knocks a business plan and marketing strategy out of the park and will save you a fortune on expensive business and marketing consultants at the same time. We really want to help you save money and time, so let's take a few minutes to delve a little deeper into what it is and how it can benefit your business by investing in it now...

A brand growth strategy is an intensive process that drills down deeply into every aspect of your business in order to create a strategic plan that will position you as the obvious leader of choice in your industry. It takes on average five days to create, two days of which are spent directly with you and should include a customer acquisition and retention strategy, a communications roll-out plan, an online marketing plan and a brand positioning strategy... all in one. Basically, it rules out anything that is found to take up a lot of your time or investment, and instead includes everything you need to attract, engage and convert more of the customers you want to do business with, at the same time as forming a strategic plan that can be tested, measured and adapted as you grow.

This process can be done yourself. In fact, you are touching on the very beginnings of your brand growth strategy right now just by following the exercises in this book. If you feel you are too close and emotionally attached to your business to create an effective strategy yourself (like many business owners), you will find that bringing an external team of experienced strategic and tactical branding experts into your business is a very beneficial and wise investment indeed.

You can create your own brand growth strategy, for example, on our B.R.A.N.D. Accelerator programme, cutting out the need to spend your money on an expensive marketing consultant. After all, a professional branding expert is not just someone who makes things look great. It's a given that they should do that for you. But like us, they should also have experience and current knowledge in every area of brand extension; sales, persuasive language, marketing, online strategy, influencing tactics and communication skills that you need to help you attract the right customers to your business by looking at the brand as whole and not just as a logo.

It makes good business sense to bring in an expert who knows exactly what to do to attract your ideal customers and speeds up the process for you massively. To risk doing it yourself without the knowledge needed to get it right first time, could cost you years of time, money and wasted energy that would quite frankly be far better spent focusing on delivering great customer experiences while the branding experts do their job. We meet far too many business owners who wish they had put more focus on this area of their business before they found out the hard way. You will enjoy the lifestyle you truly want in just a fraction of the time when you invest in the right team of communications experts who really know what they are doing, and who are up to date with the very latest practices in business growth, marketing and communications.

We have personally worked with hundreds of business owners over the years, that had all spent money on various different plans to help them grow their business before they came to us. They all felt they had wasted their time and money on business plans, marketing strategies, online marketing plans and sales plans, because they realised after working with us that they just weren't necessary to the needs of their small growing businesses. Even their branding was wrong because the strategy didn't match the outcome of their ideal lifestyle. The design company had literally given them what they needed to look great there and then, rather than creating something they could grow and expand into up to the point of exit.

The brand growth strategy on the other hand really did help them to progress and gave them exactly the focus they needed to start attracting the right customers, and make the money they really wanted. Let us share with you what we now know, based on what they told us they spent and the results they achieved:

★ On average a business plan created by a professional business advisor will cost you about £5,000, and will very rarely get used after the bank manager has seen it. After that, it will just sit there gathering dust.

★ A comprehensive 12-month marketing strategy will cost you between £3,000 and £5,000, and it will last around three months before the industry has changed, customers buying behaviours have shifted, and your strategy will have to adjust with it, costing you more time and money to update it.

★ An online marketing specialist from a professional website company will cost you between £2,000 and £5,000 for a 12-month plan, and within 24 hours it could be out of date because Google change their ranking criteria so often.

★ A sales strategy delivered by a professional sales coach will cost you around £1,000 a month, and your strategy will be out of date the minute you add a new product or service to your offering.

★ A good branding agency will cost you around £5,000 to develop your brand image across the most common customer touch-points, and then you have to find a way of marketing it yourself. Plus, if you choose to evolve your business into other avenues as it grows, you will have to rebrand if your design agency didn't brand your business in a way that it can grow with your strategy.

The list could go on and on. Why do we tell you this? Because we want to make sure that every penny you spend on your business gets you a return on your investment, and soft talking to you is not going to get you anywhere.

Yes, you'll need every one of the above aspects of business strategy to achieve great results and you'll need a plan and a way to attract new customers. You'll need a professional brand that sticks like glue in the minds of the people you want to spend money with you. However, as a growing business, you could easily rack up over £20,000 before you have even sent out one sales letter. Would you agree with that? It would be a far better investment of your time, energy and resources to invest in one strategy that covers all of the above elements in enough detail so that:

★ You have a constructive plan to follow.

★ You can build your brand effectively to attract your ideal customers.

★ It is simple to understand and...

★ It is easy to implement.

Whilst a 200 page marketing strategy or business plan will give lots of information, it's simply too much for one person to do at the same time as running a business. Plus, you need a strategy that gives you more money to invest on attracting new customers, rather than spending money on unnecessary things that eat up your marketing budget. Here's what a solid brand growth strategy should include. This will stop you going down the loose cannon route that so many business owners are suffering from that is:

Aim > Fire > Ready > Broke!

Your brand communications strategy should focus on the following aspects before going into 'action and activity' mode:

1. Where you have come from...

Education, experience, qualifications, achievements, failures, successes, unfulfilled dreams, untapped potential etc. Knowing your history will give your branding experts the basis of a great brand story that can be used to ignite your campaign and set the world on fire.

2. Where you want to go...

Vision, mission, goals, dreams, targets, expectations, lifestyle dreams, philanthropic ideas, etc. Singing from the same hymn sheet is vital if your branding experts are to help you achieve the lifestyle you want, faster than you can get there on your own.

3. Who you want to go there with...

Target clients, strategic partners, celebrity endorsements, stakeholders, staff/team, outsourcers, values matching etc. This is the most fundamental part of your strategy because attracting the wrong customers will kill your enthusiasm for your business, killing your business with it. We'll be talking about this later. Attracting the right customers is the lifeblood of your success and wealth – both financial and emotional.

4. Where there are market gaps...

In-depth competitor analysis, online research, cross referral opportunities, keyword planning, competitor weaknesses, & strengths, best practice modelling, customer needs analysis, pricing, etc. This is one of the most vital areas of your strategy if you want to compete on excellence and expertise as opposed to getting into a price war with competitors. This is your opportunity to differentiate your business from your competition.

5. How to get there profitably...

Strategic planning, resources, tools, technology, operations, systems, investment, customer buying behaviour, testing & measuring, etc. This is the compass that leads you to your destination efficiently and profitably.

6. When you are going to be fulfilled...

Setting standards, vision, measurement of successes, boundaries, exit strategy, etc. Quite simply, if you don't know what great looks like, how can you know how close you are to achieving it? This is vital in measuring your success, at the same time as setting standards that both you and your team can aspire to.

The reason this process works so well, when you get outside support from a branding expert, is because it is far more challenging to sit down on your own and map out what is in your head, than it is to have an outside expert who will keep digging and digging until they are satisfied you have given them every opportunity to help you move forward. An outsider will be looking and listening to everything you do and say from a customer's perspective, while you on the other hand are going to be looking at everything from an emotionally attached or financial perspective. It just isn't the same. You need to give your prospective customers a much broader and bigger picture of your brand so that your customers aren't too overwhelmed to make a purchase. As the business owner, it is far too easy for you to go into too much detail, which can be very off-putting.

Getting the beginnings of your strategy in place now is a great start, and certainly better than half-heartedly, or worse still, not at all. However, you will get only get a fraction of the information from your mind that is actually possible. When you have someone else helping you to extract it, and seeing the gaps you are too close to see, your brand will truly come alive. It's also important that your brand strategy demonstrates the following qualities to ensure your business stands the best chance of attracting the right customers. It must:

 ★ Appeal to both logic and emotion.

 ★ Demonstrate a common value set between you and your ideal customers to build rapport and a common ground.

 ★ Inspire loyalty and quality relationships.

 ★ Demand company-wide and family-wide support and commitment, and…

 ★ Excite all stakeholders – customers, employees, suppliers, partners and investors.

Your brand growth strategy, at the very least, should communicate who you are, what you are known for, why people should trust you, and why they should buy from you NOW - not wait. This not only gives your customers a clear idea of who you are and what you stand for, but a great deal more control over your designers, developers, marketers and anyone else representing your business as you grow.

Without giving them this, you are handing control of your brand over to someone who knows only a fraction about your business compared to you. So you are doing absolutely the right thing by getting this step right before you go any further.

Your brand is essentially the most important customer touch-point of your operation, as it is the first connection a prospect has with your company, whether that be via your website (most likely), your business card, your letterhead, your brochure, your social media accounts, or even a friend referring you to someone they know. This demonstrates that your brand is far more than just your logo. Your brand is every single touch-point your prospects have ever had and will ever have in future with your business, whether you are there or not. It's an emotional experience that bonds your customers to what you believe in.

If your brand is consistent across all the methods of communication and you are in control of how each piece of marketing collateral is perceived by your target customers, they are more likely to trust you. If your brand identity has consistent key messages going out about you, people are more likely to listen to you. And if your brand is visually stronger than your competitors, they are more likely to buy from you, regardless of price.

If your brand is consistent, people will believe what you deliver is consistent.

If your brand is inconsistent, they'll assume what you deliver is inconsistent.

Consistency is the key.

To create a true brand of **Value** and **Purpose,** you must have all seven of the following elements in place and working hard for you. In a nutshell, your entire brand is underpinned by **Trust**. Without **Trust** you have no **Credibility** and without **Credibility** you have no **Customers**.

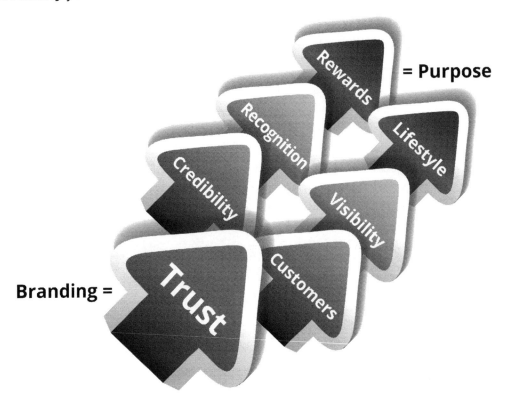

Without **Customers** who believe in your **Credibility** you cannot achieve **Recognition** and without **Recognition** you have no **Visibility** to build your brand.

Your brand is what other people say it is, not what you say it is.

Without these seven fundamental steps in place, you have no brand and therefore no **Purpose** to your business existence. Create a brand of true **Purpose** and meaning however, and you will have created a brand of true **Value** & **Success**.

It doesn't matter if you are the only company in the world to provide your products and/or services, your brand must stand out and represent the promises you make. Your brand growth strategy has a fundamental importance in moving your business forward to build and maintain a strong image that people connect with, buy into, and believe in. Your brand growth strategy is the foundation that increases positive emotional associations between your brand and your target market. Without a good strategy behind your brand, you have a pretty logo with no real foundation to give customers the 'why I should buy from you' factor.

No foundation means you are potentially building your business on quicksand, as you don't know what lies ahead on each step you take. That is no basis upon which to build a strong business and lifestyle. To create a successful launch and brand marketing campaign, a good strategy that covers at least the following areas of growth will help your visibility and credibility go far. You will:

★ Have a clear and carefully analysed target market that you can communicate with.

★ Have successful and consistent advertising and marketing messages in place.

★ Be flexible to the business climate and foresee challenges before they arise.

★ Create your brand promise and over-deliver on it every time.

Whether you are launching a new product or service, revitalising an existing business, or striving to be known as the best in your industry, it's important to remember that no matter what size your business is, there is always room for growth.

The most successful businesses revisit their brand communications strategy at least once every three to six months.

Without a strategy that continually evolves or a communications plan that you and your team can follow, your success is likely to dwindle and your competitors will win the business you could have had.

7

So what are the top seven questions your prospects want to know about you before they consider buying into your products and/or services?

It may seem a little harsh, but the reality is you need to have a very good answer to them all if you want to lead the way in your industry. Any pause to think and you will look like you don't know what you are talking about. Be prepared because the reality is that if you can't answer these questions one of your competitors will:

1. **Who Are You?**
   I want to know whom I'm working with.

2. **What Is Your Mission?**
   I want to know if our goals and values are aligned.

3. **Who Is Your Ideal Customer?**

   I want to know if you work with other people like me so that you have the relevant experience to help me.

4. **What One Single Message Tells Me All About You?**
   I want to know what kind of person and personality I am going to invest my time and/or money with.

5. **Why Was Your Company Created?**

   I want to know if you are passionate and have a background history in helping people just like me.

6. **Why Should I Care That You Exist?**

   I want to know, why do you care so much about what you do? If you don't care about it, why should I? So tell me, why I should care about what you do?

7. **What is your competitive advantage?**

   I want to know why I should choose you over anyone else who offers what I consider to be a similar product or service to you.

There are a few other questions that are subconscious, and if you add these, you'll remove any nagging objections to spending money with you and increase your chances of making the sale. These are:

8. **How Can You Help Me To Solve My Problems?**

   I want to know what you have done forpeople like me in the past, how you did it and what results it got them, so I can trust that you have expertise where I need it.

9. How Can I Find Out More About You?

I want to know how credible you are so tell me clearly where I can go to find out more about you and what you do.

10. How Can I Take This Relationship Further?

I want to know how simple your process is to get started once I have made the decision to choose you.

These questions may seem intense, but it's highly likely you've asked at least one or two of them before yourself when making a decision to buy something. Your prospective customers are no different when they are about to spend money. Now you know what these seven questions are, let's go into each one in more detail to help you answer them.

By the way, you should grab a pen to make notes in this book as you go, because this is a great time to start keeping a record of your progress...

CHAPTER 1...

Who Are You?

★ A happy meal from the drive through tells us a story about that family's eating habits.

★ The Starbucks coffee cup you see people carrying around tells you about their mind-set around disposable money.

★ The choice of car and how clean it is tells us a lot about that owner's personality.

★ The designer laptop with an apple icon on the lid tells us the owner demands quality, creativity and success.

★ That pair of trainers with a distinctive tick tells everyone who's got them branded.

★ Those jeans with a red and white label tagged to the back pocket tells us the wearer is a fan of fun and adventure.

★ The watch with the 'Hey look everyone, I made it big' on the face, tells us what kind of personality that person has...

You get the picture. Whether these brands describe you or someone you know, each brand you associate with tells a little story about who you are, your standards, what you like and how you live etc.

Thinking about that now, how would you like to be perceived?

Oh and by the way, how someone labels you happens in the first few seconds they come into contact with you. First appearances remember.

Each person and business has a set of values associated with it that tells you a story about the brand. These values will either compel you to buy into the brand or repel you away from it – either way, you are making a visible choice that demonstrates your values to the world. We will talk in much more depth about values later on.

Regardless of age, size, gender, or the position you hold, you understand the importance of branding – Whether consciously you know it or not.

When you run your own business, it's vital you understand the brand called '**YOU**' and that YOUR brand communicates and demonstrates YOUR core values, with which you want to attract the people who you want to spend money with you.

Communicate the right values and your business will flourish to give you the lifestyle you want. The customers you attract will not only value and respect you, they will also treat you as if you are an extension of their family and pay you what you are worth. Imagine what your life will look like and feel like when you have an order book full of your ideal customers? Very rosy indeed.

However, if you communicate a set of values that aren't true to the integrity of your inner you in order to win new customers, you will very likely build a brand that both you and your customers will end up resenting. A brand that doesn't pay you what you are worth, and the type customers you attract will make you miserable.

"Will this really happen if my brand is built on the wrong values?"

Definitely. It will because it's not what you know or even whom you know... it's who knows you and how they label you. If you're putting the wrong values out there, your label will be wrong and you will attract people with the wrong values in return. If you're putting the wrong message out there about your business, you are going to attract the wrong people to it - simple.

Most people brand themselves by association, so when you attract the kind of people you don't want to work with, it's highly likely your ideal customers won't either. By seeing you working with them, they will automatically assume you are the same and disassociate themselves from your brand. Sometimes this is a subconscious decision but most often, it's a very conscious one.

So for example, if you want to position your brand to work with the higher end customers who are prepared to spend more in exchange for quality, yet your brand looks cheap, or is designed in such a way that it attracts lower end customers who don't have the budget to work with you, then any higher end customers will pigeonhole you and paint a picture in their mind that stops them from spending any money with you. They will, perhaps wrongly, assume that you either don't have the necessary experience to work at a higher level, or you aren't interested in playing a bigger game.

They may even choose to work with one of your competitors, simply because they are more expensive than you – positioning them as better than you, even though your expertise may be far superior. The wrong brand cannot be positioned or priced to attract the right customer. It needs to be completely in flow.

The wrong brand can be a total disaster for you, your business, and everyone around you, as they will be affected by you not being happy. Plus, you will not just attract one customer you don't want to work with. You'll attract far more of the less desirable customers than the ones you want and before you know it, you'll have no time or energy left to work with the customers who will really value and appreciate what you do for them. We know because we've been there and have most definitely felt this pain more than once within the first few years of being in business.

On the other hand, if you want to work with small businesses and your brand is designed in a way that positions you as expensive to work with, or too grand, you will repel smaller customers who will, perhaps wrongly, assume you are out of their league and instead you will attract clients who expect a lot more from you than they are perhaps paying. This is great if you only need a few bigger clients to live the life you want to live. However, this could spell disaster if you don't have enough of these customers converting quickly enough to keep you in business.

We have seen it all and the good news is, there are many ways to position yourself to the right customers - as long as the brief you give your design company is highly directive and you are of course working with a design company who truly understands your future brand and your target audience. Whatever brand you choose to be now is what you will be labelled with for the lifetime of your business. Choose wisely now to save having to rebrand your business in future.

Here's an interesting question for you: Would you agree that when you run a more service based/customer facing business, as opposed to a less 'face to face' organisation (selling online products for example), it is important you like the people you do business with? Would you agree? Yes or No?

Let's face it; you could end up spending quite a lot of time with someone you don't like, if you attract the wrong kind of customer when you are providing a face-to-face service for them. Does it make sense to you that if you spend all your working hours with people you don't like and who don't value you, you will become miserable?

The people you spend time with outside of work will also be miserable because you will always be moaning about your customers to them (hey, we are speaking from experience here). Well you might be surprised to find that even when you sell products, this still applies. We have heard many people who sell products online say:

"It doesn't matter for my business, because I'm selling a product to people I'll never meet. I don't need to like my customers!"

But when you look at their customer retention levels, the amount of complaints they receive on a monthly basis, the amount of time taken out of their business to deal with these complaints, and the volume of refunds they have to process, it quickly becomes clear that they aren't running a business that is enjoyable, profitable or one that provides them with the lifestyle they want to live. They aren't attracting all the right customers and even when they do, they aren't following through on the promises they make, giving their brand an incredibly bad name.

Rather than building a brand based on a great reputation, they are instead stressed, building a brand that cannot be trusted and they can never take time out of their business because they are constantly taking the flak from unhappy customers. At the same time they are probably losing money by paying staff to deal with it instead. Do you know someone who is having problems like this in their business? If so, you should give them a copy of this book!

What is worse than anything, in this situation, is that it is very difficult to bounce back in the eyes of your customers, peers and suppliers, once your reputation is in tatters. When trust is lost the brand is fundamentally damaged for life. Get it right now however, and you will reap the rewards of your investment many times over.

So what kind of brand do you want to be and whom do you desire to inspire?

The good news is - and it is VERY good news – you have a chance **NOW** to make a difference to your brand and truly **STAND OUT** as the brand **YOU REALLY ARE**.

It isn't too late to define who you are as a brand. You can start positioning your brand to influence the customers you really want to work with, as soon as you decide who you are and brand yourself in that way. This means you not only need to start living, breathing, walking and talking that brand wherever you are… whether that be at a business networking event, a dinner, a wedding or even in the queue to board an airplane like we did a few years ago! You also need to invest financially in getting an experienced branding company to create that visual identity for you so that your 'trust mark,' or as we call it, your 'visual filtering device' (your logo and strapline/tagline), positions you clearly as the expert when your prospects come into contact with your brand at any customer touch-point that you create.

So how do you create a strong brand that has many magnetic touch points?

Well firstly, your brand isn't something you should leave in the hands of a freelancer who has no experience in the area you want to do business. Like any area of your business, if you want to get a good return from your branding investment, you should invest good money in getting your brand right with the right designer from this point onwards. Going cheap now with a plan to invest later is futile because you will spend wasted time attracting the wrong customers. Think cheap toilet paper and you'll get the picture!

Have you ever bought something and then wished you spent that bit extra on getting the better quality version? Don't treat your brand in the same way that you treat your toothpaste or toilet roll. It's not a commodity, so invest properly in it and respect it from the very beginning. When you respect your brand, your brand will respect you in return, and you shall reap what you sow. Start as you mean to go on, invest properly in your branding and you'll attract your ideal customers a lot faster. Your investment will be paid back a lot quicker too. When you get your branding right, your brand will be an investment that pays you dividends many times over and get this… when you brand your business in the right way to attract the right customers, you can even sell your brand for five times more money than you paid for your branding, before you have even started trading!

We know this because we've done it. You can do this simply because you have already created a strong identity that is a ready-made business for someone to step into and start running with.

An experienced brand designer should create your brand to position you now with the brand you want to have in future - NOT the brand you are now. It should be created as a brand you can step into, rather than one that becomes dated and you outgrow within the first two years. A lot of companies make this mistake and think they can just launch now with a cheap logo, and then create a brand later. This approach adds a considerable amount of confusion to you, your customers, and other people you want to do business with. If your brand identity is strong, you should never need to change it. Rather, simply continue to build on it. You cannot walk and talk one brand while your visual identity presents another face to your business. It would be like having the right face attached to the wrong body. It will feel incongruent to people and they'll have an internal siren going off that something is wrong with your business.

For example, have you ever met someone for the first time and then, after having a conversation with them, you think 'I don't know why I don't like them." They didn't say anything offensive to you and they didn't do anything to upset you, but for some reason, you just don't like them. Something doesn't add up. Well this is exactly what your brand will be putting out there to other people if it isn't consistent to your core mission, vision, values and purpose as we explained before.

Your brand, whether verbal or visual, must be completely consistent from the start, leaving no room in your prospects minds that you cannot be trusted, or that you aren't a credible company to spend money with. It's worth repeating what we said a few pages ago:

Once you have decided who you are as a brand and you have a visual identity that recognises you as the leader in that particular field of expertise to attract your ideal customers, you can then enjoy all the benefits due to you that having a solid, reputable and congruent brand gives you. **All you need to do is decide who you are and then become your brand.**

A great example to share with you that demonstrates this perfectly, is about a dog training expert who just a few years ago was trying to position her dog training business to attract high net worth customers, thus enabling her to command higher fees for her time. She agreed that one way to attract such a customer would be to attract celebrities and so she started to think, act and talk about her brand as if she was already THE 'Go To' Celebrity Dog Trainer in her industry - even though she didn't yet have any celebrities on her client list. She invested in a strong celebrity brand that positioned her as the market leader in her field and started using every opportunity she could to practice her new pitch.

Shortly after, a high profile radio station that she had contacted to get publicity, offered her a radio interview that perfectly promoted her to her target audience as 'THE Celebrity Dog Trainer'. Sure enough a celebrity was listening, one of the Spice Girls no less, and she contacted the radio station to get 'THE Go To Celebrity Dog Trainer's' contact details. What happened? The Spice Girl (who shall remain un-named) became a regular client. Then as a result of her new celebrity status and the circles of influence these celebrities dominated, it wasn't long before other celebrities joined her client list. Within just four months she had gone from the point of invisibility and making a decision about who she was as a brand in the future... to walking, talking, living, breathing, eating and sleeping her brand. She didn't just attract this status position into her life, she attracted the money that comes with it too.

What is the difference between her and every other dog trainer in her area? She simply made a decision to differentiate herself from her competitors and stepped up to the brand she wanted to become.

What lesson is there to learn from this story?

Well you need to make sure your business is branded in a way that positions you as the brand you will be in the future, not the business you are now. It should be a brand that inspires you and others too. It should be simple, attractive and easy to remember. It must communicate a truly congruent message that visually demonstrates the values you want to be known for. Whether you want to position yourself as a family brand such as Amazon, Coca-Cola or McDonalds. A no-frills brand such as EasyJet, Ikea or Poundland. Or you want to position yourself as an inspirational leader such as Nike, Apple or Virgin, you must create an identifiable 'trust mark' logo that tells your brand story and the values that it is built on from the very first time people come into contact with it.

So who are you and what values do you stand for?

On our B.R.A.N.D. Accelerator Programme we teach our students how to define their values and show them the colour psychology behind each value set. We determine what colours your brand should be based on the values upon which your business is being built, in order to attract your ideal customers. It's so important you get this bit right as your business and brand are going to be built on this foundation.

We don't have time to go into your values or colour psychology here in this book. However, if you would like to take the values test, email: advice@howtobuildabrand.org and it will be sent to you.

Here's another great example of why designing your brand based on values is so important…

When we designed the branding for a company called 'Ultimate Music Entertainment' in West Yorkshire, England, we initially spoke to the two business owners about how they wanted to build their brand. They were very clear about the direction of their business and where it was heading. Now most designers at this point would say, 'great, let's get started' and brand them as the business they are now. That is what they understand of the business at this time and they would go straight into visual mode.

However, we believe that you should never create the visual brand for anyone without working on their strategy with them first, simply because assumptions could be made, the brand could go out of date quickly, and a lot of time and money will have been wasted all around. This is not good for the reputation of either company involved.

Rather than base their entire future brand on assumption, we first worked with them on their brand growth strategy. As we delved deeper into their business, we uncovered a massive amount of untapped potential, including the realisation that their existing brand was communicating the wrong values in the wrong colours with the wrong typefaces. The name was wrong and to top it off, the logo was also the wrong shape to attract their target audience.

Their previous designer hadn't stepped into the future and asked these two incredibly talented business owners the right questions. Here they were just a few years later, lots of money spent on a struggling website, struggling to build a brand that just didn't fit their business growth strategy. The brand looked good, but these five major faults alone in the brand identity were putting the ideal potential clients off.

Their brand simply wasn't attractive to the right people. Their new brand identity needed to position them with a different set of values behind the brand, using colours, shapes and typefaces that stood for their core brand values in order to attract a higher level of target clients. It also needed to look more established and position them as the company they wanted to grow into, with several sub-brands designed ready for the company to transform, evolve and expand.

Within a couple of weeks of working on their brand growth strategy, based on the existing company name that they wanted to keep, the new brand concepts had been created and there was a flurry of excitement as our design studio prepared the concepts ready for presentation.

ULTIMATEMUSIC™
E N T E R T A I N M E N T

However, just one day before the brand presentation, one of the two business owners dropped a bombshell…. They announced that our new strategy had sparked them off with lots of ideas about new things they wanted to deliver under their new brand. They agreed that the name we had recommended to them was far more likely to attract the right customers and they now wanted to change their name from Ultimate Voice to Ultimate Music Entertainment!

This could have been a disaster because most design agencies would have to start the whole design process again. However, because we create all our clients brands based around their core values, the logo didn't have to change at all. It was simply a small amend to the wording in the logo design and WHAM, they achieved more impact with a wider offering.

Had we just designed a pretty logo that looked good, without basing it on a solid growth strategy with the brands core values at its heart, the entire logo would have had to been changed. So whomever you get to design your brand identity (hopefully us!), make sure you are working with a company that thinks in this much depth and cares about your future business as if it were their own.

When it comes to values, how important is it that you continue to ONLY work with customers and clients who share the same values as you?

It would be foolish to over-ride your gut instinct, knowing the values your business stands for when it comes to taking clients on; you have something to measure people by, rather than blindly guessing whether you'll get on or not. You will have definitive criteria they have to meet or you'll simply concentrate your time, energy and resources on someone else who does. There were probably cases where all was not as it at first seemed, right?

Have you ever made the mistake of agreeing to something you later regretted? A favour perhaps that ended up costing you a lot more time than initially promised? Or you bought something that looked like a bargain and then paid more than it was worth to get it how you wanted? You will possibly have had a gut feeling that something wasn't quite right at the beginning, but you wanted to believe it was the real deal so you went along with it anyway, only to regret it later. Perhaps you've experienced a relationship like this? Well, you will most definitely encounter this feeling if you take on clients who don't share your values. Here's why…

Many years ago we made the mistake of taking on a client who we had that 'gut feeling' about. They had very different values to us, but we didn't know much about values in those initial first stages of our business, so we didn't know how to recognise them. They were financially motivated and lacked integrity, whereas our top two core values have always been quality relationships and integrity. Knowing what we know now, our core values are non-negotiable and the match then couldn't have been further apart.

Having different values doesn't mean they were not likeable people. On the contrary, they were. However, at that time we hadn't carried out the values exercise that we do now and while we didn't 'feel right' about the relationship, we just didn't know why. This is where we learned a big lesson and if you had been with us in our first designer glass panelled design studio, surrounded by a design and development team of four full time staff at that time, you would have learned a big lesson that would have changed the way you do business too.

We liked these two business owners as people and we couldn't stand to see them in so much pain, so we wanted to help them. They told us how badly they had been let down by two previous design companies and being the trusting people we are, we totally bought into it. At first it seemed to work out really well. But as time went on they were taking advantage of our good nature more and more. Do you recognise this?

Well they became a big drain on our resources, financially, mentally, physically, emotionally and they sucked up a lot of our time and energy. We would go to bed dreading the next day. They would be the last thing on our minds at night and the first thing on our minds when we woke up. Have you ever felt like that about someone you know or something you were doing?

Our gut instinct at the start was telling us, "hang on a minute". How could two companies let them down so badly? Isn't it strange that two companies both did the same thing? Could these people be the common denominator and not the companies they are blaming? Could it be the client who is actually the problem in this case? Why have they had so much trouble finding another provider? How awful that they've spent all the budget on these other two companies, which means we have to do everything at cost to help them in the hope they will follow our advice and pay us back later.'

But even with all of these alarm bells ringing, after all these subconscious thoughts and our 'gut instinct' warning us not to go ahead, we continued to help them because they told such a good story each time we spoke to them. It's clear now that we made a personal, emotional decision, NOT a commercial, business-minded one. The truth then began to unfold. They were always difficult to get hold of when we wanted them, but when it was the other way around and they wanted something in a hurry from us we had to be at their beck and call, almost clicking their fingers to get what they wanted from us. They also never paid on time and it got to the point where we had to start saying no to them after six months because it was not just holding our business back, it was killing it... killing our relationships at home, the atmosphere in our studio and killing us at the same time.

When we started saying no, and offering them alternatives in the nicest possible way, they started to get very rude about it, making demands on our time that they weren't prepared to pay for and threatening ultimatums.

They would go to our team saying we had authorised a request that we clearly hadn't, and a few days later we would find that another project was two days behind because this company had lied to get their way. Not good at all, and in

fact a highly toxic relationship to be in. Consequently, we decided to sack the client because it just wasn't worth what we were going through. It was a very difficult decision to make based on what we thought at the time was a valuable, long-term client relationship to have, but what happened next totally dumbfounded us.

Within the first month of making the decision to sack the client, we noticed we were all finishing work a lot earlier. We were actually starting to enjoy a social life again. The business we were attracting was of a much higher value and connected us with nicer people to work with. We were getting a lot more branding and marketing work from our existing clients because we had the time to dedicate to them again. The offending client just slunk away never to return. The best thing of all was that we were sleeping again at night, looking forward to the next working day.

When we sat back and thought about it with fresh heads on our shoulders, we hadn't realised how much time and energy this client was really draining from us by not sticking to our brand values. We also hadn't accounted for the amount of

opportunities we had missed to work with people who really deserved our time, by having our heads down working for this nightmare client. We then realised we had a number of other clients who were draining our time and resources too. Around this time we had both completed our National Advanced Diploma in NLP (Neuro-Linguistic Programming) and with our new found skills and knowledge in recognising these signs, we drilled down deep into our own core values.

For the first time in our lives, we understood what really drives and motivates us. We learned about our core values and the values of others who we wanted to attract, and those who we wanted to repel. A new standard of client had been set.

We carried out a client grading exercise to determine who should stay and who should go. It couldn't have come at a more perfect time as we were about to start a new marketing campaign. One by one we went through and measured each of our clients based on his or her values compared to ours. If we thought their number one core value was Quality Relationships like ours, they went into the 'Love To Work With' list of people we wanted to work with again. If they also had Integrity as their number two value like ours they went into the 'Premiership' list'. If they didn't share either of these two core values within their top three (based on their performances in the past), they went into a pile of people we would refer to another design agency that we felt shared their values the next time they needed help.

While this sounds like a ruthless measure, your business is so important that nobody should be allowed to undervalue your time where it can be avoided. By making the decision to focus our time only on clients who genuinely valued us and also took action on our advice, within just 6 weeks our turnover doubled just through repeat business alone, and the business grew from a team of 4 to a team of 9 in just over 12 months. Our values are now non-negotiable. We would rather lose a customer than lose our time, because time is something you can never buy back. Would you now agree that your values should be non-negotiable? Yes or no?

When you know who you are and what you stand for, you have a great deal more power in yourself and your business. Your customers and clients have greater confidence in you, respect you and your time more and are more likely to tell others about you because people are attracted to genuine confidence. The lesson here is:

Stick to the values at your core and people will value you more.

When it comes to valuing your time more, a very astute business friend and advisor of ours, Steve Phillip of www.linked2success.co.uk, once said: "If you were stood at a bus stop and someone stole £20 out of your pocket, you'd chase them up the road to get it back, wouldn't you? So why let people steal 20 minutes of your time without doing something about it?"

He had a very good point, wouldn't you agree? Although it might feel uncomfortable for you to say no, or state that you are busy, you must be ruthless with your time or it will just get sucked away by people who don't deserve it, who aren't willing to pay for it, and will likely waste it when they get it anyway. We're just speaking from experience.

Another good friend of ours, business coach and mentor, Lisa Clifford of www.lisaclifford.co.uk, made another excellent point from which you can learn a lot too. We were climbing Pen-y-Ghent together (one of the three Yorkshire Peaks in England), during the summer of 2011 as we trained for the Yorkshire Three Peaks Challenge. As always, the topic of conversation touched on business and on this particular day we were telling Lisa about how frustrated we were becoming with people who wanted our help without paying for our time. Lisa looked pensive for a moment as she took in the words and then said something that we have since taken throughout all our life decisions. She said the following eight words:

"Just because you can, doesn't mean you should".

WOW! This stopped us in our tracks. We realised that yes, we wanted to help everybody and treat everyone equally. But not everybody was ready for our help and not all clients could be treated equally because that's not actually fair on our clients. Let's expand on that statement for a moment. 'Not all clients should be treated equally'... it's usually at this point we hear "But all clients should be treated equally and fairly".

Yes your clients should be treated fairly and yes they should get the value they pay for. However, if you have one client paying £100 and another paying £5000, those two clients must be treated differently either by receiving different products/ services or different levels of that product/service.

The £100 client should get £100 worth of value, not £5000 worth of value for £100. Like-wise the £5000 client should get £5000 worth of value and more of your time, products or resources, not £100. If you treat a £5000 client the same way you treat your £100 client, you will soon lose that client. The ensuing word of mouth publicity will damage your reputation enough to prevent you attracting higher paying clients again in the future. Plus, you will be exhausted and broke by over-delivering products or services to clients who aren't paying enough for it. You are worth more. In fact, this is so important that we need to repeat that again.

YOU ARE WORTH MORE!

If your £100 client calls you up and asks you to deliver something extra for them that the £5000 client is getting, and you say yes **just because you can**, you have just opened yourself up to a whole world of pain. You might feel great and so will this client because they just got something for nothing, and the joy it gave you to make them happy just notched up your feel good factor of significance for a while. However, believe us, it just isn't worth it. Why? Two reasons:

#1. If your higher paying client finds out, they will be extremely unhappy that they are paying more for something other people are getting for free and this could end very badly.

#2. The next time this lower paying client asks you for another extra product or service and you decline, you'll go straight down in their estimations and they'll ask you why you did it last time, but this time you won't. You just damaged your brand because by saying no they now think you have treated them unfairly. Now they'll go and tell everyone how badly they have been treated because they are no longer good enough for your business. That's a lot of bad publicity you don't want or need, isn't it?

The reality is, you should have politely declined the first time, offering them the higher package should they require the extra support. At least they would have upheld their respect for your time. When you give someone something for free, very rarely do they value it and it ends up costing you more in the long run. If this has already happened to you, you will know exactly what we are talking about. If this hasn't happened to you before, make sure it doesn't by following this advice from now on.

Just keep it simple and provide exactly what they are paying for. As harsh as it may seem, it's simply a commercial decision to give your higher paying clients more time, resources, services, products etc. than the clients who are paying you less. Set your standard now, set your levels of service or grade of product and then let your lower paying clients upgrade when they are ready. Always give them great value, unexpected rewards and WOW experiences that encourage them to buy into your future upsells. But never give them more than they are paying for, or their expectations will be shattered at some point along their journey with you, shattering the relationship and your reputation along with it. We have seen it far too often to ignore the facts.

There is most definitely a difference in the way your clients should be treated at certain price points. In fact, you can read a whole article we have written on pricing strategies in Issue 3 of The Brand Brains:
www.howtobuildabrand.org/brand-brain-magazine/publications.

When we thought about what Lisa had said in her statement, *"Just because you can, doesn't mean you should"*, we looked historically at some of our clients in the different 'Price VS Value' brackets to see how many extra things we were doing for people *just because we could*.

To be honest, we weren't shocked by our findings. It didn't take a rocket scientist to realise that our higher paying clients tended to follow our advice. They trusted our expertise, paid us on time and let us get on with the project so they could do what they did best – run their business. The lower paying customers took up more of our working time, wanted more of our resources for nothing, didn't respect our personal time and they didn't want to find the extra money they needed to invest in our higher value services. When they didn't invest in us they only ended up coming back to us once it had gone wrong anyway.

What was more frustrating was that the people who paid less for our time actually valued our time less so they didn't follow our advice, wasted our time and then blamed us for not getting the results they wanted. Have you ever found that?

At least with our higher paying clients we were getting brilliant results because we were doing it for them. Aha, there appeared to be a pattern emerging! It wasn't even that these two grades of client were getting equal treatment, because the higher paying clients were in fact getting less attention, due to the smaller clients that were taking up all of our time. This had to change, so we applied the 'just because you can, doesn't mean you should' rule to every request from that moment on. It will pay you to do the same.

Perhaps you resonate with what we have just shared with you. Maybe you have helped someone who didn't pay you for your time or resources and he or she wasted it. Maybe you gave someone advice and specifically told them what to do, but they didn't do anything about it and then blamed you for it not working. Frustrating isn't it? So the next time you are asked to provide your time for free or for a value less than you know you are worth, knowing 100% that you can do whatever it is you are being asked to deliver, heed this advice. Saying the following eight words could make a huge difference to how you spend your time, where you focus your energy, how much more rewarding your relationships are and how much more money you will make by saying to yourself:

"Just because you can, doesn't mean you should"

This is a key learning skill for you to take away and use in your own business as you grow. It's also one that will help position who you are in the minds of your customers and prospects.

One of the greatest things about knowing who you are as a business is in that moment when someone asks you: "What kind of organisation are you?" and you can tell them exactly who you are and what you do shortly and succinctly from the heart, with absolute clarity, confidence, certainty, courage and conviction.

People still want to buy from confident people and the reason WHY they actually buy from you comes down to the nuts and bolts of who you are as a business. If they like who you are and what you are about, they will more likely trust you and buy from you no matter what you are selling. If they aren't sure about you, on the other hand, it won't matter if you have the greatest widget on the planet, they still won't buy from you even if you are giving it away for free.

Just imagine somebody like Sir Richard Branson, Bill Gates or Steve Jobs answering this question 'Who are you as a business?' Do you think they would babble on and on about all the reasons why they are so great, boring you to death with how great they are? No! You have probably had this happen to you before and you know what it's like to be on the receiving end of it. Would their response more likely be to

sum it all up in one short sentence that gives you the **WOW** factor? We have already heard their answer to this question a number of times for the different products and services they have promoted over the years and yes, you guessed right if you thought it was the second response.

You see, they will have taken time out to consider this question before it was even asked by writing down all the responses they can think of and then picking out the best and most clarified answer of them all. Having done this exercise on launching our very first business together, we were surprised at just how many answers we came up with that had never come to mind before. The standard, sales type answers came up first of all but the more responses we wrote down the better quality the answers became. In fact, it turned out we would have been selling ourselves very short with the first things that came to the forefront of our minds if we'd given up there. We ended up using the responses we came up with after our fourteenth or fifteenth response. It really serves you well to spend some time on this answer and write as many things you can think of. What we were going to say compared to what we now say, after this exercise, is completely different and has changed our results by increased conversions.

Let's take some time now to answer the following questions about who you are as a business and consequently as a brand.

By the way… as you do this exercise, place yourself into the future. Imagine yourself three years from now, talking about yourself and your business as if you have already achieved the success you would love to have achieved – both as a business and the brand you would love to build. If you like to think further ahead, think five years from now or even ten years from now. This way you can create a statement that positions your brand as the brand you want to be, the brand you want to step into in future, and the brand people want to grow with. That is the brand you need to get designed!

Grab your pen, let's get started!

1. What business are you in? (10 words max)

2. What kind of organisation are you?

3. What size is your organisation?

4. Where is your business based?

5. What kind of people / roles do you have within your organisation?

6. How much collective experience do you/your team have in your industry?

7. What are your core services or products?

8. What makes your business special compared to other businesses in your area of expertise?

9. What do your competitors do that you believe should be done differently and why?

10. What do you do that is so genuinely different and innovative to them?

11. In life, what values do you stand for?

12. What values in others do you despise in others?

13. What are some of the things you consider to be a threat to your industry and why?

14. How do you add value to your customers?

15. What character traits make you a great company to work with?

16. Place yourself into the future. If your company could do anything or be anything, what would it do and what would it be?

Now you have a much fuller picture of your business, the next set of questions will create an even greater overview about what kind of brand you will be in the future.

1. If your business were a walking, talking, living, breathing person, what kind of personality would it have? For example, would it be logical, serious, analytical and methodical, or crazy, fun, exciting, adventurous, creative, etc...

2. What would be their favourite type of place to go for a drink? For example, local pub, wine bar, country pub, nightclub, café, etc...

3. What make, spec and colour of car would they love to drive? Be specific, to the finest detail...

4. What kind of friends would they have?

For example, would they be teachers, students, lawyers, accountants, entrepreneurs, tradesmen, CEO's, stock traders, property investors, etc...

5. What kind of clothes would they wear?

For example, would they wear a tie, dress casually, always be formally dressed, etc...

You may think some of these questions aren't relevant to your branding. However, your answers will give you, your designer, your website developer, your marketing manager, and any other person who has responsibility for your business development as you grow, a brilliant overview of what kind of brand you are, who you are as a business, what kind of friends you want to associate your business with and how your brand needs to conduct itself in front of prospective customers. Why is this so important though, we hear you ask? It's important because...

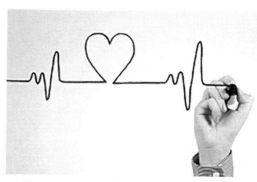

You need to start thinking of your brand as your 24/7 sales force... out there making sales on your behalf even when you are sleeping.

Your brand is the first thing your prospective customers will come into contact with on behalf of your business. It's also the last thing that will go through their filtering system while comparing you to competitors, thinking about whether they trust you enough to spend money with you or not. These are the key questions your customers will be asking about whom to choose:

★ Which brand walks its talk?

★ Which brand do I identify with the most?

★ Which brand looks like it can deliver on its promises?

★ Which brand do I think I am going to get on with best?

★ Which brand has the most testimonials and case studies that help me to trust them?

Just as you wouldn't employ a sales person who is totally the wrong fit to sell your product or service, neither do you want a brand that is a totally wrong fit for your product or service, because your brand IS your sales person. Just as people have a character that others are either drawn to, or compelled to move away from, so does your brand. The personality of your brand has a lot to do with the response you will get.

For example, a brand that dresses casually, drives a family car, and loves to drink in an old country pub, is a very different kind of brand to a brand that dresses formally, drives a sports car and always drinks in a wine bar. A brand that surrounds itself with lawyers as friends is very different to a brand that surrounds itself with local tradesmen. A brand that has a logical or methodical personality is very different to a brand that has a creative or fun personality. Can you see how this will impact on the design of your logo, your strapline, the colours of your brand, etc.? You get the picture.

Make sure you give your answers in as much depth as possible to create a brand that gives your ideal customers a great idea about your brand personality. This will determine the kind of character your brand takes on as it is being designed. Your answers to these questions will make it much easier for your designer to get it right first time for you. If you think you can add more detail to them, or you haven't filled your answers in yet, stop reading any further and DO IT NOW before you move on.

What you've just been through is part of the first stage we take every brand strategy client through on our B.R.A.N.D. Accelerator Programme, because this gives you and the people who are going to help you build your brand, a fundamental understanding of who the brand is, what it stands for, and what promises it deliver. Obviously we cover this exercise in a lot more depth on the course, including looking at your whole business model. However, in this book we want to get you started on the first part of your journey :)

If you skip this part of the process, as many failing businesses do, you are in danger of getting to the stage where your business controls you. You also risk turning into a complete bore that people avoid! You know... that person everyone avoids speaking to, watching, or referring business to because they don't clearly state who they are and you think they are 'fluffy'. In your mind you're thinking, "Well if you can't clearly give me the answer to my questions, how can you deliver exactly what I need you to do?" You can probably call to mind right now someone you know who is like this, can't you?

But you wouldn't want other people to think of you in the same way would you? So don't leave this vital area of communication to chance or risk damaging your business reputation by blagging your way through it. Get this part of the process right **NOW**, and you'll become a magnet in the room, and THE go to expert in your industry. The one people talk about, refer business to and want to spend their money with. As a rule, the shorter and more succinct you can narrow your 'Who are you?' statement down to, whilst still giving a meaningful answer, the better. We go by the principle of getting it across in around 120 words, which should take no more than about 60 seconds to communicate.

Once you have completed this exercise a number of times, and refined what you want to say about your business, write your final answer as if you are talking to your next, best client. Here goes:

Who are you as a business in approximately 120 words?

_____

_____

_____

_____

_____

_____

_____

_____

_____

_____

_____

_____

This isn't a rigid statement you'll keep forever. It's the beginnings of your brand story and you will tell it over and over until you embellish it with other stories as your business grows. We advise you to test it out on people and notice how they react and respond to it. Make a mental note of the following things and become conscious about what people do as you are talking:

★ Do they ask you more questions and eagerly await your response?

★ Do they ask you questions that suggest a lack of clarity? Perhaps you need to change something you are saying?

★ Do they look overwhelmed, fidgety or break eye contact with you?

★ Do they ask you for more detail because you aren't giving them enough, or

★ Do they ask you questions that you consider to be obvious?

Remember, you are the expert in your field. They are not. Their response will give you a goldmine of intelligence that can help you to improve your presentation beyond compare.

This reminds us of a conversation we had with Gill, a cheerful lady reminiscent of Julie Andrews and a branding client we had been referred to, to help her attract better quality clients. Having delivered our 'who are we?' message during the conversation, she asked what we, at first, thought to be an obvious question: "Do I get to keep my brand once you have created it for me?"

"Yes of course", we replied.

"Oh it's just that I've spoken to three other design agencies and they quoted less than you, but when I asked them if I owned the copyright to my brand, they all said no. When I enquired further, it turns out that I'd be committed to get all future design work created by those agencies at a higher price, or it would cost me the same again to receive my brand on a disk that I could take wherever I wanted to go. But you are saying I get to keep my brand once I've paid for it and take it anywhere I like. Is that correct?" She said.

"Really, is that what other agencies do?" We said in amazement. "We've never considered doing that to the people we work with. Once you've paid for it, you own it. Yes we cost more to deliver the work, but that's because there is more thought, research, time, and attention to detail put into everything we do and we package everything up to give you complete control, which takes a little extra time. It naturally costs more for us to do this and get it right first time, rather than cutting corners to make it cheaper and then waste your time going back and forth with amendments to get it right. It's not more expensive because you own it, it's more expensive because it is better quality. You own all the artwork so you can go to any designer or printer in the future and give your artwork to them to continue working on it. That's why none of our clients need to come back to us for rebranding. We get it right first time, every time and our clients stick with us because they know they are getting a great value service. How would you like to proceed?" we said.

"I would like to work with you", she replied.

Now we could have totally dismissed this conversation and answered a question we thought had an obvious answer. But what Gill gave us was a brilliant insight into *what our competitors do, who we are and the value we give our customers in comparison to our competitors.*

This was a golden opportunity to include a fundamental piece of information in our 'Why' statement and position ourselves even further ahead of our competitors. Too many people flat line their presentations at networking events or seminars, bulldozing their way through their pitch because they aren't doing the fundamental things that we are teaching you right now in this book. They just carry on talking about 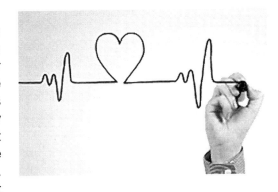 themselves as if it is really interesting to everyone else. They don't think about watching the other person's body language to see if they are glazing over, falling asleep or practically heading for the door. You know the sort don't you? They just continue to do what they've always done without changing anything, yet they expect different results and wonder why business is so quiet?

Einstein would have called this the definition of insanity.

To conclude this first chapter, here is an overview of your task:

#1. Keep shaping, re-writing and editing your "Who Are You?" positioning statement until you are truly happy with it. Once you have a strong and compelling statement that is completely congruent and true to your values, you will know because it will feel right to you.

#2. Practice delivering it over and over until you have it so clear in your mind, it is as natural as breathing oxygen.

#3. Always look for visual and verbal feedback when you're delivering your statement, so you can consistently improve it for next time.

Well done. That's chapter one complete! Let's go to chapter 2 to work on your Mission Statement.

"Miles and Sammy are extremely thorough and their skills complement each other's in a way that is very rare in business. Their business offering is unique and packed with value."

Joe O'Connor, The Transformer

"Sammy & Miles dive deep into the soul of your business to uncover the priceless gems that the world needs to access. They are like midwives, supporting and guiding the birth of your new venture... Perfectly formed to thrive and survive."

Marion Bevington, Tantric Sexpert

"Sammy and Miles helped me to reconnect my personal values to my business. It made me realise that the message I was sending out to my customers was totally wrong. Since getting back into alignment with my values, I am now launching another business doing what I love."

Rafael Dos Santos, Entrepreneur

CHAPTER 2...

What Is Your Mission?

When the reason you want to be in business becomes greater than the reason you need to be in business, you will be compelled to achieve your goals in a much greater way.

We all have our reasons for going into business. Perhaps you have always been entrepreneurial. Maybe you are going into business with someone you know. Perhaps you were made redundant or you are about to take redundancy. Maybe you want to turn your hobby into something you can earn money from. Perhaps you are stepping up to inherit the family business. Whatever your reason for being in business, you now need a much stronger and compelling personal reason as to why you want to continue growing it.

Most websites and other promotional literature have a mission statement on them. This is because a mission statement is a vital component in the brand-building process. Your company mission statement compliments your brand story, demonstrates who you are, tells people why you exist to serve them and sits nicely alongside your positioning statement. Without a company mission statement, your business looks as though it has no purpose or greater reason to exist.

You already completed a great deal of work in chapter one and that will help you create your mission statement. However, for this exercise we want you to focus more on creating your own personal mission statement. Why do we want you to focus on creating your personal mission rather than your company mission? Because it is important you look after yourself while growing your business. Your business must exist to serve what you want in your life - not become your life.

A personal mission statement will help you stay true to your purpose. Without it, you are in danger of becoming like 97% of the other business owners who right now feel tired, stressed, undervalued, underpaid, unhappy, and burned out in a business that has left them with no life or fulfilling relationships outside of it.

What kind of life is that? Not a fulfilling one that's for sure. What is the point of having a flourishing business if your quality of life is diminishing? How do we know? Because you guessed it... we have been there and it was extremely PAINFUL.

It's one thing to have a great mission for your business so you can serve others. But it's quite another to ensure you serve yourself and the people you love outside of work.

Having been on the receiving end of business burn out, we really don't want you to have to go through it as well, or go through it again if you have already been there too. Quite simply, we forgot our own personal reasons for growing the business and lost touch with the life we had outside of it. Instead we got caught up so much in helping other people, focusing on growing our six figure business, and consistently doubling our results month after month and year after year. And yes, we made the mistake we mentioned in chapter one. We were over-delivering on customer service and running the business far too hands-on.

Inevitably something had to give and what suffered most were our personal lives, relationships, friendships and health. In fact we both suffered to the point of divorce, insomnia, near stroke, regular heart pains and a huge amount of lost time with loved ones. What hurts most is that we will never get that time back. We learned a valuable lesson that we can now pass on to you.

Had we looked after both ourselves and our relationships outside of work, at the same time as looking after our business, these are challenges we wouldn't have faced and our business would probably have flourished even more. But we didn't and you don't need to go through that too. We realised the error of our ways when we attended Andy Harrington's Power to Achieve event in Heathrow, London in July 2011 (www.powertoachieve.co.uk). It was the first time in five years that we had taken three consecutive days out of the business to do something that wasn't work. Quite simply, it was truly transformational.

During the event we were able to step out of the business and look from the outside in – in all areas of our life. We realised what a fun life we were missing out on by being so caught up in business all the time. We realised that our nieces and nephews were growing up without really knowing who we were. We realised that the people we loved most were getting older quickly and we were missing out on their lives. At one point we were forced to take a good hard look at our lives and think about what would happen if we didn't change what we were doing. It was the harsh wake-up call we needed and it took a very scary panic attack on the way home from the event to face up to the fact that something needed to change, or we would die for our business.

We knew that our lives were about nothing other than business. Because we enjoyed what we did so much, we weren't making time for anything else. Our friends were business friends. Our drinking buddies were our staff. Our spare time was filled with discussing what we were working on and what we would like to do to grow business profits by an extra 200% in the next quarter. Even dating was a nightmare because we had nothing to talk about other than business, so you can imagine how boring we must have been to our dates! We laugh about it now, but it was certainly no joke at the time.

Year on year we continued to double the turnover of the business, but when it came down to the real nuts and bolts of how happy and personally fulfilled we were in our personal lives, it was pretty much zero. Something had to change.

By creating our personal mission statements to demonstrate what we personally stand for, and what we wanted to have achieved in our lifetimes, it gave us a huge boost and interestingly we became more productive. For the first time in a long time we had a reason to finish work. Over the eighteen months that followed, we changed pretty much everything in our business to serve the lives we now live. In fact, we encouraged the majority of our employees to start their own flourishing businesses and we now pass business to them in a way then serves us all.

Our brand strategy has evolved into a plan that delivers a great deal of fun and adventure in our business. We use the technology that is available to us to communicate with our teams and this enables us to spend quality time doing what we love with the people we love, whenever and wherever in the world we want to do it.

Why do we tell you this? Because you have the opportunity now to do the same, before you get caught up in the same position that we did. Learn from our painful mistakes and give yourself the gift of foresight by creating your personal mission statement now and then stick to it come hell or high water.

Let's be clear about the difference between your company mission statement and your personal mission statement. Here are our definitions:

Your company mission statement is:

★ The driving force of your company.

★ The reason for your company's existence in the eyes of your customers.

★ Something your workforce or outsourcers focus on and align with.

★ Something your suppliers trust and look up to.

★ Confidence for your customers that you are an organisation that cares.

Your personal mission statement is:

★ The driving force of your life.

★ The reason for your personal existence in terms of what you want from life – to achieve, to be, to see, to do and to have.

★ Something to focus on and align with when things get tough.

★ A greater reason outside of yourself to achieve your goals.

★ A good reason for your family and friends to support you and hold you accountable to your mission if you go through a tough patch or start to stray from the plan.

For example, the difference between our company mission statement and our personal mission statement at How to Build a Brand is:

Our Company Mission Statement...

*"How To Build A Brand supports growing businesses internationally by consistently testing, innovating, developing and sharing the most powerful brand building concepts, techniques, strategies and ideas that will **dramatically increase the value and credibility of your business.***

*Our team is committed to growing How to Build a Brand through **embracing technology,** developing **strong partnerships** and placing strong emphasis on providing **high levels of customer satisfaction.***

We strive for excellence, always aim to exceed expectations and provide valuable information to maximise your business potential.

*Retaining our competitive edge through **innovation** is central to how we operate. We are not interested in being the biggest, but we certainly do want to **be the best.**"*

Our Personal Mission Statement...

*"To enjoy a life filled with **love, laughter, passion, fun** and **adventure** with the people we love, while **travelling the world** and **inspiring** people to get paid for doing what they love. This gives us the freedom to work with charities close to our hearts, such as Basket Brigade, Street Love, as well as actively help other people who are less privileged than us".*

As you can see, our company mission statement tells you what we do to serve YOU as our customer, how we do it and who we are as an organisation.

Our personal mission statement, on the other hand, tells you who we are as people behind the business and what we care about. It also shares our reasons for why we get up in the morning and continue to work through the many challenges that confront us all the time.

Your reason 'WHY?' has always been, and will always be more important than the 'HOW?'

The 'how?' becomes far less challenging when you have a compelling reason to get what you want. It's incredible how resourceful you get when you really want something badly enough.

For example, seeing the beaming smile of a cold, tired, and hungry homeless person when giving them a cup of tea, a blanket and something hot to eat is hugely rewarding for us. Especially when other people are just walking past them as if they don't exist. Spending the day putting together food baskets and delivering them to families who are too poor to eat on Christmas day is massively gratifying when you sit down to your own Christmas meal and truly appreciate what you have. Just stopping in the street to give your time to help a fragile person cross the road or to help a struggling mother pack her shopping is enough to fill our hearts and want to help others more.

However, these things are only possible if you are in a good place yourself. You cannot truly help someone else until you yourself are strong enough to give to others. Here is a really good analogy to demonstrate this point: Picture a cup resting on a saucer. You are the cup and the people in your life are the saucer. As you continue to invest your time, talents, passions and energy in yourself, the cup will fill and eventually it will overflow onto the saucer. You are being refreshed and the people around you get to enjoy the overflow of your time and support. It sounds strict, but you can only put other people first for so long. Work on filling up your cup so that you will have something to share with others.

For the same reason emergency instructions on an airplane instruct you to put the oxygen mask on yourself before you give oxygen to others. It is no good you giving it all away and then depriving yourself. You are limiting yourself by not being what you are truly capable of when you are strong. The same goes for your business. When you are strong you can help others to become strong. So make your mission clear, set your intention to make it happen and then you will have all the time and money in the world to help others. Even when the going gets tough you'll do whatever it takes if you are doing something for a reason greater than yourself (especially for others), which gives you a compelling reason to succeed... whatever the weather.

We say 'whatever the weather', because if business were so easy then the sun would always be shining and everyone would be doing it. But what happens with so many business owners is they don't put a solid brand strategy in place at the beginning of their business. They don't have a mission for the business or themselves, and they don't believe they should take time out of their businesses to do what you are doing now to create one as their business grows. Why waste years running your business in a way that is nowhere near as productive, efficient, or profitable as it could be? Why not take time out now to ensure the time you do spend on your business in future is productive and will achieve its purpose – for the business, for your customers and for your life?

Unfortunately they aren't like you. They don't think this way. So, what happens to these business owners who don't do what you are doing now? Well, when the weather gets rough, as is inevitable at times, they have nothing in place to see it coming and will have to batten down the hatches. They won't have a plan to keep them strong and steady, or to help them continue building their brand as the storm hits. Quite often their business dies and they go back to employment until they realise they aren't doing what they want to do and then, they usually try again. But they make the same mistakes again because history so often repeats itself and they didn't really learn the lesson.

The reason they quit their first diet is probably the same as why they will quit their next one. The New Year's resolution they made on 31st December last year that they failed to complete will likely be the same resolution they make this year. The problems they had in their first business will likely surface again in their second. The problem with these people is that they don't do what you are doing now. They don't take the necessary steps and time out to create the strategy for their business growth, and look to others who have already achieved what they want to do. Instead they become insular, usually focus on the money they need and voilà… history repeats itself. Congratulations on not being like them. If you don't have a brand strategy or a mission, the business will naturally lack focus.

A lack of focus means no consistent messages will be going out about your business and you have no compelling reason to continue when you most need it. No consistent messages going out about your business means people don't know you exist, will forget that you exist or will be confused about why you exist. Whichever way, they will stop listening to you or get confused. When people stop listening or get confused it leads to doubt on a large scale. Doubt leads to a lack of customer conversion and a poor reputation. Lack of customer's and/or a poor reputation mean no sales. No sales equal no business and certainly no lifestyle.

So how can you give your business more certainty, significance and flexibility?

Putting your personal mission statement in place now, as part of your brand strategy, will give you a greater reason to continue with the mundane and sometimes laborious tasks that you need to do when the going inevitably gets tough and your goal is out of reach. Sharing your mission and goals with your team as well will clarify their reasons why they too are helping you achieve your goals. And a great reason to share your personal mission with your customers is that you will attract loyal people who love what your business stands for, will pay you what you are worth and support you in your cause. Anyone who doesn't believe in your mission can go and do business somewhere else. After all, there is plenty of business to go around and you don't want to work with people who don't appreciate what you stand for, as discussed in chapter one.

Knowing your mission and why you want to achieve the goals you set for yourself will give you the reason you need to keep going. By sharing that mission with your clients, family, colleagues and friends, you will achieve greater significance in your industry and you will create some great publicity by being someone in your local community who genuinely deserves success.

You will also be strong enough to weather any storms that come your way and bounce back a lot quicker than your competitors because you will face the storm head on to achieve your mission and live the life you want to live.

Before we get started on creating your personal mission statement, please be warned that you can actually turn this creative process against you if you do not adhere to the following advice:

As you start thinking about the life you want to live, what you want and how you want to do it, you may naturally fixate on the life you don't have yet. You may start to focus on how big the gap is currently between all that you don't have, everything you haven't accomplished yet, and the things that you are not. Therefore it is absolutely vital that if you feel yourself going down this route of negativity, you must clear your mind, centre yourself and celebrate all the successes you have achieved that led you to the point in life where you are now...

Breathing, alive & ready to thrive!

Let's take some time out now to focus on your personal mission statement. Here are five areas that will help you to think about what is most important to you, the life you want, and how you are going to achieve it. Answer in as much detail as possible.

By the way, the more detail you give and the more specific you are, the more choice you will have from which to create a true personal mission statement that really stands for what you believe in and what you want to achieve.

Grab your pen and get started.

1. Family and Relationships…

a. Who are the most important people in your life?

b. Why is it important to you that your business gives you the freedom to spend more time with them?

c. What would life be like if they weren't around or you didn't see them?

d. How could you make the biggest difference to their lives through this business?

----

e. What are you going to do from now on to build a business that will make the biggest difference to their lives and to your own?

----

f. How will you know when you are making that difference?

g. What are you going to do to ensure you continue making that difference?

h. What is the first thing you are going to do to ensure this happens and by when?

----

2. Lifestyle...

a. Your business is going to provide you with your ideal lifestyle. What does that ideal lifestyle look like, sound like, and feel like to you?

----

b. What is important to you about living the lifestyle you just wrote down?

c. What will that lifestyle give you and your family that you don't have now?

d. What would it mean for you to truly live the lifestyle of your dreams?

_____

_____

_____

_____

_____

_____

_____

_____

_____

_____

e. How would your life and the lives of the people around you be affected if you didn't have your dream lifestyle?

_____

_____

_____

_____

_____

_____

_____

_____

_____

f. What do you need to do to make sure you achieve the lifestyle goals you have written down so far?

....

....

....

....

....

....

....

....

....

g. Achieving your dreams and goals is much easier when you break it down into smaller chunks. What interim goals could you put in place en-route to the dream lifestyle you have written down?

....

....

....

....

....

....

....

....

....

3. Emotional...

a. What are some of the things you must achieve to be completely fulfilled and happy before you die?

_____

_____

_____

_____

_____

_____

_____

_____

b. Why are these things that will make you fulfilled an absolute MUST to you?

_____

_____

_____

_____

_____

_____

_____

_____

_____

c. What will it mean to you and the people around you if you do not achieve the things?

---

d. How will it impact on others around you when you DO achieve them?

---

e. What will your life look like once you have achieved complete fulfilment and happiness?

_____

_____

_____

_____

_____

_____

_____

_____

f. What micro-goals are you going to put in place to ensure you do achieve them?

_____

_____

_____

_____

_____

_____

_____

_____

_____

4. Business...

a. When you step five years into the future, what does your business look like, sound like and feel like at its most successful?

_____

_____

_____

_____

_____

_____

_____

b. What would achieving that level of success enable you to be, do and have with the people around you?

_____

_____

_____

_____

_____

_____

_____

_____

_____

_____

c. What would it mean to the lives of the people around you?

_____

_____

_____

_____

_____

_____

_____

_____

d. How would you spend your time making the most of it all?

_____

_____

_____

_____

_____

_____

_____

_____

e. What would it mean for you to see the people around you benefiting from your success?

f. What else would your business enable you and others to do once you have achieved this level of success?

g. Where would this level of success take you personally?

_____

_____

_____

_____

_____

_____

_____

_____

_____

h. What do you need to do to ensure you achieve this level of success in your business?

_____

_____

_____

_____

_____

_____

_____

_____

_____

i. What is the first thing you are going to do to ensure you achieve it and when are you committing to achieve it by?

---

5. Financial...

a. What would you be able to do more of if you earned more money and had more free time?

How much personal income would you like to generate in the next twelve months and what would you spend it on? This is so you can see the amount of extra things you will be able to do when you are attracting great quality customers and bringing more money in. Let your imagination run loose and have fun with this. Make your list and then total it up at the bottom so that you know exactly what income you need to generate.

For example:

3 week holiday to Thailand. 1st class

tickets and all expenses paid   Cost: _£5,500_

1 year golf membership

    Cost: _£5,500_

Your turn...

    Cost: _____

    Cost: _____

    Cost: _____

    Cost: _____

_____

_____   Cost: _ _ _ _ _ _ _

_____

_____   Cost: _ _ _ _ _ _ _

_____

_____   Cost: _ _ _ _ _ _ _

_____

_____   Cost: _ _ _ _ _ _ _

_____

_____   Cost: _ _ _ _ _ _ _

Total amount over 12 months: _ _ _ _ _ _ _ _ _ _ _ _

What does this total annual figure break down to as a monthly figure?

Amount broken down per month: _ _ _ _ _ _ _ _ _ _ _ _ _

   b. How many of your lowest priced products/ services would you need to sell
   in order to achieve that monthly figure?

_____

_____

c. Alternatively, what products or services could you sell less of at a higher price?

_____

_____

_____

_____

_____

d. What products or services could you sell more of at a higher price?

_____

_____

_____

_____

_____

_____

e. What would happen (both positive and negative) to your business if you raised your prices by 30%?

_____

_____

_____

_____

_____

_____

f. What would happen to your lifestyle if you increased your prices by 30%?

g. What added value could you include with your existing products or services that would enable you to increase your prices by 30% to the customers you want to work with? Write a number of different ideas below:

h. What other higher priced products or services could you add to your existing offering that compliments what you already deliver?

----

i. What kind of clients would buy these from you at a higher price?

----

j. How might it affect your business in a negative way?

k. What could you do to minimise the negative impact it may have?

l. What would it mean to your family or those closest to you if you focused on your personal financial goals?

_____

_____

_____

_____

_____

_____

_____

_____

m. What would you be prepared to do less of in order to achieve your personal financial goals?

_____

_____

_____

_____

_____

_____

_____

_____

n. What would you be prepared to do more of in order to achieve your personal financial goals?

_____

_____

_____

_____

_____

_____

_____

_____

o. What could stop you from achieving your personal financial goals?

_____

_____

_____

_____

_____

_____

_____

_____

_____

p. What is the first thing you are going to do to take you closer to achieving your goals and when by?

Finally...

A great way to summarise how you want to have left the world a better place for having had you in it is to write down what would be written on your tombstone. This will help you to define how you want people to remember you – not just after you have emigrated to heaven, but now, whenever you come into contact with someone who you want to remember you in a certain way.

How would you want them to have remembered you?

Here are a few pointers to help you out:

★ Who you were

★ What kind of life you lived

★ Who you helped/touched, and

★ What legacy you left for the world to be a greater place

Grab your pen. Here goes!

If you are anything like us, you will have learned a lot about yourself and your goals throughout this chapter. Perhaps you surprised yourself with some of the things you wrote down. Maybe you realised you are closer to achieving your goals than you thought. Or perhaps you even realised that you don't need to build such a big business to earn what you need and live the lifestyle you want to live after all.

The rewards and pay-offs are huge when you invest the necessary time and resources into getting this vital part of your brand strategy right for your business. They are even greater when you continue to build and evolve your strategy once you have achieved the great business and life you dreamed of. Your brand strategy isn't something you 'do' at the beginning of your business and then forget about. Rather it is something that evolves with your business as you grow.

Our brand strategy document started off around twenty pages when we first sat down to conceptualise our business and answer all of the questions we have just asked you. It's now hundreds of pages long, with different sections for Business Development, Marketing, Financial, Health, Spiritual, Family and Relationships, Charitable, Emotional, Business Operations, Project Management, Email Templates, Brand Guidelines, Preferred Suppliers, HR, Business Ideas, Products, Future Projects, Sub-Brands, etc... It supports our systems and ensures that everyone in our company is singing from the same hymn sheet. Since we started our business it has been opened at least once a day and it continues to evolve as our business changes.

It has been used to create all of our core documents, company literature and external communications, ranging from a two-page document we give our strategic partners to increase referrals and introductions to new customers, through to staff welcome packs, systems documentation and social media

communications planning. Our brand strategy beats at the very heart of every communication that goes out about our business. Oh and we have a brand strategy for every business, because each company has a different DNA, a different heartbeat, a different brand and consequently different messages that go out to describe and promote it. After all, it is no coincidence that the last three letters of the word BR**AND** when spelt backwards spell **DNA**.

People make comments to us all the time about how lovely it must be to run our business from wherever we are in the world. However, we only work this way and manage our business using the technologies that are available to us because this is the way we decided we wanted to work when we re-evaluated and evolved our brand strategy.

We didn't foresee us working from different countries when we first started, and we thought it would take us a lot longer to get where we are. However, we are able to do what we are doing now because we continue to grow and evolve our strategy at least every 3 months. This means our business is always flexible to the business climate. We foresee what is happening in our industry and can be what we call 'pre-active' rather than 'pro-active' to ensure what we do enhances our lives and relationships, rather than affecting them. This is also what we help our clients to do when we create their brand strategy for them.

Having learned the hard way how not to run a business in our own separate companies before we built our first business together, it taught us some of the valuable lessons that we are now sharing with you in this book. What you do with them is up to you.

You can choose to stay where you are and watch others continue to grow around you. Or you can design and create the life you want to live by being specific about your mission and reason for doing what you do. Only by knowing your mission can you truly attract the kind of clients who care about the same things you do and who will pay for you to live the life you choose to live. Either way, as our very good friend and Finance Director, Roy Lancaster, from the North of England would say; "you don't get ought for nought"

Now it's time to put what you know into practice and create your final personal mission statement. There is no right or wrong way to write this. Just write it from the heart and make it meaningful to you. As before, when you were writing your positioning statement, we will start by writing your first draft. For now, let your words unfold across the page without worrying about perfecting sharp, fancy sentences. Write whatever comes to mind easily and refer back to your previous answers in this exercise when needed.

Be honest with yourself. The more honest you are with yourself, the stronger and more applicable your statement will be.

Then finally, as before, write your second or third drafts as needed until you are happy with your final personal mission statement. By the way, we have given you enough room to write it. If it is any longer than this, it won't mean as much as if it is short, to the point, powerful and punchy.

Grab your pen, here goes…

Personal mission statement version 1:

You probably wrote a lot down that doesn't need to be there. Now see how you can revise it to make it shorter, sweeter and more concise.

Personal mission statement version 2:

_____

_____

_____

_____

_____

_____

_____

_____

_____

Personal mission statement version 3:

_____

_____

_____

_____

_____

_____

_____

_____

_____

Now you have at least three versions of your personal mission statement, go back through each one and ask the following questions...

★ Which one stands out the most for me?

★ How could I improve it further?

★ Is it compelling enough for me?

Once you are happy with it, write your final personal mission statement here:

My personal mission statement is...

Congratulations! You now have a compelling personal mission statement. You will also by now have at least 50 key messages written down about your business that you can tailor to promote yourself immediately, and even more reasons why your prospective customers and clients should do business with YOU over and above anyone else.

What you have done by cementing your personal mission statement is to give yourself the very best chance of success when you are faced with your toughest challenges.

There will be points along your business journey when it feels like summer and you have an abundance of work. But then you get so busy working on what you already have that you forget to continue feeding and watering your harvest and a drought catches you unaware.

There will be times when you feel like it has been winter for too long, work is cold and potential clients are frosty because they are not ready to buy from you yet. Then all the work you have been doing, and the investments you have made to come into play and this converts into a great avalanche of business and you are swamped again. Just as you start to get used to the ever-changing seasons, a competitor comes along like a hurricane, swooping up business that could have been yours if you had just kept your eye on the forecast for potential threats.

Keeping up to date with your brand strategy will help you to foresee these challenges and ensure it is sunny all year long for your business. However, should a cloud appear, just look at your mission statement to give you a compelling enough reason to keep going. Blow that cloud away and persevere through all the seasons to achieve your goal.

Congratulations! Chapter 2 is now complete. Let's move onto Chapter 3 where we will define who your ideal customer is.

"I recommend Sammy & Miles for brand strategy and also increasing your customer conversions through a focused analysis of your business."

Richard McMunn,
BookPublishingAcademy.co.uk

"Sammy and Miles are like professional make-up artists who give businesses a great foundation and then make them look beautiful. Imagine Hollywood. This duo creates blockbusters."

Steven Woodward,
Website Developer

"Miles and Sammy are dynamic, individual, personal & passionate branding and marketing leaders who are exceptional at understanding and helping people in business to achieve their goals."

Alexander Vince, Entrepreneur

CHAPTER 3...

Who Is Your Ideal Customer?

Your brand is your individual trust mark and sorting device for those prospective customers who are looking to buy what you sell. It's what people use to make a distinction between buying from a company that they trust and bond with, versus a company they don't share values with or feel a connection with.

Your logo is also a mark of authority. It will either give them feelings that they want to buy from you and remember you forever, or instantly forget you and never return. This is a crucial point for you because, if your ideal customer doesn't feel what you deliver is aimed directly at them, you may have quite possibly lost them forever to one of your competitors.

Whoever your ideal customers are, it's no good investing your time, resources and energy into attracting them to your brand if you don't yet have a brand that engages them when they get there. You could drive 1000 new visitors to your website every day for example, but if they don't trust you when they get there, or see what they are expecting to see within the first 3-4 seconds, they will click off of your website and onto another to buy from your competitor. While you cannot guarantee that every person who clicks on your website is going to buy your products and/or services, you can be more certain they will spend money with you if you have done everything you can to match your brand solution to their pain or problem.

It's up to you as the owner of your business, or a manager of the business you represent, to create an identity and build a brand your prospective customers can trust, immediately associate with, instantly connect with, totally bond with, and will have them happily tapping into their bank account to spend their money with you.

If you receive lots of questions about your product or service, have a low conversion rate, have to constantly explain what it is you do, spell your company name out all the time, find your business is changing direction quickly, or you receive an unexpectedly higher than average return/refund rate, these are sure signs that your brand isn't understood by your target audience or it has changed and needs to be developed further to adapt accordingly.

If you don't seriously invest in your brand, how can you possibly expect other people to seriously invest in you?

It takes an experienced design team at least two to three days of careful thought, strategic planning, visualisation of the future, specialist research, targeted customer profiling, skilled positioning methods, and a natural creative talent to design a number of logo concepts and brand designs that will position you specifically to the target customers you want to attract. This process, when delivered properly, is managed by a branding specialist and their graphic design team. You'll get the perfect brand for your business working this way, because the branding expert is strategic while a graphic designer is tactical. The branding expert is constantly out on the front line, testing and measuring to see what works and what doesn't for each specific business, while the graphic designer has his or her head down in a studio somewhere accessing their creativity from within – two different skill sets that when brought together are very powerful. One without the other however, just will not work, as you may have already found out.

Once you have chosen your future brand from the concepts shown to you, that brand is then applied to each of your customer facing touch-points to ensure every interaction you have with a future customer is completely consistent from your business cards and stationery, to your website, brochures, email signature and social media channels, etc...

From concept to completion, the proper brand design process should take around five days to complete and will cost you between £2,000 and £5,000 depending on who you work with and what part of the country you are buying it from. It's like going to the hair salon and working with a junior stylist or the salon owner. Which one do you think is going to give you the better haircut? The one who has been doing it for a short time, or the one who has lived and breathed it for their entire career? Branding your business properly is a very time intensive and front loaded process. Invest any less and your designer is probably going to cut corners to cut the cost.

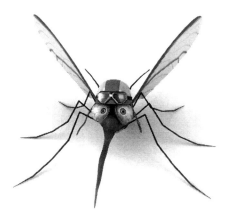

Five days might seem like a lot of work just to create one little logo design that represents your business. However, as has been proven time and again, the smallest things can take the longest time and make the biggest difference to your business. You only need to spend one night in a room with a mosquito to know that size doesn't matter – it's what is packed inside it that counts! So is this part of your business building process worth investing in? You bet it is.

So many business owners go wrong at the branding stage. They try to take the place of the branding expert to cut costs and go direct to the graphic designer or cheaper online alternative. Bad move. A graphic designer or online logo design service doesn't have anywhere near the same level of commercial or strategic experience as the branding expert and neither does the business owner. With the greatest of respect, it is like the blind leading the blind. They both come up with something nice together at the beginning and get excited about the future.

However, two years later when the business is still struggling to get off the ground, the business owner is exhausted, frustrated, financially struggling and blaming the designer for getting it wrong. It's not the designer's fault however; as they just followed the brief they were given. The buck lies with you who, the person who made the decision to cut out the branding expert in the first place and not seek specialist help. I guess this is where you could be right now. Hopefully you are reading this before you make the same mistake.

A £5000 investment is a drop in the ocean compared to how much money you are losing when people aren't attracted to the brand you have. You can charge far more for a well-branded product or service than you can for one that has a 'kind of' brand or no brand at all. Look at Nike versus HiTech, for example. They both sell sports footwear, yet one has an immediately recognisable identity - even without the name displayed on it and the other has a product with a typeface on it. One charges £200 for a pair of trainers, while the other charges £20 and the type of customer it attracts still thinks £20 is too expensive. This is the difference a good brand can make to the kind of customers you attract and what they are willing to spend with you.

We have seen business owners cut corners hundreds of times over the years and it isn't pretty. Can you see how this part of the process has the potential to go VERY BADLY WRONG if a branding expert does not set in place the right foundational brand growth strategy for your business first? Plus a lot of time, energy and money are wasted in the process like this. You wouldn't expect to build your ideal family home on a plot of land without first speaking to an architect, getting a land survey and developing the right foundation for your particular property would you? So too must you apply this same thinking to your business.

If you lay a foundation that is too small for your business, it will topple over and hurt a lot of people in the process. If you lay a foundation that is too big, your customers may find it difficult to get to you. Your foundational brand growth strategy must be absolutely right for your business and it must be flexible so that it can expand as your business grows, like the strategies our students create on our B.R.A.N.D. Accelerator Programme.

A brand growth strategy is not a 'one size fits all' for every business. You can't just pick up any old template and build it up from there. YOUR brand strategy is totally unique to you and is right for your business only, just like your fingerprint. Make sure you work with an expert who will work with you from the ground up. You do not want to work with a company who uses a one-size fits all approach.

To create your business identity without the direction of a branding expert, is to set off on your journey of a lifetime without a Sat Nav.

Create The BRAND For Your Business

Make Your Brand Visible To Ideal Customers

Branding Specialist

Graphic Designer

THE TWO WORK IN HARMONY TOGETHER

Let's set out the responsibility of each role in its most basic form before we go any further, so it's clear to you who needs to do what for your business as you move forward…

Branding Specialist:

Branding specialists are the driving force of your company image and identity. Your branding specialist should work with you to create and oversee:

★ Your brand strategy.

★ Your marketing & communications plan to attract your ideal clients.

★ Your branding brief for the graphic designer.

★ Your website design brief for the website designer.

★ Coaching support for the lifetime of your business to ensure you are continually building your brand in a way that attracts your dream customers.

This is because a branding specialist is best placed to strategically direct and oversee the process that will get you the greatest response, who with, where, how and why.

Graphic Designer:

The graphic designer will then design the logo and graphics that are set out in the design brief given to them as overseen and managed by your branding specialist.

Once your logo design has been approved, your branding specialist will oversee the design of your stationery and marketing materials, including the design of your website with the website designer, to ensure there is complete brand consistency across every customer touch point. Your website design will then be given to your website developer to build your website, ready for you to add your content.

By the way, your branding specialist can also create your logo design, website design and marketing materials for you because they will have worked their way up from starting as a graphic designer to specialise in branding. If they are not designing it themselves they can direct it extremely well because they know how it should be done efficiently, effectively and creatively.

Website Developer:

Your website developer is responsible for the DEVELOPMENT of your website - NOT the design of your website. They are given a website design and will create the structure (using programming code) that makes it easy to use when your customers click on a button.

A website developer is logical and thinks systematically in programming code, while a website designer is creative, knows how to design a website that works for your customers and thinks in more of a visual form.

Just like the branding specialist and graphic designer - please don't try to mix the two into one person as the results can spell disaster. Neither the website developer nor the website designer necessarily know an online strategy that will work. They can only interpret that from someone who does (branding or online marketing specialist) and then turn that into the brand themed, working website.

Website Designer:

Your website designer is responsible for the DESIGN of your website - NOT the development of your website. This is not a job for a graphic designer either. That it why website design should be created by a website designer and your marketing material graphics should be created by your graphic designer.

The main responsibility of your web designer is to ensure your website is appealing to your ideal customers and, as a result, both catches their attention and engages them to look further.

As well as making your website look visually appealing to the eye, your web designer should also be experienced in various user experience techniques. User experience design looks at the way in which your ideal customers will interact with your website. Different types of customer will be looking for a different type of user experience, so you must ensure you are working with a website designer that has experience in working with a large variety of clients, for whom they have successfully delivered a design that converts. Ask your website designer for introductions to some of their clients so you can get an idea of their results straight from the horses mouth. Also make sure you are working with a company who already has experience of targeting the ideal customers you want to work with. By working with someone who understands these key principles, you will maximise the opportunities your website converts for you, such as clicks through to more information, upsells, down-sells or purchases.

You – The Business Owner:

You, as the business owner, should concentrate on bringing it all together by building, growing and running your business. By focusing on profit generating activities and following the agreed brand strategy to deliver great quality service to your customers. You should also ensure the communications plan is delivered either by yourself or by a marketing manager.

The more you come away from focusing your attention on your business to interfere with something you don't know about, the more customers you are neglecting to support, which means you will be making less money than you have the potential to make. Leave your branding specialist, graphic designer, website designer, and website developer to do what they do best and in turn, you do what you do best. That way you will get the best results out of everybody, including yourself. The more you micromanage, the less they will do and the less effective you will become.

When you work with a good branding company, they will manage this whole process for you so you only have to deal with one person, making it far easier on you to just let them handle it all and approve everything with you as they go.

It's important you continue to liaise with your branding specialist on at least a quarterly basis, once your brand has been launched, to ensure your brand stays true to your growth strategy as your company expands and evolves. Keeping in regular contact with your branding specialist will also ensure you are informed of all the new ways you can reach your target customers. A good branding specialist will be constantly testing and measuring brand exposure, visibility strategies and direct response marketing techniques. While this may sound like we are putting graphic designers down in their ability to create a great logo, this is certainly not the case. Graphic designers are incredibly talented individuals who are brilliant at producing beautifully creative artwork to a specific design brief. They are also perfect for creating great designs that help your brand to get more exposure once your brand has already been created. However, they are not strategic, logical or commercial – all the things you need your branding specialists to be, at the same time as creative, when it comes to creating your brand design. That is why you are going through the exercises we have created for you in this book, because a graphic designer needs to be given the answers - as does your website designer. Whereas your branding specialist will come up with the answers for you.

You will not get the best out of your graphic designer by asking them to work with you to create the answers for you as well. How do we know this? Because we have worked with hundreds of graphic designers over the years and they rely on a very strong brief to enable them to get totally into their creative flow and come out the other side with a work of inspired genius. Try to get them to think strategically, logically or commercially during the creative process and you will end up with something that looks pretty, but doesn't work practically where needed. Having spoken to 63 graphic designers during the creation of this book about this very subject, we know they agree and appreciate us fighting their corner to receive proper design briefs!

Creativity is not a tap you can turn on and off as and when required. It has to be on all the time or you are messing with a process that needs to be flowing constantly to achieve the best results. Keep turning that tap on and off to work on other things, like strategy or marketing, and the creativity will dry up quickly. This will not give you the overall desired result you need from your designer in order to create a successful brand that will last you the lifetime of your business and continue to attract your ideal customers as you grow.

Graphic designers are best left to do what they are best at - being creative. This means they are not constantly out in the big wide world testing and measuring marketing methods that do and don't work. That's the bit we do as brand managers and strategists. Graphic designers work at their peak when they are left alone to get in 'their zone' and go underground until they are totally happy with the concepts they have been briefed to create. It is a micro-managed process that takes an experienced brand manager three to four days, going back and forth with the designer to get the best result, amending the design until they are happy to present it to the client, and then preparing the chosen design for production.

If you really want to build your brand, you need to work with a design team who have the necessary experience in branding across all the various platforms and mediums, such as online, offline, print and social media too. This guarantees far greater success in attracting the people who need to know about you.

Ideally you want to work with a brand management company who has specialist knowledge in online marketing, website design, search marketing, direct response marketing, email marketing, strategic marketing, social media marketing, print and product creation to create a brand that you know will work and evolve across every medium.

This is why we have had a 100% success rate with every client we have ever created the branding for. Between our branding team and us, we are each specialists in every specific area of building a brand both online and offline.

Before each project starts, we get together to discuss the client, the extended brief, their ideal customer profile, how their brand needs to work online and the potential for business growth in other areas that hadn't been thought about previously by the client. All of this happens before the brief goes anywhere near the studio so that everyone is singing from the same hymn sheet.

Throughout the entire branding process we are all connected with our design team to ensure the brand works across every area of brand extension. The risk you take in not working like this is time intensive, energy draining and expensive later on.

Why are we so thorough? Because it's highly likely at some point that your brand is going to be presented across most, if not all, of these methods of communication as you grow your business. Without this in-depth level of thinking and strategic intervention, your designer will not create a brand for you that can grow to work across all mediums.

All too often you see a logo that looks great on a business card, but will not work on a website, a promotional gift or a shop front because it is the wrong shape. Sometimes the strapline text looks great on screen but it is so small on a business card that it's not legible when the logo is reduced in size to fit certain media.

Another problem is that very often your logo colours will work well in print, but they don't work at all well on a computer or TV screen. These are all things your branding specialist should know when managing the branding process for you.

Any less than three to four days spent on the design of your brand is not the sign of a true brand process and it's certainly no good cutting corners to reduce the price, because you will regret it later.

Your brand is a process you should NOT rush or get done cheaply. Otherwise, you risk creating a face for your business that is totally wrong, has a confusing personality and sends out messages you don't want it to. Ultimately, this will damage your reputation.

This is not the kind of behavior you would tolerate from an employee sales person is it? So why would you risk employing the wrong face to represent your business? You wouldn't go to a plumber for major heart surgery; you would go to a specialist heart surgeon, wouldn't you? Well the same rule applies to your brand. Don't go anywhere other than an experienced branding company or agency who live, breathe, eat and sleep branding and have lots of case studies to demonstrate how they helped their clients to build a brand. They are not just creating a logo for your business. They are creating the entire face and foundation of your business.

If you don't like the look of a person, you won't do business with them, simple. If people don't like the look of your brand, they won't do business with you. An experienced branding company will know exactly what you need to do to get in front of your ideal customers and they will lead you directly to them. Why are we so passionate about you getting it right first time? Because…

Attracting the wrong customers can kill your business. They will suck up all your time, eat up all your profit and expect more of you than you can possibly give.

We know the damage and negative impact a poor brand can have on your business, your confidence and your reputation because we have seen hundreds of business owners over the years who have made the fatal mistake of going cheap or getting it wrong. The following situation is one we are very familiar with:

The client approaches us, usually via word of mouth referral from an existing delighted customer, to help them create the brand for their product or service. They really want to work with us, but they think they can't afford to and they forget to ask us about payment options. So off they go and get their design created by a lower level designer that they can afford. Two to three YEARS later, they come back to us saying they wish they had continued to get their brand designed with us and can we now help them to put it right?

Not always can we step in to help them put it right because the damage has already been done and their reputation cannot be repaired. However, in all the cases where we did step in, the only way we could help was to carry out a complete rebrand, starting right from the brand growth strategy, as explained. Usually we would do everything we could not to rebrand a business.

It is not good practice to rebrand unless it is absolutely necessary. We would rather turn business away, than to take the money for the wrong reasons just to fill our studio with work. However, if we feel that based on the history of the business, it really does need to reposition the face of the company, we have all the expertise, experience and knowledge to help them do that.

In each case, the clients we have worked with to rebrand have achieved greater results within the first twelve weeks of rebranding than they achieved in the whole two to three years they had been in business, limping along with a brand that wasn't right for them. Check out what Phil said about the work we did for him...

"In 2007 I approached Sammy and Miles to increase our brand awareness. They first identified our brand strategy, which I now realise the importance of, because during the session they gave us so many light bulb moments and we realised we were not even targeting the right customers! They then used our brand strategy to design us a fantastic new logo and brand image that transformed the look and feel of our company completely.

Our monthly business dramatically increased within a month, doubled within two and tripled within three!! There's no doubt that this incredible team of brand specialists has had this positive effect on our business and 6 years later we continue to recommend them to everyone we come across who want to increase the value of their company."

Phil Holmes
Managing Director of OfficeTech Supplies.

It's no coincidence that we got it right for Phil. It is because we are experts in what we do and we have many years' experience in creating tangible results. You can take the long way to success, go cheaper and regret it, or you can achieve the success you deserve straight away, saving time and money by not having to design it twice. Which would you prefer to do?

It's far better to get it right now than get it wrong and struggle along.

The wrong brand, communicating the wrong message to the wrong customers will cost you a great deal of time, money and energy – all of which would be far better invested in working on your business, rather than working in your business trying to make a failing brand work.

Plus a good design agency will always offer you payment options to help you get your brand out there in front of the customers who are paying for it, so do ask about payment plans if you need financial support to get you going.

Who needs to know about you is a fundamental decision you have to make and think about in great detail before giving the branding brief to your chosen design company. You must make sure that all of the information lines up to create a winning brand so you continue to grow a business that consistently delivers great paydays.

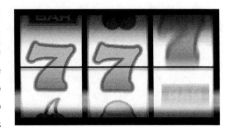

Attracting the right customers isn't just about thinking who needs your product or service the most. It's about you being very selective about whom you want to sell your products and/or services to. You can either try to sell to anybody at the risk of attracting nobody. Or you can get really specific about who you want to work with and help a select group of people who are willing to pay far more to work with a specialist in one area of expertise.

Yes you reserve the right to be picky because this is YOUR business. Oh and yes, you do need to do this now before you give your brief to your designer. Changing your mind at a later date will simply confuse everybody – especially those you want to spend money with you. Whether your ideal customers are male or female, young or mature, happy or sad, fat or thin, tradesmen or entrepreneurs, health fanatics or couch potatoes, hippies or upper class gentry, sun worshipers or snow lovers, price selective or aspirational buyers… there is someone out there who precisely fits your ideal customer profile.

This is where we started with Phil to help him attract his ideal clients. On the following page you will find some of the questions we asked him during his brand strategy session. Had we not spent some in-depth time working with Phil on this exercise, he would still be targeting male, middle aged, Managing Directors of companies with more than 10 employees, rather than the Personal Assistant who actually orders all the stationery in the business. He needed to target the same businesses, just a different person in the organisation. This tiny switch to who he was targeting made the greatest difference and achieved the results you saw previously.

To get the most out of this exercise, answer the following questions in as much detail as possible and they will help you too. This exercise will not only help you to define who your target customer is. It will also enable you to target them more precisely when you come to develop your marketing strategy, because you'll know who they are, what they like doing, where they hang out and what they spend their money on.

If you want to further develop your ideal customer attraction strategy further after doing this exercise, ask us about the Advanced Customer Profiler from the B.R.A.N.D. Accelerator Programme at advice@howtobuildabrand.org. The Advanced Customer Profiler stage of our 5-step programme has been responsible for some serious increases in customers for the people we work with, including raising their prices by up to 500% and cutting their hours to work with higher quality, better paying customers. These are the same businesses that just six months before had struggled to attract any customers at all, let alone get them to pay what they are worth. The Advanced Customer Profiler goes into the following areas of your customer attraction strategy to ensure you never pick up a bad customer again and attract only the very best customers who will pay for the lifestyle you want to live. Here are some of the things we cover with you during this stage of the programme:

- Your Ideal Customer Profile

- Your Customers Pains Analysis

- Your Customers Spending Habits

- Your Online Positioning

- Your Online and Offline Locations

- Your Benefits Driven Proposition

- Your Internal And External Capacity

It really is a great section to work on and a lot of fun too. You can contact us about that later though as for now, we want you to get started on this exercise here...

We will first start by working out what your ideal lifestyle will cost, so we know what kind of customers are going to pay for it.

The reason we start here is because you don't pay for your lifestyle, YOUR CUSTOMERS DO - or the customers of your employer do. So this is the first vital question you need to answer. Once you know this take home figure, you'll have a better idea of who your ideal customers need to be and how many you need to work with to take that monthly figure – remembering you'll need to earn roughly double what you want to take home to cover the running costs of your business.

For example, in chapter 2 you worked out how much money you needed to bring in if you wanted to live your dream lifestyle. You also worked out how many customers you would need to help you achieve that figure.

For example, if your dream lifestyle costs £10k per month and your service is £50, you are going to be exhausted and probably won't hit your target, because you'll need to exchange a lot more time with a lot of customers than you can healthily give. However, if you add value to your service, increase your prices and target a higher profile client, you could achieve your monthly take home figure a lot easier. Better still, you could create a product once and sell it many times over to thousands of customers without ever seeing them. The choice is yours, but you must start by knowing what you want so you know who to target in order to achieve it.

1. Where do your ideal customers hang out/ spend their time? Here are some ideas...

Attending local events – which ones?

_____

_____

_____

_____

_____

At exhibitions and seminars – which ones?

_____

_____

_____

_____

_____

_____

Social media channels – which ones?

_____

_____

_____

_____

_____

Watching YouTube videos – What topics?

Reading certain newspapers – which ones?

Reading industry specific publications – which ones?

Surfing online forums – which ones?

At the golf course – where do they play?

At the gym – which one?

At church – which church?

_____

_____

_____

_____

_____

_____

Walking the dog – Which walking place?

_____

_____

_____

_____

_____

Other?

_____

_____

_____

_____

_____

_____

a. What hobbies do they enjoy most?

Playing sports – which sports?

Seeing shows – which shows?

Walking or climbing – where?

Watching movies – which movies?

Reading books – which books?

Beauty treatments – which treatments?

Clothes shopping – what brands do they buy?

_____

_____

_____

_____

_____

_____

Wherever your customers and clients are hanging out or spending their time, this is where your brand needs to be seen and heard and where your presence is felt. You cannot wait for them to find you or your business will die. You absolutely cannot expect them to have to fill in the gaps. You must find them, make it obvious that your brand is targeting them and make sure your brand is repeatedly seen by them wherever they are. For example:

1. If you know they use LinkedIn more than Facebook, make sure you are regularly posting updates, videos and images on LinkedIn around the topics you know they are interested in. If your outcome is to meet for coffee, you will eventually get the opportunity you want and they may even ask you first.

2. If they are keen golfers, regularly frequent their golf course to appear on their radar. You'll soon introduce yourself and get to know them better. Sooner or later you'll have the conversation you want to have with them and exchange business cards without it feeling too much like a 'sale'.

3. If they read a certain publication, place an article in it or become an 'Ask The Expert' columnist on a topic you know will catch their attention. Once the publication has been printed, send them a copy with a handwritten note asking them to have coffee with you to discuss the topic further.

4. If they like to pamper themselves, buy them a voucher or send them a treat. You'll get their attention if it's something they especially love doing. The thought of you going to all that trouble to find out what they like will really get you noticed.

5. If they subscribe to a certain topic or channel on YouTube, create some videos around that topic. Email them a link to your video and let them know they can find more of them at your YouTube channel.

Whatever you need to do to find common ground, build rapport and become 'sticky' in their mind, do it. We've just given you five ideal ways to get in front of your ideal customers. Here are five more to help you along; taken from the TOP 100 Brand Building Activities we share with our students on the B.R.A.N.D. Accelerator Programme:

1. Create content for a series of at least five YouTube videos that will give your ideal prospects a really good idea about each of your products and/or services and what the benefits are for each one.

2. Make sure your social media profiles are up to date and post an update, tip or news item at least once a day. If you have answered all the questions in this book so far, you will have more than enough to say about yourself and your business.

3. Write regular 600-word blog articles using the key messages you have written so far in this book. When you consistently talk about a certain topic, you'll naturally appear as an authority in that subject. So start writing! Turn it into a 'How To...' guide too as Google loves sending customers to 'How To' type resources.

4. Create a press release to go into the literature your prospects are likely to read. Use this to generate more content for your blog and use social media to point people to your blog and press release once it has been printed.

5. Set up an email signature strip (the part in an email after the "Kindest Regards" at the end) to ensure you never miss an opportunity to update people on what else you do. Put buttons at the bottom of your email signature that take people to your Facebook Page/Social media profiles, website landing pages or put offers or testimonials at the bottom of your emails. This is prime advertising space that costs nothing; so make sure you use it.

You are making great progress by answering all of these questions and taking action on them. We know there are a lot of questions and it isn't always easy to answer them. However, you are doing the very things that will stand you head and shoulders above your competitors. They aren't even thinking about any of these things and that's why you'll be able to charge more than them.

Just imagine how much more direction you are giving yourself, your designers, developers and marketers to help you build your brand to the place you want it to be. No longer are you putting your business in the hands of fate like so many business owners around you are doing.

YOU ARE DIFFERENT.

You are telling the world exactly what you want, who you want to attract and how you are going to attract them. A clear brief like this gets clear results.

Let's now look at what else you can do to attract your ideal customers in chapter 4.

"Sammy Blindell and Miles Fryer are the brand magicians of the 21st Century. They really embody what true relationship marketing is all about."

Tosin Ogunussi,
The UK's No.1 Empowerment Coach &
Performance Improvement Specialist

"Sammy and Miles are the Brand and Marketing experts who will take your business onto a level of infinite possibilities."

Claire L Perry, Internet Marketing Expert

"Sammy and Miles are genuinely excited by the prospect of creating a brand that will grow your business. They don't work off the peg and definitely think outside of the box!"

Greg Garrity,
Entrepreneur & Changemaker

CHAPTER 4...

What One Single Message Tells Your Customer All About You?

As a business owner, you will often get asked the following question: "Hi, what do you do?"

What you say next will either make or break the rest of the conversation.

This is your opportunity to pitch your product, service and/or expertise in a single positioning statement that gets a response like "WOW that sounds great! How do you do that?" or "Where can I get that?"

Give them too much information at this point and they'll be overwhelmed. Give them too little and they will think you don't know what you are talking about. So getting your positioning statement right (otherwise known as your elevator pitch) is fundamental to your brand engagement and

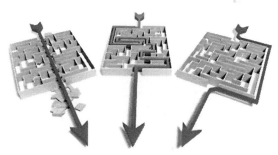

conversion; whether you are delivering it verbally one to one at an event or over the phone, one to many at a seminar, via video, or through the wording on your website, brochure, blogs, books, etc., when you are totally happy you have successfully created your introduction pitch / statement about your business, it then needs to be applied consistently across every touch point that your prospects and customers will ever have with your business.

Sharing this single most important message about your company with passion, conviction and belief as well as with clarity, confidence and certainty (as we discussed in chapter 1) will capture the attention of the people you want to do business with and hook them in so they want to know more about what you do. We don't recommend you take longer than 60 seconds to deliver your pitch, which is the equivalent of around 120 words.

You could go back and look at the answers you wrote down in chapter one to help you create your positioning statement. Or perhaps you have something completely different in mind as you have probably had lots of ideas since you started reading this book.

Let's set up a scenario to get you in the right mind-set to answer this question...

You arrive at a popular local networking event, bustling full of eager business owners of all shapes and sizes. The room is buzzing as they are all deep in conversation, sharing their knowledge, catching up since the last event and talking about their products and services to fellow colleagues and contacts. As you walk through the crowded room to get yourself a drink, a fellow businessperson who you know well, stops you to say, "Hi". They happen to be talking to a person that you've wanted to arrange a meeting with for a long time. This is THE opportunity that you've been waiting for. The tension mounts as the pleasantries come to an end and you know you're going to get asked that question. Then it comes. You line yourself up for it...

"So tell me [name], what do you do?"

Write below what you would currently say so you can see your progression later on:

_____

_____

_____

_____

_____

_____

_____

_____

_____

_____

You may have noticed we gave you a lot of lines for you to write on. That's because most business owners at this point, (who haven't done what you are doing now), babble on about things that are important to THEM instead of what's important to the person they are speaking to. They totally miss their opportunity to take the conversation to the next level and the other person feels like a train has hit them.

A babbling introduction, or one that overwhelms the person you are talking to will get you a "that's nice" response and they'll be thinking about how to make a quick exit with the first excuse they can think of. Perhaps you have experienced this yourself at an event or even a personal engagement where you got stuck talking to someone and you really wish you hadn't engaged them in conversation.

A well-delivered pitch, however, will get you the "WOW that sounds great! How do you do that?" kind of response that you really want. So how can you sharpen your response and know exactly what to say in future?

Before we get started, you should know what 60 seconds / the equivalent of 120 words of content looks like, so here it is:

> The quick brown fox jumped over the lazy dog. The quick brown fox jumped over the lazy dog. The quick brown fox jumped over the lazy dog. The quick brown fox jumped over the lazy dog. The quick brown fox jumped over the lazy dog. The quick brown fox then quickly jumped over the lazy dog. The quick brown fox jumped over the lazy dog. The quick brown fox jumped over the lazy dog. The quick brown fox then quickly jumped over the lazy dog. The quick brown fox jumped over the lazy dog. The quick brown fox jumped over the lazy dog. The quick brown fox then jumped even higher over the lazy dog. The quick brown fox jumped over the lazy dog again.

60 seconds is the maximum amount of words / time that we would advise you use to communicate your positioning statement. If you can't get your message across in 60 seconds, revise it until you can. This is why it is otherwise known as an elevator pitch, because you literally have the time it goes up a few floors to get your message across.

You may not think a minute is a great deal of time, but when you are on the receiving end of it, 60 seconds feels a lot longer than it actually is. Getting your message across in 60 seconds will give your prospects a clear idea about what you do, in a short period of time. They can then repeat this easily to others and create a WOW impression of you that makes people think:

★ This person stands out.

★ This person is incredibly professional.

★ This person knows what they're talking about.

★ This person cares about how they present their business.

★ This person is clearly prepared and looks like they are the kind of business that will look after their customers well.

★ This person is not going to waste my time as they clearly value his or her own time.

★ This person really walks their talk and can therefore be trusted.

★ This person is someone I am happy to recommend to others.

It's amazing what goes on subconsciously in the minds of the people you are talking to. You want to create a great impression on the people who are coming into contact with you and your business for the first time so they remember you and they will tell others you are great too.

Do you remember the last time you asked someone a question and then really wish you hadn't?

Horrible isn't it? Not wishing to be rude, you keep quiet while they bore you to death and all kinds of things go through your head… probably everything except what they want you to think.

It's your responsibility to ensure your prospects are thinking about how they can take the next steps with you, rather than how they can make their escape to the toilet or coffee queue, how much work they still have to do when they get back to the office, or how much housework they've got to do when they get home. You know what we mean because you have probably been on the receiving end of someone else who has done this to you. So step into your prospective customer's shoes now and give them what they want to hear in an honest way. You don't have time to waste in 60 seconds and neither do they. Make it powerful.

If you have ever heard the expression "You never get a second chance to make a first impression", this is where it most definitely applies. So let's get started.

The best way to create your positioning statement is to first of all look at what you want to say from three different perspectives:

★ Your customers

★ Your marketplace

★ Your business

First of all, you need to get into your customer's head, step into their shoes and find out what matters most to them? Don't assume. To

ASS.U.ME
Makes an ASS out of U
and an ass out of ME!

assume is to risk completely missing the point and affecting not only your sales, but also your reputation. If you create a negative impression, this is what they will remember and repeat to others. So make it a positive impression by taking control of what you are saying and how you are saying it.

You need to interview existing and potential customers. Survey them and pay attention to what is being said both in person and online. Google your topic and connect with them via the various social media channels. Ask them when you see them at networking events or when they are out shopping. Ask friends and family who fit your customer profile. You need to start thinking about what your customers value most, what pain they are in and keep a track on the words you hear them repeatedly using to talk about this particular pain or problem that you can solve.

In order to understand your customer, you must become your customer. This is the best way you can serve them and increase their loyalty to you.

For example, when we first set up our design agency we went around using the terminology 'branding' because that was the industry term we used. We wrongly assumed that it was widely used by our customers as well. We continued to use the term 'branding' on our website, our marketing materials and verbally whilst out networking. It wasn't until we did our own keyword research and asked our customers what terminology they were searching for when they needed what we provide, that we realised more people use the terminology 'brand design' or 'brand strategy' than 'branding'. This gave us brilliant intelligence as to what language our customers actually use to search for what we provide. This is what you need to do too.

We changed our language and saw an immediate difference, both in customer referrals and online enquiries through our website. This demonstrates that just one word or phrase can make all the difference to your pitch and only by doing your research properly and asking the very people who will spend money with you, will you really find out what your customers want.

For your positioning statement and brand promise to be totally effective, it must also be true.

Here are five questions about your business. Your answers will give you ideas you can use to start pulling together your positioning statement. This exercise is important for you to further refine how you positioned yourself in chapters one, two and three. By the way, each time we ask you to answer a question that may appear similar to one we have already asked, it's because we want to draw out a bigger variety of answers from you to cherry pick the best ones for you.

Each set of answers you give is building your brand yet further, and often the first answer that comes to your mind is a good answer. However, we usually find that it is your fifth or sixth answer to that same question which proves to be THE best and most effective. So stick with it, grab your pen and let's get started…

1. What are some of the things you do that are the same as your competitors?

----

2. What are some of the things you are doing that makes you different from them?

----

3. What are some of the things that make your product, service or knowledge totally unique in your industry?

_____

_____

_____

_____

_____

_____

_____

_____

4. What is different about your manufacturing process or the process by which you create your content / products / deliver your services?

_____

_____

_____

_____

_____

_____

_____

_____

5. What are the top three most important things to your client about what you deliver?

1. ---

2. ---

3. ---

Let's now look at your competition. Only one brand in your industry can own the market leading position for what you do, so how do your top 3 competitors position themselves? Step into the future and look at the companies you want to be competing with in 3 years' time, rather than the competitors you compete with now. This way you can build your business to compete in a bigger way than the competitors you currently compete with.

Pick 3 competitors and write below what you think they are doing well to position themselves as the leader in YOUR industry.

Competitor 1:

Competitor 2:

Competitor 3:

What are their company straplines / taglines?

An example of straplines / taglines are:

- Tesco - 'Every Little Helps'
- Nike - 'Just Do It'
- Gillette – 'The Best a Man Can Get'

1. _____

2. _____

3. _____

What do they say on their 'About Us' page about their company to make them stand out?

Competitor 1:

_____

_____

_____

_____

_____

_____

_____

_____

_____

Competitor 2:

Competitor 3:

What do their customers say about them on their website testimonials?

Competitor 1:

Competitor 2:

Competitor 3:

_____

_____

_____

_____

_____

_____

_____

_____

_____

_____

Weeding out what you do in comparison to what your competitors do is not so you can actively put your competitors down in your positioning statement. Rather, it's a statement you create to distinguish you from them. It should talk honestly about what you deliver and position you as the better option over your competitors, without disparaging them. Virgin, Nike and Ryanair do this very well in our opinion. Here are some mission statements to give you an example:

> '**Virgin** believes in making a difference. We stand for value for money, quality, innovation, fun and a sense of competitive challenge. We strive to achieve this by empowering our employees to continually deliver an unbeatable customer experience.'

> '**Nike** brings inspiration and innovation to every athlete in the world. If you have a body you are an athlete.'

*'**RyanAir** is an Irish airline that offers flights at a much lower cost than other commercial airlines. It was established in 1985, but has since grown and is still rapidly expanding. RyanAir aims to provide its passengers with low prices, punctuality and great customer service'.*

As you can see, Virgin's positioning statement is very simple. It doesn't focus on price at all. Rather, their core message focuses around investing in their employees to deliver unbeatable customer service. They make it clear they go above and beyond their competitors, without putting them down and they make you feel part of their family in just 37 words.

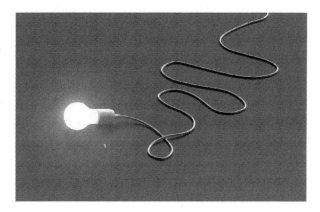

If you can master your positioning statement in this way and also extract your brand strapline from it so it's completely consistent with all brand messaging and values, your brand will flourish and be highly memorable.

Nike's positioning statement is short, sweet and easy to remember – therefore easy to pass on to someone else through word of mouth. It gives you a direct hit of what their company is about. Their strapline 'Just Do It' is consistent with a brand that is all about taking action. If you sell a product or service that is about taking action this is a great brand for you to model.

Ryanair's positioning statement at the opposite end of the scale to Virgin is very focused on price and the environment, which at a guess, are two of the most important things to their clients when buying flights abroad. If you can encapsulate the two most important things to your clients in your positioning statement and brand strapline, you will spend less time explaining what you do because your message is loud and clear. You can then spend more time answering the valuable questions you'll no doubt get because they are so interested in how you can specifically help THEM.

There are two more things to consider when writing your positioning statement… Be memorable and steer clear of incontinent language. What do we mean?

In 2005 we were at a BNI networking event. If you are unfamiliar with BNI, it stands for Business Network International and is now a worldwide brand that is made up of thousands of business networking events. It was founded by Dr Ivan R Misner in 1985. At BNI, business owners meet for breakfast one morning of every week in their local region. It's perfect for small businesses to connect, refer business to one another, learn how to sell and gain experience by pitching your business for 60 seconds in front of a room full of 20-40 other business professionals. We used to think of it as our weekly board meeting.

Their meetings usually happen at the start of the day, between 6.30am – 8.30am, so it's a great way of doing business before the business day has even begun. We were both members of BNI for over five years and have many things to thank it for, including meeting each other there. Having met at a regional BNI networking event, after 12 months of referring business to one another we formed our first business together and went on to build five more businesses together before we launched 'How To Build A Brand' and 'The Brand Brains'. The rest, as they say, is history.

Having both been individually recognised for our networking excellence, business expertise and being extremely well connected, we were both asked to become Assistant Directors for the BNI organisation to launch and grow more BNI groups (otherwise known as Chapters) in our local regions. This gave us a huge amount of scope for networking on a much bigger scale while continuing to run our own businesses.

Our names were also well known in our local business community for giving so many referrals to our contacts each week, simply because we were both launching and growing new chapters with hundreds of members in the region and also we were still members of our own individual BNI group.

We attended at least 2-3 extra networking events every week, including a monthly Business Development Academy we had set up together. So we were speaking to an average of 100-150 new business owners every week. Each business had challenges, which led to hundreds of referrals and introductions to the high quality people we know.

In fact, people knew we were so well connected that one day a lady was referred to us to ask if we knew a really good chimney sweep. We didn't, but within minutes of putting the request out to our network of contacts, we were given the name of a very highly recommended chimney sweep in her local area. She was delighted, and funnily enough, six months later she came to us for her branding and website design simply because she knew we were the kind of people who would go the extra mile to help. There is a lesson there for you about being the 'Go To' person.

As you can imagine, we got to see hundreds of business owners pitching their businesses and marketing themselves in many different ways. Some were hugely successful, while most of them were incredibly poor at doing so. The best presenters did eight things very well. They used visual props and told us 'YOU' focused stories that sparked intrigue to stick in your memory. They were also very specific about the business introductions they wanted and always ended their 60-second presentations with a memorable strapline or call to action along with a hook (a compelling reason to take action).

This made them stick in our memory. The most professional presentations were always well rehearsed and kept within their time slot.

Interestingly, it was the people who did all of the above in their presentations that were cleaning up all the referrals in the room and giving the most back. Let's cover what they did well, so you can model them in your own business:

★ Use visual props.

★ Tell stories that spark intrigue and stick in your customer's memory.

★ Use 'YOU' focused language that engages people and makes them feel like you are talking to them directly.

★ Be specific about what referrals or business introductions you are looking for.

★ End your presentation with a strapline, call to action or memorable hook.

★ Be prepared and well rehearsed.

★ Always stick to the timeslot you are given.

★ Be the person who gives the most back.

Now let's look at what everyone else was doing. Most of the other presentations were boring. They would stand up, ramble for 60 seconds about irrelevant stuff, and use what we call 'incontinent language'... "We" do this, "We" do that. "We", "We", "We"... They'd sell to the room. They would go way over their time slot and then sit down again, ready for the next person to speak. They wouldn't listen to the advice they were given to improve their presentations and as a consequence, they didn't get many referrals – then complained they weren't getting any business out of it. Can you see a pattern?

What they couldn't understand was that the way they were conducting themselves was giving the impression that this is what they are also like in business. Unrehearsed, ill-prepared, boring, not sticking to timescales given, constantly talking about themselves, selling at you, unprofessional, not listening to feedback, etc... Then they blamed the system for not working. Basically these people were at the total opposite end of the spectrum to the successful people, and you could tell which type they would be from the time they arrived in the morning – those arriving before everyone else arrived, ready to smile and shake the hands of everyone that came in... and those rushing in at last minute as the door was shutting or even walking in halfway through the meeting. Guess which business owner stood out as the professional one you wanted to do business with compared to the one you didn't?

This brings us to very reason we started talking about BNI, because it was at a BNI meeting on a cold December morning in 2006 that we met a very interesting and memorable chap called Guy, whose presentation and strapline still sticks in our minds to this day... As we walked into the room at 6.30am, he was the first person to greet us with a huge smile and a bright red tie, which at the time we thought he must have worn to wake everyone up at that time of the morning. He went out of his way to get us refreshments and made sure we had the best seats in the room. He'd written a poem for his presentation, which had the room in fits of laughter. This built instant rapport and impressed everyone with his attention to detail. He ended his 60 seconds with a hook... "When you've got PC problems,  don't try to get by. Contact Guy with the red tie." Okay, so it wasn't the most perfect piece of poetry, but we remember his presentation because it stuck in our minds. He has had countless referrals as a consequence of that red tie!

The first thing you are going to do is write your statement a number of times, altering it as you go, to give you a number of versions to choose the best one. We find writing it three times has given us what we need to create our best statement. You may find it easier to go back through all the answers you and make a list of between three to five key words that you want to get into your statement and then weave them in. Let's get started.

The key words you want to include are:

_____   _____

_____   _____

_____   _____

_____   _____

_____   _____

Positioning statement version 1:

_____

_____

_____

_____

_____

_____

_____

_____

_____

_____

_____

Positioning statement version 2:

Positioning statement version 3:

Now you have at least three versions of your statement, you must put yourself in your ideal customers' shoes and go back through each one.

As you read, ask yourself the following questions:

- Which one stands out the most for you?
- How could you improve it further?
- What are you thinking by the end of it?
- Are you compelled to find out more?

Let's refine it one more time?

My final positioning statement is:

_____

_____

_____

_____

_____

_____

_____

_____

_____

Congratulations! You are almost half way through this book! If you have completed all of the exercises so far you will already have at least 50 to 100 key things written down about your business that you can highlight, adapt and tailor to promote yourself immediately in many different ways.

You will also by now have at least 10 reasons why your prospective customers and clients should do business with YOU over and above anyone else.

Let's continue to build your brand strategy in chapter 5 to start building your brand story.

"I literally can't recommend Sammy & Miles highly enough; they are absolute stars, extremely knowledgeable & very creative! They are bursting with ideas on how to develop the brand of your business, in ways that you won't have even thought about before. Their enthusiasm knows no bounds, and they genuinely want to see your business succeed. If you're serious about taking your business to the next level then get in touch with Sammy & Miles today!"

Lizzie Tailby, Jewelry Designer

"Sammy and Miles are the most professional and personable people I have ever worked with. They stream with innovative ideas and know their business inside out. Always there with suggestions and help, they really live their business. Giving sound strategic advice they have helped my business advance in leaps and bounds. The website that they have built for me and the back-up they give is second to none. I have no hesitation in giving Sammy and Miles my whole-hearted recommendation and thanks for all they have done."

Gillian Cossins, The Craft Workshop

CHAPTER 5...

Why Was Your Company Created?

People love good stories. You can almost see and hear the cogs turning in their heads as you engage them in a story that taps into their imagination, heart and soul to bring your experience to life in their mind.

As storytelling extraordinaire and Jet Set Speaker, Andy Harrington, often says;

"Good stories are not just re-told, they are re-lived"

A good story taps into people's passions, emotions and purpose. Stories get embellished and grow each time they are told, retold and passed on. The senses explode as you increase the intensity of your story using smells, sights, sounds, tastes and even feelings that tap into their memories and subconsciously spark off a state change within them.

You have a brilliant story. It may be buried deep, or it could be bursting to get out! Either way, you MUST tell it.

The story of how your company was created is one of the most important aspects of your brand. You might not think it's that important, but your customers do. When it comes down to the nuts and bolts of why your customers will choose you over and above your competitors, it will be because there is a level of rapport, respect and trust with you that they just don't feel with any other company elsewhere because they connect with your story more than any other.

People like to do business with people they have experiences in common with, and it's likely they will choose you if your brand matches up to their values, beliefs, past experiences and expectations. They like to know they are right, so if they hear or see your brand story and it makes them think, "Yes, I knew I could trust you", then the hardest part of your sale is complete.

Imagine speaking to someone you are thinking about spending money with. You ask them why they started their business, looking for some common ground to put your mind at rest so that you can trust them. You are expecting to hear a fantastic story about how they got started, their experiences, their failures and what led them to be the expert in their industry now. Instead, they give you a few words along the lines of, "I don't know really. I just kind of fell into it". Well, they may as well have just taken a pin out of their pocket and burst your balloon!

Maybe you have heard this type of response before. We hear it all the time from people who come to us because they want us to brand them. How can we possibly create a vision and a brand for a business that has no soul or story within it? The soul is the story behind your brand. There must be depth and soul to your brand, otherwise you just have a logo sat on top of a product or service that means nothing to anyone, and people don't pay for 'nothing'.

You must feel connected to your story or your customers won't be. Short answers (like the example we gave above) don't mean anything to you, let alone your ideal customers. This is not what your future customers want to hear. They're looking to tick all the little boxes inside their head that give them trust in you. It won't make them believe you are the best in your field of expertise, and they certainly won't feel any rapport with you. They will just go somewhere else. Put simply...

If people can't connect with your past, they will struggle to connect with you in future.

It's your experiences they want to know about. Limited answers like "I just kind of fell into it" will not cut it, especially if you are selling a product or service that is highly emotive and works with people on a deeper, emotional level. You have the opportunity now to create, master and share your brand story. Re-live it for your customers and create a memorable brand they'll instantly connect with and tell their friends about.

Right now, as you read this book, there are thousands of business owners all over the world creating their brand story. Some will compete with you for business. Many of them will boost sales. Some may engage people and some may even inspire them to take the next step. But how many brand stories will be truly remembered? How many of them will be compelling enough that they are passed on from person to person, giving your brand even more exposure each time it is told?

It's just not enough to simply share your ideas. Today you need to tell a compelling brand story that stands the test of time and builds a momentum all on its own with a title, a plot, a twist and a summit.

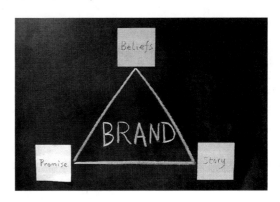

Now is your opportunity to create your brand story, take your customers right to the very heart of your business and motivate them to do business with you.

1. Let's start this exercise by accessing memories you have in your head, so you can commit them to paper. Photo albums or looking through your Facebook photos are great if you get stuck, as they'll lift memories from your subconscious, ready to re-live the story that sits behind each photo. Don't limit yourself to experiences about work because you are promoting a business. Each and every life experience you've had has shaped you to become the person you are today. So make a note of whatever comes into your head. It will all be useful to you at some point. It's time to open up your memories like a treasure chest and surrender the gems inside.

2. Once you are happy that you've exhausted as many life experiences as you can remember, you can then go through and choose the experiences that best fit the story you want to tell. Experiences that lead you to the summit, that made you start your own business and decided to create the brand you are building now.

3. Perfect your story. Embellish it with characters. Describe who was present and relevant to the story. Add speech and dialogue to bring them to life. Relate your story to your audience to make your story relevant to your brand. Then polish it for presentation and prepare to tell the world.

Below we are going to ask you a series of questions that will help you get started, so grab your pen... let's go!

1. List some of your first ever memories?

----

2. List some of the best experiences and adventures you had whilst growing up.

_____

_____

_____

_____

_____

_____

_____

_____

_____

3. Are there any childhood experiences (good and bad) that really stick out in your mind?

_____

_____

_____

_____

_____

_____

_____

_____

4. List some of the worst experiences you've had that taught you some major lessons.

5. How did you deal with them?

6. Did the way you handled these situations impact on you later in life? If so, how?

_____

_____

_____

_____

_____

_____

_____

_____

_____

7. What was it like the first time you earned your own money?

_____

_____

_____

_____

_____

_____

_____

_____

_____

8. What did you spend it on?

9. What did you do in your first job?

10. Why did you leave?

11. What happened next?

12. What was the biggest lesson you learned in your first job?

13. How did this shape your career?

14. What was the turning point that made you decide to start your business?

15. How did the people around you respond to your decision?

16. Why did you choose to go into the industry you are in?

17. What are some of the things you love about what you do in your business?

18. What are some of the things you are best at in your industry?

_____

_____

_____

_____

_____

_____

_____

_____

_____

19. Name the #1 thing you do better than anyone else you know and tell us why you believe it to be so.

_____

_____

_____

_____

_____

_____

_____

_____

_____

_____

_____

20. What do other people say about you and your business? (If you haven't started your business yet, make a list of the things you want to hear them say)

Extra notes:

Before you choose which experiences to take forward into your brand story, there are two things that we always do and we recommend you do the same...

1. Think about what state you want your audience or your prospect to be in once they have finished listening to your story, reading it or watching it. Do you want them to feel happy? Confused? Stressed? Emotional? Scared? Unfinished? Elated? Hungry for more? One, some, or all of the above? Whatever state it is that you want your audience to be in at the end of your story, make sure you choose a story that can be embellished to influence their state.

2. Make a list of the beliefs you want to instil in your audience. You may want your audience to believe that no matter where they are financially, there is a way to get out of debt and live the life they want to live. Maybe you want them to believe life won't change unless they take responsibility and change it. Perhaps you want them to believe they can achieve anything they put their minds to. Whatever belief you want them to have about you by the end of your story, you must choose an experience from your list that you can share with them to seed that belief all the way through.

Once you have written your brand story, here are 10 places you can share it to spread your message out to more of the people who can share it with their contacts too...

1. Create a blog post to share your story.

2. Share the link to your blog post as a status update on LinkedIn, Facebook, Twitter and Google+.

3. Use the content from your blog post to create a press release for your local business paper or publication.

4. Create a shorter version of your story (around 400 words) that can be added to a page in your sales brochure.

5. Write a book and weave your story into the content.

6. Deliver your story to your ideal customers at an event or seminar.

7. Turn it into a video to introduce yourself on the homepage of your website.

8. Take the audio from your video and turn it into a podcast.

9. Upload the video to your YouTube channel.

10. Share your video from YouTube to Facebook, Pinterest, Twitter and Google+.

11. Upload your video to your Facebook Fan Page and pin it to the top of your page so it's the first thing new fans will see when they land on your page.

If writing a book is something you'd love to do, then there has never been a better time to write and self-publish in both printed format and Kindle to get your brand story out there. Richard McMunn is our publisher and is one of the UK's most successful authors, which is why we chose to work with him. Having self-published over 150 books to date, he is best placed to help you achieve your publishing goals, as he has done with us.

To find out more about how Richard can help you to get your book published and on sale through Amazon and in High Street stores such as Waterstones, go to:

www.BookPublishingAcademy.co.uk

These are just a few ideas taken from our B.R.A.N.D. Accelerator Programme, where we go a lot deeper into your story. We also share a lot of resources we have found to increase exposure and show you how to use low cost and no cost marketing techniques to reach more customers with your story.

If you would like to develop your brand story further on the B.R.A.N.D. Accelerator Programme, email Sammy for more information now at: advice@howtobuildabrand.org.

"Our team spent half a day with Sammy and she helped us to gain real clarity about how we will be communicating our brand to corporate businesses. She also helped us to feel more confident about offering our services at a price point higher than we had initially intended, whilst still feeling comfortable about doing so. Sammy's style and approach is engaging, energetic (4 hours, stood up, no break) and always considerate. She listen's well and was able to reflect back our ideas to great effect. I would absolutely recommend using Sammy & Miles to any business that wants to position itself to its clients in the right way."

Steve Phillip, LinkedIn Trainer

"Sammy & Miles have a huge passion for what they do and this comes flowing through in everything they touch. They are the epitome of positivity, bringing vision and energy to every engagement. They are inspiring, fun and looking to do the best for whomever they work with."

Colin Pinks, Practitioner, Coach and Mentor

CHAPTER 6...

Why Should Your Customers Care That You Exist?

One of your greatest challenges as you grow your business is going to be that your prospects are not always going to be ready to buy from you when you are ready to sell to them. Yes you will get lucky occasionally, and the introduction of referrals to your business will certainly speed up the process of turning strangers into lifetime customers. But so much intelligence and research is done online now that you aren't always going to be there to make the sale in person. If you aren't already making it easy for your customers to trust you and buy from you, then now is the time to take this seriously. Quite frankly, if you aren't giving them a great enough reason to care about what you provide then why should they buy from you at all?

☐ *Brand X?*
☐ *Brand Y?*

In this 'information age' where it is so easy to find exactly what you are looking for within just a few clicks online, people just aren't content anymore with finding what they want and then buying it straight away. With so much choice available to them, they now find exactly what they are looking for, but they don't buy it there and then... they almost buy it. They visit your website and read through your sales page. They watch your videos and look at all the glowing testimonials you have received. They've seen your brand in other places too, which gives them reassurance about who you are. But there are still some little niggling thoughts in the back of their mind that stop them from clicking on the 'Add to Basket button, 'Contact Us' button or saying yes to your proposal.

This is incredibly frustrating because that click could have been the start of a very profitable relationship for you. It's also frustrating to your customers because they almost just saved themselves a load of time, stress, hassle and perhaps even money by buying into a product or service that could help them to solve the very problem they came to you with in the first place - But they didn't and this makes it a 'Lose – Lose' situation.

If you don't have a website, business card or brochure yet then this is your opportunity to get your design brief right now before you give it to your graphic designer or website developer. If on the other hand you do already have existing marketing materials in place, then you must stop any more future customers from haemorrhaging away from your business right now and evaluate what you do have.

It's not good for you to lose out on potential business, and it's certainly not good for potential customers in need of your help. If your marketing materials aren't working, STOP trying to limp along with what you've got, because every day they aren't working for you is another day you are losing money. Recognise instead that they aren't working for you as well as they could be and change them NOW. It will do you more harm having the wrong thing out there than having nothing out there at all. We have advised countless businesses, large and small, who have all made this mistake before.

How can you get new prospects to stick around long enough so that they not only care about taking that next vital step with you, they also actively want to spend money with you as well? Here are three steps that will help you to achieve massive leaps toward this outcome. We don't have time to go into each step fully, because we have taken these snippets from the B.R.A.N.D. Accelerator Programme. Let's get started...

Step 1 –
Increase The Perceived Value Of Your Product Or Service...

It's highly likely your prospects already have some preconceived ideas and beliefs about what you sell before they come across you and your business and their opinion of your industry might not be all rosy. Maybe they have been hurt in the past by a company who over-promised and under-delivered. Perhaps they know somebody who had a bad experience with a different company in your industry and it has made them nervous or wary about investing in anyone else 'like them'. Or potentially they feel they were 'ripped off' by someone in the past and are now overly cautious, effectively pigeonholing you with the same values of that other person.

Whatever it is that's holding them back from buying your products or services, it's vital you challenge any negative beliefs head on and challenge them early. Your reputation is riding on it. You can't afford for them to go elsewhere with the thought in their head that you failed them in some way. If you believe your product or service can genuinely help them, then it's your duty to ensure they don't leave your website, office or shop until they've bought something from you. List three ways now that you can increase the perceived value of your product or service:

1. --

----

2. --

----

3. --

Step 2 – Enhance The Perceived Value Of The Outcome...

You must demonstrate clearly that you created your product or service based on a fundamental understanding of your customer's pains, problems, challenges and desires. To do this you must think like them and the best way to think like them is to actually become them. It may be a long time ago since you last placed yourself in your customer's shoes or had the same problem they have. If you've done this recently, then you'll be more prepared for this short exercise. This is a great opportunity for you to get back to basics.

For example, Sir Richard Branson regularly flies on his own airline to experience his products and services just as his customers do. This is how his marketing is so spot-on and it's no coincidence that he directly attracts the exact people he wants to fly on his airline and spend money with him. As they say, 'success leaves clues'. Model this successful person in how he wins customers and you'll achieve at the very least a fraction of his success too, even without his marketing budget!

List three ways now you can increase the value of what you leave your customers with after they have spent money with you:

1. _____

_____

_____

_____

2. _____

_____

_____

_____

3. _____

_____

_____

Step 3 – Reduce Their Perceived Risk...

Getting people to part with their cash is a challenge for even the greatest salesperson if you cannot offer some sort of money back guarantee that gives them security should something go wrong. So many companies now offer a money back guarantee. It makes you look like you aren't confident in what you're selling if you don't give one. Having had many a conversation with some of the world's greatest marketers and business people about how they offer guarantees, here's what they found after intensive testing:

30-day money back guarantees work really well because they say 'If you don't like it, I'll refund you completely'. Depending on the item, you may get a few people coming back to you for a refund. However, many people think about getting their money back, but then they miss the deadline to do it. This is good for you because it hasn't negatively affected your bottom line, but it could still be bad for your business. How so?

Well, in this blame culture that we now live in, there will always be a small proportion of people who get peeved with you before they'll take accountability for their own decision to buy. This means that even though they know they only have 30 days to take it back for a refund, and even though it is they who haven't made the time to sort it out, they are still going to blame you for being stuck with something they don't want. This damages your brand in their mind and they will never buy from you again. Some people think, "Well, that's ok because it's their problem that they didn't get it back to us on time so it is their loss". But we personally think this is your loss if you think this way, because your reputation is worth far more than a few refunds.

You genuinely don't want people to go away displeased with your product or to associate your brand with any unpleasant feelings, because people will talk far more about a negative experience than they will talk about positive ones. This means negative word of mouth about your business has the potential to spread bad news quicker than good news.

Based on this, we highly advocate that if someone asks you for a refund, no matter what, you should have a contingency in place for this eventuality. You can either just give them their money back anyway and move on quickly, or find out what you could have done to have improved their experience so you get something from the exchange and then provide something extra that is of little or no cost to you, but of added value to the customer. This will equip you to take measures that minimise the risk of that happening again.

This may seem a ridiculous thing to do, because you have clearly put guidelines up and the customer didn't follow it, yet you got penalised. Surely there is a way to offer a guarantee that keeps everyone happy? Well yes there is and that it to offer lifetime money back guarantees.

Now this might send a shiver down your spine and your gut reaction might be to reject the idea completely because you are seemingly leaving yourself open to lifelong problems. However the results speak for themselves and even with a 30-day guarantee you're probably going to give them their money back anyway if they come back after 60 days for example, so you actually have no greater risk by implementing a lifetime guarantee. Also, something psychological happens when a customer is given a lifetime guarantee as opposed to a defined time limit.

Tests have shown that they very rarely request their money back at all. Why? Because they know they can do it any time they like. They consider getting around to it one day and never do. The accountability is totally on them to take the action. In the meantime, your brand reputation stays completely intact because they tend not to blame you for something that they haven't even challenged yet. Personally we prefer this second option to the first, but only you can decide which route you take when it comes to offering a guarantee on your products and services.

Let's focus on covering the top 3 objections you think you'll get to make your guarantee stronger:

Objection #1:

Objection #2:

Objection #3:

You'll no doubt think of many more objections, so continue this exercise on an extra sheet of paper to ensure you cover every angle that could risk your sales being compromised. The greatest businesses are the ones who take time to answer these questions, put measures in place and offer a guarantee that overcomes those objections.

This is one of the most basic areas of building trust that most businesses fail to succeed at. Putting these measures in place will help you to increase trust and credibility in your brand, while reducing objections and gaining your prospects confidence in you as a business. This will make it far easier for you to sell them any product or service you want to offer in future.

Let's now focus on your competitive advantage in chapter 7.

"At a recent presentation I found Miles and Sammy's communication skills outstanding; they were warm and welcoming, whilst being knowledgeable and professional. They connect with their audience and provide an interactive experience, which is something most presenters shy away from. Sammy & Miles offer a valuable insight into branding and marketing which they deliver in an interesting, jargon-free way."

Laurra Nalty, Social Media Trainer & Consultant

"Sammy & Miles really know how to 'get under the skin' of any business and to then showcase that business in a true, professional and inspirational light. They really think deeply about what your message is and what you are trying to convey, then will add suggestions, advice and input before allowing you to come to your decision. I think their design work is excellent and they are so easy to communicate with. They just 'get it' - every time."

Nadine Hill, Speaker, Blogger & Freelance Writer

CHAPTER 7...

What Is Your Competitive Advantage?

According to NASA.gov it takes a whopping 500,000 gallons of super-cold liquid oxygen and hydrogen fuel to send a space shuttle into lower orbit, and once it has reached space, as little as 46 gallons of fuel to power the shuttle in space for up to 2 years. You can see from the numbers that it takes a much larger amount of fuel and resources to launch into orbit than it does to continue moving through space for a much longer period of time.

Once it has reached its initial target, the energy and resources required to maintain the shuttles position are actually very little in comparison to the energy used to gain that initial momentum and velocity. Also, by the time you watch that space shuttle launch on the news, you are only seeing the end result. What you don't see is the vast amount of research, expertise, planning, preparation, investment, design, implementation, man hours and time that goes into getting that space shuttle even as far as the launch pad, ready for the world to see it take off. Can you see where we are going with this?

Yes that's right... the same principle applies to you building your brand to gain advantage over your competitors. Once you launch your business and it starts to fly, you then have to maintain your position as the market leader of your industry, sector or niche. It's not as simple as creating a website and hoping people will find it. For you to gain enough momentum, credibility, visibility and what we call 'mind market share' in the minds of your ideal customers, you are going to have to apply these same principles as the shuttle launch to your marketing campaign.

Without the necessary resources, expertise, creativity and groundwork to build momentum, you won't achieve the competitive advantage you need to make **_THE_** difference, instead of just **_A_** difference.

Just as it takes a lot more fuel, resources, time, energy and strength to propel that space shuttle into orbit, you will need all this and more to build the necessary momentum required to position yourself on at least the same level as your competitors. We know you though. You are like us or you wouldn't be still reading this book! You are the best in your industry and want the recognition and reward that comes with being the best, yes or no?

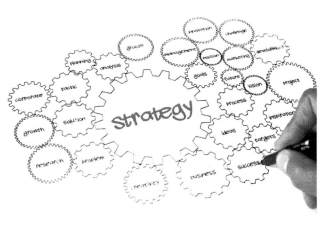

Just being perceived as being on the same level as your competitors is not good enough for you. You want to be seen as **THE BEST**.....Right?

Why would you want to be seen as anything less?

To exceed your competitors, you must add extra fuel, creativity and thrust to your campaign. Once you've achieved mind market share as THE authority and the 'Go To' person in your industry (and therefore gain the competitive advantage), you need to make sure your marketing campaign is topped up with the right fuel so it continually propels you two steps ahead of your competitors.

When you have customers referring you to more customers, who refer you to even more customers, you know you have become the obvious choice in the minds of the customers you want to do business with!

Based on your competitor's strengths, you can create a strategy that takes all the best things that are clearly working well for them, and implement them straight into your own strategy. You can avoid the weaknesses of their brand within your own and even use them as an opportunity to overtake them in the marketplace. Every weakness to them is a potential strength for you, so make sure you look at every area of their campaigns to undertake a proper analysis of your competitors and overtake them.

Your competitive advantage will result in your prospective customers perceiving they will get far greater value working with you than working with anyone else. Most businesses don't take the time to do what you are doing now and as a consequence, they are failing and their business is dying in the process. However, by continuously taking action on the exercises we are showing you in this book, you are putting into practice the top seven foundational actions that make our very own clients' strategies successful to get them significant results. You are also completing another step forward with every chapter, which is pushing your competitors further backward.

Let's take a look at five things you can do to find out whom your real competitors are and how they position themselves as experts in your niche. Finding out whom your real competitors are is something many failing business owners aren't doing. The real test of who your competitors are is when you do what we are about to show you…

1. First, make a list of the words you think your ideal customers are likely to type into Google to search for what you provide. Once you have a list of say 10 keywords you want to be found for, type your chosen keywords into the search bar of Google one at a time to see who shows up in the top results for that search.

★ Are they appearing for more than one search?

★ Do they take up one or more of the top search results rankings in Google?

★ If so, what for?

    Spend some time on this, putting different words from your list into Google to see who shows up. The more these competitors show up, the more you need to see them as someone to beat and do whatever it takes to knock them from those top spots and position yourself in their place.

2. Now go into YouTube and just like you did in Google, enter your keywords into the top search bar. It will give you a list of all your competitors who are creating videos to promote their products and/or services. It's likely you will find there are one or two companies who are doing it really well and using

video as a big part of their marketing strategy. You should be watching all of their videos to see what they are talking about, promoting and advertising. Look at the amount of views each video has so you know which topics are the most popular ones. Using videos on your website, in your social media marketing, your email campaigns and your blogs (otherwise known as 'video logging' or 'vlogging'), is a great way of establishing rapport with your target customers without you having to be there.

There are so many ways you can use video to position yourself as the market leader above your competitors, because it gives you a voice and personality that other marketing mediums simply aren't capable of giving you in that way.

Video is a major part of our marketing strategy as you'll see on our Facebook page: www.facebook.com/BrandExpertTips & YouTube channel: www.youtube.com/howtobuildabrand.

If you want to build a strategy using video as one of your key marketing tools, check out our monthly publication The Brand Brains and our resident video marketing expert, Ben Brophy, who gives you all the latest tips, tools and techniques every month that he uses to get great results using video.

3. Sign up to Google AdWords to use the Google Keyword Search Tool. You'll get a much clearer picture of how many times those search keywords are being used each month. This will help you understand what demand there has been for those words in the past 30 days, both in your country and worldwide.

It will also give you a range of results that show you the other keywords people have searched for, which may be more effective. When using this tool to search, make sure you select the search options [Exact] and unselect 'Broad' (these options appear on the left of the screen) to ensure you only see results of exactly how many people are searching for each keyword. Selecting "Phrase" will display how many people are searching for each keyword as part of a sentence or phrase. This tool is fantastic for finding where the demand is, if there is one, and you can be far more accurate with your competitor research too.

4. Ask 10 friends or colleagues (who fit your ideal customer profile), which companies in your industry they have heard about, have used in the past and/or would recommend? You'll find out who's on their radar so you can check them out, do your research, ask your friend or colleague some questions about the service they received/were told about and give yourself an even greater chance of a competitive advantage.

We also ask our customers to keep us updated on what they find, because they are more likely to come into contact with what our competitors are doing than we are. Just putting these little touch points in place with your existing customers shows you care about the level of service you provide and gives you insider knowledge that you wouldn't otherwise acquire. You'll more than likely find this will strengthen the relationships you have with your customers and will also increase your customer repeat order value, because they will come back to you to deliver another product or service.

5. Sign up to www.socialoomph.com to monitor what's going on in your industry all over the world. When you sign up, you enter all the keywords you want to monitor and then tick a box to say how often you want to receive the updates. When your keyword is mentioned on Twitter, you will receive an alert to let you know all the posts and blogs that have been posted with your chosen keyword in it. This is a great way of keeping you up to date with what is happening in your industry all over the world, whilst at the same time giving you some ideas for content you can write about to position you as the expert in your industry, and keep your name fresh in the minds of your prospects and clients.

Competitor analysis is something you should do regularly to keep you ahead of the game. Our suggestion is to review your competitors at least every six months. If we hadn't done our analysis again six months after we launched our design agency, we wouldn't have found out about a company we didn't consider a competitor at first.

However, we did do our research at that six-month point and we found out that they delivered a lot less value than we did and were charging three times the price. We followed this up with more research and spoke to a few of their clients (NOT as a design agency, but as a potential client of their design agency). Our intended outcome was to find out what service they had received, what they paid and if they were happy - NOT to steal their clients. We found out these clients were happy with the amount they had paid, what they had paid for and what would have made their experience even greater.

Their answers gave us a massive intelligence and from the next day we added even greater value to our services and doubled prices going forward.

The amount of value we added meant there was still no quibbling on price regardless of the increase. In fact, clients felt they were receiving a greater value for the price charged and that we were worth more. Imagine that… your own clients telling you to put your prices up. So we raised our prices again and even to this day we know we still do not charge what we could for our strategies, design and branding services.

However, we are not focused on just getting more money from our clients. Our focus is more on long-term relationships and delivering extra value and therein lies our reward.

The crazy thing is, if our competitor had called their clients more often as part of their aftercare service, they would have found out exactly the same information that we had about how their clients perceived the value of their service.

They didn't consider this as a worthwhile strategy but we did, so we went from a small design business charging small prices to a boutique design agency charging what we were really worth. Doing this also changed the way we behaved because when you think small, you act small.

When you think big, you deliver bigger value and can charge more.

You also have a different presence about you and you start to attract higher value customers pretty much immediately. Fancy some of that? Well just make sure you continually keep your eye on what is happening out there in your industry. Don't do it once and think that's enough. You must keep up to date with who is doing what and what they are charging for it. That way you will see what is working so you can:

★ Emulate and model what they are doing well in your own way.

★ See what isn't working so you don't waste time doing the same things.

★ Know what opportunities there are for you to overtake competitors.

Now that you've completed all seven of the exercises we have given you so far, you should have a clearly defined customer profile with a great deal more intelligence as to how you need to communicate with them when promoting your products and services to them.

You can at the very least give them seven solid reasons why they should do business with you over and above anyone else. If you have answered every single question you have been asked so far with lots of variations on your answers, you will have written easily over a hundred things that can act as key messages to help you promote your business. And from your answers throughout this book you can create a brand growth strategy to give to your brand designer, website designer and marketing manager so they GET IT RIGHT for you FIRST TIME. This is a great achievement, well done.

But there's more if you want to really push your competitors over the edge?

As promised, we have added three bonus chapters to this book that will enable you to speed up the process of conversion from strangers to friends, and engage friends into lifetime customers. Want to know what they are? Let's continue onto chapter 8 to discover how you can help your customers solve their problems.

"Sammy and Miles are amazingly clever and their out of the box, funky thinking process has a massive impact on the ends results. They get right into your business model and your thought trail to make you think about it differently and always positively. Talking positive, Sammy and Miles are probably the most positive thinking people I have met, which is infectious to you when in their company and for a time thereafter!"

Lisa Bohanna-Tang, Debt Doctor & Entrepreneur

"When we first worked with Sammy & Miles the products and the services we provided were already very strong. As our client base is diverse we asked for help to create a new face and feel for our company. What we asked for was a strong brand that would leave a lasting impression.

What we got was quite frankly some of the best creative design I have seen. We here at Quite Frankly Water are obviously very pleased with what they have created. But what really matters to us is what our current and prospective clients think. We have had a very positive response to our brand. The reaction we now get is something to behold, and for this we are very grateful."

Paul Ulett, Cost Reduction Specialist

CHAPTER 8...

How Can You Help Your Customers Solve Their Problems?

Imagine you are standing in a pub you love to go to. You can overhear two people talking animatedly at the bar a few feet away while you wait for the bar person to serve you. One of these people is listening intently to the other person speaking and is clearly trying to offer advice to calm the other person down, as he/she appears to be distressed.

You can't help yourself... you start listening in to what they are saying. You can hear the distressed person say to the other that they are having trouble with a problem that has been frustrating them for a long time. It has now come to a head and they need to do something about it. After a few minutes you have heard enough. Without saying anything, you know exactly what this problem is. Even better than that, you know how to help them solve this problem because this is exactly what you are an expert in. Without you even having to say a word, the other person steps in to say they have heard about this great company who can help them. They have a friend who went to this company and you start to hear them telling the distressed person all about what this brilliant company did to help them. Much to your delight, you realise they are talking about you and your business.

In that moment you feel a huge sense of pride as you hear someone referring your business to another person. Then you start to listen even closer to what they are saying about you, because you have absolutely no control over what is said next. This could be your next best customer, but the sale is pretty much in the hands of the person giving you the referral. Will they promote your business as you would yourself? Will they get across what is more important than anything else? Or will they say all these great things about you and then move on to a different subject before they discuss a call to action? You have no control over this next move. How frustrating.

Perhaps this is a scenario you have actually experienced or maybe you have been that person down the pub referring your friend who has a problem, to someone you know who can help. Regardless of who is referring business to you, you need to make sure there is a clear and consistent message that goes out about your business when you aren't there.

It's vital that you are in control of the messages people are using to communicate with your future customers. What you say and how you say it can make a big impact on whether that person goes ahead with the enquiry, and consequently the sale. But what if it's not you who is in control of what is being said? You need more control over your brand than that. You also want to be sure that the people being referred to your business are people you actually want to do business with.

This is a great opportunity for you to take control of whatever people say about your business in future, and create a number of different scenarios where person 'A' has a problem, challenge or situation that you know you can solve, and person 'B' gives them the perfect response to refer you and open the door.

For example, at How to Build a Brand, here are a couple of our own scenarios to give you an idea of what you need to do for your own business in this exercise:

Conversation Scenario 1...

Customer pain, challenge or problem:
"I'm gutted about being made redundant. I loved what I did, just not the money I was getting. Maybe I could set up my own business? I'd love that but I just wouldn't know where to start. What do you think?"

Our Dream Response:
"I know where you should start. There's a fantastic resource called HowToBuildABrand.org that I came across when I first started my business. I'm now a Diamond member and use it every day. Business owners all over the world are using it to start, build and grow their businesses. Their monthly publication TheBrandBrains.com is also brilliant and their daily branding tip videos are really helpful on Facebook and YouTube. If you've got a business idea, this resource will

help you turn it into a massive success by giving you daily tips that tell you what you need to do to continue building your brand and therefore your business. I know quite a few other people who are using it and they love it as well. Plus it saves you at least £24,000 a year on employing a Marketing Manager. You really should give it a go. I tell you what, I'll send you the link."

Conversation Scenario 2...

Customer pain, challenge or problem:
"I've had such a terrible couple of months sales-wise. The marketing that used to work just doesn't work well anymore. I must try something different and bring business in soon. I don't have enough money to employ someone to do my marketing, so I need to do it myself. I just wish I had someone telling me what to do every day so I could get on and do it and then get back to running my business. Any tips?"

Our Dream Response:
"A friend of mine swears by this amazing marketing resource he has joined online which emails him every day to tell him what to do. There are different levels of membership, so you can choose how much support you need, from just getting a weekly email, up to daily marketing tips, videos and group masterminds at the higher level. You really should take a look at it. I'll send you the link now." You get the gist... Now it is your turn so grab your pen and get started:

Conversation Scenario 1...

Customer pain, challenge or problem:

Your Dream Response:

Conversation Scenario 2...

Customer pain, challenge or problem:

Your Dream Response:

Conversation Scenario 3...

Customer pain, challenge or problem:

Your Dream Response:

It's worth you creating at least three different scenarios to give yourself and others a full overview of what pain your prospective customers find themselves in before they find out about you. Then you need to write down what you want people to say on your behalf to open the door for you.

Word of mouth referrals are the best form of marketing because the trust between friends, (which stacks up the strength of the referral) means most of the sale has taken place before it even reaches you. If they can open the door long enough for you to walk the prospect through it, you could have a very successful word of mouth strategy in place quickly and easily. However, you can't expect people to take loads of time out of their business to refer you when they have their own businesses to run. So make it easy for them and give clear instructions on what to look for, what to listen for, and what to say or do next.

This is a particularly good exercise for you to do if you are building up your network of trusted colleagues. Help them to help you find more business opportunities. Networking organisations such as BNI or 4Networking are brilliant for helping small businesses connect with other like-minded business people who get together regularly to refer business to one another.

Likewise, if you use your scenarios to highlight your products and services through social media, you will start to give people the verbal tools they need to get you through the door. You can also use the scenarios on your websites FAQ section and in the videos that you publish on YouTube to get you even more visibility and exposure. Speaking of social media, it really is a fantastic way to get your message across and have your friends, family and colleagues sharing it with their own networks, to give you even greater exposure. But what messages do you want them to share with their friends? What image do you want people to make of you in their own

minds when they hear about you? What action do you want them to take once they know you exist? These are key things you should think about now so you have control over what is said and what call to action you want to be passed on.

For example:

- Maybe you could have a great offer on the homepage of your website that your friends point people to. You can then get these new contacts into your sales funnel and continue the relationship with them?

- You might want them to pass on a particular number or email address so they can contact you directly?

- Perhaps you want to cut yourself out of the loop altogether and have them contact your office line instead?

- Maybe you want them to go to your Facebook page or YouTube channel?

- You might want them to give your card or flyer to that person so they can get in touch with you.

- Perhaps you simply want the person referring you to keep control of the relationship and simply introduce you?

Whatever it is you want them to do next, you need to be very clear about what action you want them to take. If you don't make your call to action clear and obvious you will be in danger of people having really nice and flattering conversations about you that lead to nothing because there was no course of action to follow.

Another good reason for creating many different scenarios is this... Google will love your website if you add lots of different pages to it, using each scenario as a way to educate people about the variety of ways you can help people to solve their problems.

A great example of this is when a metal sheds business, which at the time sold most of their products in a physical shop, approached us a few years ago to help them build their brand online, enabling them to move their business to an online model that exchanges very little time for money. They wanted to make their metal sheds brand far more attractive and needed our help to do so. They did have a website, but it was getting a very small amount of traffic compared to the level it was capable of. We set to work on doing a few things very well:

First we got the whole team together, to build a list of every single use we could think of for a metal shed. Together we came up with over 100 different uses for a metal shed, from bike store to man cave, fishing shed to garden tools store... you name it, we put it on this list.

Next we set to work researching which of the keyword terms were used most in the Google Keyword Tool. For each of those terms and purpose of shed we wrote a 600-word blog article. Into each article they inserted an image of the shed being used for that purpose.

Finally, we uploaded all of the pages to their new website and then used various marketing tactics to drive traffic to the pages.

A very simple marketing plan indeed and the results were tremendous.

Not only did their business increase by 101% in less than 12 months. The number of sources referring traffic to their website went up by 76% and their website generated 152% more sales than it had the previous year. An added bonus they didn't expect was that our research and the strategy we created for them at the beginning also resulted in the launch of many other secure products into smaller lucrative vertical markets, which now make them the brand leader of their marketplace. This was before video was introduced to their campaign... and you can imagine how that transformed sales too.

This exercise should by no means be underestimated if you want to create a business and build a brand that has people referring new customers to you every day. Here's another small exercise to give your strategy that extra

VA-VA-Voom. Again grab your pen and answer the questions we have set out for you below...

What 5 key messages about your business do you want the people in your networks to share with their friends and colleagues the most? Keep them short and sweet so your friends are able to remember them. For example; '9 out of 10 clients say they would recommend [company] to their friends/another business.'

Key message 1:

Key message 2:

Key message 3:

Key message 4:

_____

_____

_____

_____

Key message 5:

_____

_____

_____

_____

What action do you want your prospects to take once they know you exist? EG: 'I want them to go to a specific landing page on my website'

_____

_____

_____

_____

Finally, ask five of your closest friends, family or work colleagues (or clients if they are happy to do this for you), to write down the top five words that come to mind when they think of you. Once you get all of your responses back, use the space below to write them in so that you have them all in one place. You will no doubt see a pattern emerging of what people really think of when you come to mind. If the result of this activity is positive, use it as marketing material. For example, "8 out of 10 people think of integrity when they think of my brand".

If however, the result is not so positive and people don't say things about you that you want them to have said, then you need to set about changing or emphasising the necessary things about you that ensure you are perceived in the way you want to be from now on.

Person 1:

1. _____

2. _____

3. _____

4. _____

5. _____

Person 2:

1. _____

2. _____

3. _____

4. _____

5. _____

Person 3:

1. _____

2. _____

3. _____

4. _____

5. _____

Person 4:

1. _____

2. _____

3. _____

4. _____

5. _____

Person 5:

1. _____

2. _____

3. _____

4. _____

5. _____

Congratulations! You are now just two chapters away from completing all the exercises in this book. You have taken GIANT leaps forward in your business already!

Let's take a moment now to make a note of some of your biggest learning's so far:

_____

_____

_____

_____

_____

"Sammy and Miles are extraordinarily creative and diligent marketing experts and pro-active networkers. Their capacity to work 'out of the box' is unrivalled in my experience. If you are looking to leave a mark on everyone you meet and live in their memory forever, I recommend you contact Sammy and Miles without delay. Why not find out for yourself about the secret marketing weapons that people in the know are raving about?"

Jason Dean, Fitness Professional & Holistic Fitness Centre Owner

"I've referred Sammy to many associates of mine and as yet I have not had one ounce of negative feedback and only have positive things to say about her. From a layman's viewpoint, her design work on branding and logo's is excellent and certainly seems to have had a huge impact on the business's she has done logo and branding design for."

David Powell, FD Time Saver

CHAPTER 9...

How Can Your Customers Find Out More About You?

Marvin Gaye once sang "I heard it through the grapevine". It's highly likely you'll now have this song in your head for the rest of the day. Sorry about that.

It does prove a point though. When you develop or create something catchy and memorable, that also has good feelings associated with it, it has the potential to grab people's attention, stick in their minds forever and be shared between friends, family, colleagues and strangers a million times over... and then some. Video is one such way to achieve great recognition at the same time as attracting a worldwide audience. It is one of the fastest ways to get exposure to your brand. According to Cisco, 48 hours of video content is being uploaded to YouTube every minute and one video is estimated to be worth the equivalent of 1.8 million words. If you don't fancy sitting down to write 1.8 million words, then video is a great option for you to start achieving worldwide recognition on a much larger scale.

Businesses of all shapes and sizes are incorporating video into their brand strategy, because more and more people are now watching everything from online content to TV and movies on their computers, laptops and smart devices. Video is everywhere you look and Cisco predicts that it won't be going away anytime soon. In fact, online video accounts for a whopping 90% of all Internet traffic.

Quite frankly, if video is not a part of your brand growth strategy, then it should be and now is the time to learn how to implement it into your marketing activities. You only need to look at some of the most popular videos that went 'viral' during 2013 to see how a little creativity on a small budget can go a long, long way.

Let's take a look at some examples of popular videos that took unknown people and brands from being invisible with little or no sales, to powerful and globally recognised market leaders within weeks…

Gangnam Style:

The original video has had 1,739,134,083 views on YouTube – to date. That is over 1.7 billion views in just over 12 months and this is just one version of the video. Check out the YouTube listing and you will see millions more views of the adaptations people have created to attract even more views. This video made PSY famous. It also showed off the dance moves that most of us now know, turning dance floors all over the world crazy with horse riding type manoeuvres every time the song is played. PSY went from being a broke South Korean wannabe Pop Star to an International award-winning Artist on the back of this video.

According to Wikipedia, on 24th November 2012, Gangnam Style became the most viewed video in YouTube history. Imagine if you had picked up on this craze quickly and posted an advert on the video through YouTube advertising. Your business would have been seen by millions of people by now. Chances are you would have had some great exposure to your brand and increased your sales in the meantime.

Orabrush:

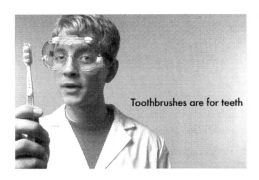

Toothbrushes are for teeth

This video boasts an incredible 18,441,743 views to date on YouTube, and it took very little investment to create. With just the aid of one man, a good video camera, a good mic, some props, a well-rehearsed script, and a little video editing, they used their creativity on a small budget to create BIG results. Could you do this too? Yes, absolutely you could.

Harlem Shake:

The original video has had 64,143,436 views on YouTube so far and again this is just one of many hundreds of videos that fans have created with hundreds of thousands more hits to each version. In fact, between drafts one and two during the creation of this book, this viewing figure jumped up by over 2 million views. It is bound to have increased even more dramatically as you read this book now. Businesses were using the Harlem Shake as a viral marketing tool by recreating the video using only the video camera on their smart phone and uploading it straight to YouTube. What did it cost them to create? Only their time. Our Facebook wall was full of people recreating the Harlem Shake in their homes and offices for months. They were even doing it on the train. It just

goes to show how powerful music is in branding when all you have to do is hear a song and you immediately associate emotions to it – whether those emotions are good, bad, indifferent or annoying. As of today there are over 160,000,000 search results on Google for the term 'Harlem Shake'. Imagine if your business had even 1% of this traffic off the back of an advert on the video. What would it do to your visibility and sales pipeline?

Ultimate Dog Tease:

This video is one of the funniest, cleverest and simplest videos we have seen to date that went viral within days on YouTube and it has received over 143,295,640 views to date. This number continues to increase every day. You'll notice the advertising pop ups and link to subscribe that come up at the end of it. These are clever FREE ways to get people interested in your material and will eventually get you onto their mailing list where they can build a long-term relationship with you. This is a great low cost marketing strategy which again was simply recorded on a mobile phone and edited using a video-editing program such as iMovie or Final Cut Pro to add the voice & promotion at the end. Using Annotations in YouTube, you can add the little pop-up boxes for free.

Now you may well think 'what has a talking dog got to do with my business?' Well the actual content in the video doesn't always have to be relevant to your business. If it is, great. However, you can create something funny like this video to engage people and add a link at the end that points them to your business, using a little strapline that ties in a link between the video and your brand. Pets always get great attention and the funnier your videos; the more they will get shared with your brand on them.

Dollar Shave Club:

This is another great example of how a low budget video can go viral quickly to promote a product. Today it has had over 11,003,649 views and their company is taking orders worldwide because of this video. What's important to note here is there is nothing special about the people who created it. The video is special because it had creative thought behind it along with a good brand strategy to direct the creative process.  However, there is nothing about this video that you couldn't do yourself on a low budget with your own brand strategy. Using a Film student or graduate from University who could do with the money, you could get them to film you and help edit it for less than £500. Win-Win. A bargain considering the exposure and sales you could get in return for your investment.

Will It Blend:

 A stunning example of how you can take an everyday, seemingly boring household product, and position it on a completely different scale in comparison to any other blender on the market. Let's face it, they could have put a pretty logo on it, enter into a price war with their competitors, spend fortunes on advertising and compete for sales. Instead however, they made the product and the brand around it fun. They demonstrated how strong the blades are by blending some of the world's most famous household objects in it on video and caught the attention of millions of people worldwide. One of the items was even an iPad.... yes, an iPad and it blended it to dust.

Another of their videos called 'Will It Blend? - iPhone 5 vs Galaxy S3', has had 7,809,674 views to date and that is just one of many videos they have launched on their YouTube channel by blending various different random objects. This means 7,809,674 people have watched this video, been exposed to their product and a percentage of those people will have gone on to purchase their blender.

No doubt they are also then up-selling another product, or insurance for example on the back end of the initial sale and boosting their sales and profit up even higher.

The viewing figures on these videos will no doubt be a lot higher as you are reading this book. Every day that goes by, another person shares it with a friend or someone else will come across it and tag it into a status update on Facebook that is then seen by thousands more people. There is nothing special about the people who created these adverts. They just took the right ACTION.

These low budget videos on YouTube have created an International phenomenon that proves it's not just the product that makes a difference to the sale. It's how it is branded, positioned, marketed & kept fresh to engage your audience.

 If you can create something that sticks in people's minds just long enough for them to share it with someone they know, you will have created a positive association and emotions that attach good feelings to your brand. This is the start of creating a bond that when treated with respect and nurtured over time, will turn strangers into friends, friends into prospects and prospects into YOUR lifetime customers rather than someone else's.

This is why it is so important to present yourself and your products/services in a way which will attract the demographic of customer you seek and inspire them to come back again and again for more. Attract the wrong clients and your campaign will be wasted, along with your time and hard-earned money. Instead, create something special for your ideal clients that you know they will love and you'll stick in their minds forever. So let's relate this to your business specifically now...

There are thousands of different things you can do to attract your ideal customers to your business, your product and/or your service. Some are more fruitful than others and in some cases you can generally predict the results. Some get quick results, while others might take longer because the price point is higher. Some can be very fruitful with the investment of your time, while others need financial investment as well to get your campaign off the ground. The more creative you get with your ideas though, the more of a buzz you'll create around your brand and what you sell.

For example, I remember a good friend of ours, Simon Coulson of Internet Business School, telling us that he once received a big box that was hand delivered by courier to his office. When he opened it up, it was a toilet seat with a message on it that said, 'Don't throw this opportunity down the toilet' - He was so intrigued (after the initial shock) that he called the number on the message and it turned out to be a very lucrative joint venture for him. Interestingly, Simon gets lots of requests from people asking him to send an email out to his list because he has a big, qualified list. However, he has worked incredibly hard and spent a lot of money on building his list of contacts so do you think he is going to just send anything out to the people on it? No he won't. He has to be very protective of his client list.

Most requests go by the wayside because all they did was try to exploit Simon's list. However, this guy (who we'll call Mr Toilet Seat) went out of his way to make the opportunity a WIN-WIN for both involved, and the very fact that he was so creative in this thinking to catch Simon's attention, told Simon that this person was an action taker. It stands to reason that if you want to get in front of someone of such a high calibre then you had better start thinking creatively about how you are going to catch his or her attention.

Over the years we have spent thousands of pounds as well as thousands of hours on marketing, on both our own businesses as well as the businesses of our clients. In fact, we just worked out that between 2003 and 2013 alone we spent just over 60,000 hours between the two of us on marketing – not including the time our employees also spent creating, testing and measuring marketing campaigns. Oh, and this is on the conservative side as we worked it out based on a calculation of 8 hours a day x 5 days a week x 48 weeks of the year. The reality is that we worked between 12-14 hours a day, 6 days a week and mostly during the holidays too, so you could say that we've got a teeny little bit of experience in branding and marketing.

We learned the hard way to find out what works and what doesn't. Some marketing activities cost us a lot of money and gave very little return. Others cost hardly anything to implement (other than time) and continue to attract new customers even now, making us money to this day. *"Which ones worked the best though?"*

Okay, okay… you twisted our arm. Here are three marketing activities out of the many we share with our students on the B.R.A.N.D. Accelerator Programme that have consistently worked well for our business and the businesses we have worked with over the years. They aren't elaborate, difficult or costly. They don't require challenging code or hours of pouring over textbooks to learn the formula. They are simply a mix of both online and offline activity which focus more on time investment to get results, as opposed to having to spend lots of money.

All three of these activities are great for you if you are working to a tight budget. In fact, they will only cost you your time and perhaps a little bit of time for your designer to make them look good, and a website developer to upload them to your website if you don't know how to do it yourself. We're pretty sure though they will work for you too, as long as you implement them without cutting corners.

If you have any questions, you can always ask us on our Facebook page: www.facebook.com/BrandExpertTips or send your question to advice@howtobuildabrand.org and we will make a video for you to post on our YouTube channel: www.youtube.com/HowToBuildABrand

Strategy #1. Give Something Away For FREE:

Yes, we know it might go against the grain for you to give away some of your best knowledge, thought leadership or content for free, but by doing so three things will happen...

1. People will think that what you have given them is so great they cannot wait to sign up for whatever it is you offer them next.

2. It will continually push you to create newer, content so you always have content you can re-use, re-purpose and make money/build relationships with in other ways.

3. The people who visit your website will find that it is so full of knowledge, information and helpful free downloads that they will come back to you over and above your competitors, because they trust that you are prepared to invest in the relationship before you take their money. This gives very clear signals that you care about delivering a great service, rather than just taking their money and moving on.

Every time you give something away, especially when you do it publicly via social media, PR or holding a public competition, you will get lots of additional prospects signing up for it who you would never otherwise have positioned your brand in front of.

Take The Brand Brains publication for example. We give two digital issues of this jam packed 24-page brand building magazine away for free on our website. Yes FREE, even though they cost us around £2000 per issue to create, once we've paid for design, editing and output. We know we could make more money by charging for these two issues. However, getting money out of a new potential customer upfront for two issues of Brand Brains is nowhere near as important as building on the relationship we would like to have with each potential **lifetime** customer. The value to you is far greater in the long-term when you invest

in the relationship up front. Once you have built their trust in you, they will be far more likely to invest in the relationship with you in return.

Is it likely that we will get people who download both issues and then don't spend money with us?

Yes of course, but the positives of doing it far outweigh the negatives. Plus you should remember that not everyone will spend money with you, but they may refer you to someone who will. So while it is the case that not everybody will read the magazine and then subscribe, more people than not will value the high quality information and content we provide each month and take the next step to invest in the other monthly issues that will help them to consistently grow their business (which saves them around £24,000 a year on a student marketing consultant). If you haven't already got your two free issues, go and get them now at www.thebrandbrains.com

Each new person you give a gift to in return for his or her email address is a potential lead to new business. However, you should still think about your outcome and encourage the kind of prospects you really want to do business with.

We find that the more details you ask people to give you, the more committed your new prospects will be. For example, asking them for their surname as well as their first name and email address on your website in return for a free download or video... You may never use their surname, but you know that by asking for it you will be weeding out the people who are just on the lookout for free stuff that they'll likely never do anything with.

If they can't be bothered to fill in their surname, they are highly unlikely to be bothered about taking action on the things you are advising them to do. This can actually damage your brand if they do only half of what you are advising them to do and then complain to everyone that your advice hasn't worked for them. You will discourage people from signing up to your free content. However, you will know that the people who are signing up for what you are offering them will be far better quality prospects and they will be better ambassadors for your brand... not to mention that your conversions will be a lot higher.

Based on the thousands of campaigns we have run in the past, experience tells us that the larger the prize, the more new and better quality clients you get in return. Plus it is not only very rewarding to give something away for free that you know will make a genuine difference to the lives and businesses of the people who download or watch it. You will also find it incredibly rewarding when you have new clients calling you up to spend  money with you. This is a WIN-WIN situation! We designed some promotional postcards with a difference for an event we were attending. We bought some little silver torches on the barrel of which we wrapped specially branded stickers that had our logo and web address embossed into them.

Using some glue-dots we stuck the torch to the postcard in line with an image of a torch and its white light beam printed onto the card (so that when they took the torch off it didn't affect the design). Under the torch was the message 'Put Your Business In The Spotlight'. We popped the ensemble into bubble wrap and brand coloured envelopes. Having given them out instead of business cards, they received absolutely loads of attention to the point that we had people running up to us to get one because they saw someone else open it up in front of them. It was like a magic trick and people couldn't get hold of them fast enough.

Our investment in that campaign was around £4.50 each to make and we had 100 made, so our total investment was around £450. Was this worth it? Oh yes. This little, low cost idea brought in sales of over £150,000 within the first two months of attending the event. Most small business owners would look at the investment and balk at the outgoings but this is very small thinking. The £150,000 return on that investment was a pretty good investment, wouldn't you say?

Whenever we hear people tell us that they either get their business cards done cheaply or pay nothing at all, we pretty much know what response they are going to get from them. We can never understand the value of going cheap on your marketing material though. Every business card you hand out is a 'mini-me' of your business. So make sure you give something out that completely and wholly represents who you are and what you do with a strong call to action. That way your marketing materials can continue to act as a top class sales person on your behalf even when you aren't there.

You probably think that £149,550 return on investment is pretty good for the sake of putting some promotional materials together for £450. However, the return on our investment on these gift style promotional cards didn't end there…

Our new clients were so delighted with what we created for them that they then referred us on to other clients. We have now lost track of the exact figure that these postcards have brought in because the links and referrals have become more and more degrees of separation away. What we can tell you though is that we still get enquiries coming in years later from people who we gave these promotional marketing pieces to.

They were effective because even if the people we gave them out to weren't ready to work with us at the time, we were so sticky in their minds for having been creative with our marketing material, that they kept them on their desk and in constant visual contact. When they were ready to go ahead, we were the first company they called in when they needed branding, graphic design, brand strategy and marketing. In fact, you can watch a video on these direct mail pieces to give you some more ideas at: bit.ly/DirectMailMarketingIdeas

Strategy #2. Get Out And Meet People:

Whilst this digital age has made it incredibly easy to meet people online and exchange introductions without actually meeting them, you still cannot beat a good face-to-face conversation.

All of our best repeat business clients are people who we have either met personally, at events or through existing clients, who became raving fans and referred more new clients to us. Even a lot of the people who buy our smaller products and services, such as www.thebrandbrains.com or our intensive B.R.A.N.D. Accelerator Programme, still get to meet us at events and seminars face to face, or see us on stage.

There is no doubt that videos are a fantastic way to build rapport with more people without you having to physically be there. Skype / FaceTime / Google Hangouts / Webinars, etc... are also all great communication tools for keeping in touch with people all over the world without physically being there. But you just cannot beat face-to-face interaction for speeding up a high-ticket sale.

If you would rather stick to smaller networking opportunities with like-minded people without being in the limelight too much, you might like to attend a local small business event, such as BNI, B4B, Institute of Directors or Chamber of Commerce events. As we said in an earlier chapter, we both met at a BNI event and launched our first business together two years later, so it just goes to show how great partnerships can be formed at such events. Also websites such as www.meetup.com and www.findnetworkingevents.com are pretty good for finding out what is going on near you.

Depending on your industry or sector, you will also find some really good industry specific events, conferences, trade shows and exhibitions that are highly relevant to you by searching on Google for events based on your topic, or a topic that your ideal customers are interested in. These are ideal opportunities for you to meet prospective customers at the same time as building your network of strategic partners who can refer you repeat business. These events are also perfect for you to put yourself forward as a keynote speaker. Contact the event organiser and ask if it is possible to speak at their event.

Strategy #3. Create A Buzz:

Create a big buzz about your product or service and it will expose you to new potential customers every time. You may be nervous about promoting something that isn't quite ready yet. However, by posting glimpses of what you are up to on social media, in newsletters or even direct mail to your existing and targeted customers, you are keeping your brand at the forefront of their mind.

A place we recommend you start is to focus on creating a buzz around your outstanding customer service. If your customers love you because you treat them with the utmost patience and respect, you could encourage them to tell other people through word of mouth that your company is the most reputable brand to work with.

Perhaps you could ask them to call three people they know who may require what you provide. Maybe they could send out an email and copy you in. Or potentially they could invite people they know, who are your ideal prospects to an event or seminar that you will be speaking at, so they can make the introduction face to face. There are so many companies that lack proper customer service that eventually it cripples them. If you are confident your customers love you enough to talk to others about you, get them involved to attract more new customers by adding to the buzz you are already creating.

Make it easy for them though. Your customers are busy people so don't expect them to take their focus off of what they are doing to help you. It is a bonus if they do, but you cannot expect them to do this. You do however have more of a chance of them helping you, if you give them what they need to make it easier.

Our B.R.A.N.D. Accelerator students get email, phone and social media templates they can use to build their word of mouth referral campaign. It's worth you creating templates, as this will make it easier for you each time you send it to someone. Alternatively, join us on the programme to get your templates as part of the course.

In the next and final bonus chapter, we are going to look at your call to action and how to give your prospects a compelling reason to contact you. Without this you are not just wasting your own time, you are wasting other peoples by making it difficult to get the help they need from you. Let's hop across now to Chapter 10 to get started.

"Sammy and Miles are two people you should have in your Arsenal. Not only are they fantastic at their job-being meticulous and passionate. They are also great people all round. I have had the pleasure of knowing Sammy and Miles for about 5 years now and have indeed benefited from their skills and experience. They are two of the most committed people you could wish to meet and they fully understand the "Givers, Gain" philosophy. I would urge you to get to know Sammy & Miles and if it is your business branding or awareness that requires attention then they are the team I would recommend without fail time and time again.

Jason Archdale,
Home Improvements Specialist

"Your knowledge and understanding is evident, your enthusiasm is infectious and it has been a pleasure to work with you so far."

Karl Collingwood-Thirlway,
Legionella Control Specialist

CHAPTER 10...

How Can Your Customers Take The Relationship Further?

One of the most obvious rules of engagement is giving your prospects a clear 'Call To Action'.

By 'call to action' we mean clearly telling your prospective customer what you want them to do next, and how you want them to do it, so you convert them from window shopping to spending money with you.

For example:

- Do you want them to phone you, quoting a special reference number to track your marketing effectiveness?

- Do you want them to email you at a special email address that has been set up to track your campaign?

- Do you want them to refer you to a friend in return for a special gift?

- Do you want them to watch a video with only one action to take afterwards?

- Do you want them to see a specific highlight that promotes a special offer or bonus?

- Do you want them to connect with you on Facebook?

- Do you want them to fill in their contact details to get started on your FREE program?

We could go on with hundreds of different calls to action, but you probably get the point by now. Whatever it is you want your prospects to do, make your call to action clear and make it quickly so they don't move on before you can get your most important point across.

Your call to action is one of the most vital pieces of information you could have on your business card, website, brochure, flyer, social media accounts, email signatures, direct mail, etc. If you don't tell your prospect what to do and how to do it, they simply won't do what you want them to do. You could miss out on that all-important sale because they'll get bored or distracted and quickly move on. You can probably think of one or two examples of when you have visited a website and it was so unclear where to find what you wanted, or what to do first due to too many options, that you just gave up and moved on. Do you remember that feeling of frustration and stress when you couldn't find what you wanted quickly? Don't do this to your own prospects. They won't thank you for it and if they do remember you it will be for all the wrong reasons.

Often we are asked to work with business owners on their brand growth strategy because they aren't getting the sales results they want. One of the first things we do is look at their marketing materials. Nine times out of ten they have the most amazing looking marketing materials, but they haven't put a call to action on them.They tell you how great they are, but not how to access that greatness! Just adding this  simple piece of text to could increase your sales conversions by 80%-100%. Learn from their mistakes and start putting a call to action on every promotion you create – even social media status updates.

If having a call to action increases sales so significantly, why is it one of the most overlooked areas of marketing? There are several reasons:

- It could be because a well thought out and executed marketing plan has so many components to its success that the call to action gets missed.

- Perhaps as a novice to marketing, most business owners put what they want to see on their marketing material without first stepping into the customer's shoes and applying the core AIDA principle (Attention, Interest, Desire, Action – in that order from top to bottom), based on knowing exactly what is first and foremost important to the customer.

- Or maybe so much planning goes into the design and layout of the page to make it aesthetically pleasing (i.e. so that it looks good), that they forget to put the focus on what content should be on the page in the most critical order.

More than likely however, it is a mixture of all three and perhaps some other things too. It is frustrating though, isn't it... when you know exactly what you want but you can't find it.

For example, have you ever been on your way to a business meeting or social engagement and as you ran out of the door you accidentally forgot to pick up the nicely designed invite card displaying the address? You think to yourself, 'Oh that's ok, I'll just look it up on my phone maps app when I get closer', only to spend your time frustratingly clicking on every Google link without any joy. 'Grrrrr' you say. 'Why couldn't they just have a website page with a link on their phone number so I can press it and it just starts calling the venue?'

Or have you ever spent your time searching for something online, found exactly what you are looking for and then wasted the next ten minutes of your life trying to work out how to find their contact details so you can ask them a question? Annoying isn't it? Think of the last time you couldn't find what you were looking for, even though you knew it must be there somewhere. How frustrated did it make you feel? Did it make you want to continue hunting on their website even more to find it, or did you give up and look somewhere else? If you gave up and looked somewhere else you are not alone. If you never went back to that website because you had such a poor user experience with that brand, you are not alone there either.

There's nothing more frustrating to a customer than not being able to find what they are looking for. In this digital age there is no excuse at all, where plugins, widgets and apps have been developed especially to make it easier than ever before for prospective customers to get in contact with you. Putting your phone number or contact details at the top of your website so it shows on every page is a simple and effective way of making it easy for your prospects to contact you. It also gives them reassurance that they can speak to an actual person if they need to.

Just knowing your details are there is enough for some people and they will likely never even call you. However, if your prospect feels that there is no way to contact you, subconscious barriers will appear in their mind as to why they should trust you. Don't give them the opportunity to do that. Think of it like the mind's decision maker having a 'No' bucket and a 'Yes' bucket. For every good element of the experience they have with you a drip will fall into the 'Yes' bucket and vice-versa. Enough 'Yes' drips will tip the decision maker in your favour. Making things easily accessible is one of those things. Make contact information easily available and you'll add another little 'trust' drip in the YES bucket.

It is even more annoying when you go to the contact us page expecting to pick up the phone or email them, only to be sent to a contact form in the hope that you fill it in and get a response within 24 hours. People don't trust this type of contact form anymore because they feel it is just a way to capture their data. The truth is, they would be right in most cases. Plus if you are looking for something urgently, the last place you are going to spend money is with a company who just has an impersonal automated email responder on auto-pilot telling you a member of the team will be in touch within 24 hours. If you want to capture their data, create a proper data capture page where you give something of value in return for their contact details. But don't add another step in the process of contacting you if you can avoid it because you are just adding another barrier to your sales cycle.

In this technological age you should be able to view a website from your mobile phone and click on the number to automatically dial it for you. It should be easy for your prospects to find your other contact details. If you are selling a product or something else on your website, it should be easy to spend money with you by having a simple payment procedure that takes as much pain away from the process as possible. The technology is available and a good web master will be able to do this for you. Don't leave it up to your prospects to memorize your number and then have to type it in for themselves. They only have to get one digit wrong before they give up and move on to your closest competitor, who is using the technology that makes it simple for the customer, and you really don't want that after all the hard work you have put into it.

OK, OK... rant over for us, but perhaps you get frustrated with these little things too? It's the small things that make the biggest difference as we mentioned in chapter three. So take note and don't put your own customers through that ordeal. Make sure you have a clear phone number or call to action in an obvious place at the top of your website that consistently stays there no matter where they are on your website. Oh, and make sure you have a mobile ready version of your website that makes it easy for them to select your number so that it dials straight through to you. Each person who visits your website knows what they are looking for when they find you. Some people may well be visiting your website for the first time and will want to look through the whole site before they trust you enough to take that next step. Others will look through only a couple of pages and will have seen enough that they are ready to take action. Some will revisit your website several times after checking out your competition and will feel they have done enough research to take it further. Others will have seen or heard enough about you that all they want to do is go to your website, find your phone number and call you up straight away. Maybe you find yourself following one of those buying patterns?

You cannot guarantee that the people visiting your website or reading your brochure are going to look at it in the same way that you are. That is why it's so important to clearly display contact info on every page in a logical and obvious place that calls out 'Hey, contact us. We're friendly, approachable, professional and we are ready when you are'. Here are five calls to action ideas that will help you to start converting more prospects into customers straight away. Put your own creative spin on them to make them more personal to your own brand:

1. The URGENT Call To Action...

This is a great example of creating an urgency to buy from you based on a compelling offer that will run out in a limited time scale. The fear of loss is enough to get them to sign up on the spot. For example, '50% Off – Ends Today' or 'Buy One Get One Free For The First 10 People To Purchase This Product'.

List five **URGENT** call to action ideas you can use in your marketing strategy:

1. _____

2. _____

3. _____

4. _____

5. _____

2. The DIRECT Call To Action...

Some websites overcomplicate their call to action by giving too many actions or options, thereby confusing the prospect into not taking any action at all. If you only give them one thing to do, you can be sure that they are going to do it.

Google.com and Dropbox.com are great examples of keeping it simple. When you land on their website, you can only do one thing and it's extremely obvious.

List 5 **DIRECT** call to action ideas you can use in your marketing strategy:

1. _____

2. _____

3. _____

4. _____

5. _____

3. The COMEDY Call To Action...

Making your prospect smile will create a personal connection that engages them onto a journey with you. Red Bull does this brilliantly, combining a simple call to action with a cheeky twist.

List 5 **COMEDY** call to action ideas you can use in your marketing strategy:

1. _____

2. _____

3. _____

4. _____

5. _____

4. The GIFT Call To Action...

Giving a gift in return for your prospects details is a great way to start a lifetime customer relationship with that person. The key here is to give something away of massive value that shows off what YOU do, as opposed to giving something away that someone else has created or is not related to what you sell.

Don't be afraid to give great content away, as discussed earlier. You need to impress them with what you can do for them, so use this free gift as an opportunity to upsell them to something else you provide of higher value, after they have given you their details, thereby giving you permission to contact them again.

Perhaps you could create a free guide to give away or give them one chapter of your book, and then upsell the rest of the book to them once they have read that chapter.

Maybe you could create a value packed video series giving away some of your best content to get them excited about buying into the rest of your program/product. We created the 6 Step Brand L.E.A.D.E.R. System specifically to give away. It delivers massive value at the same time as demonstrating our expertise beautifully and gives us at least 2 hours of touch points with each person that goes through the program. This has helped us to dramatically reduce the amount of time it takes to convert them into customers in other areas of our business, because the trust has been built during that 2-hour process.

List 5 **GIFT** call to action ideas you can use in your marketing strategy:

1. _____

2. _____

3. _____

4. _____

5. _____

5. The CURIOSITY Call To Action...

When you make your offer so relevant and compelling that it immediately grabs their attention, captures their curiosity and plays to their higher emotions, it makes it hard for them to resist taking action with you.

This type of call to action works especially well if you are tugging on the emotional heartstrings or something that is close to their heart, for example:

- 'Does Your Child Suffer From ADHD? Take This Simple Test NOW'.

- 'Is Your Home At Risk Of Intruders? Take This Security Quiz NOW'.

- 'Use Our Online Calculator To Find Out How Much Money You Are Wasting On Your Health Insurance'.

The reason we call this 'Curiosity' as a call to action, is because you are offering a solution to prospects that are looking for answers from a place of curiosity, and perhaps even vulnerability. This doesn't mean you are praying on their emotions just to sell them something... As long as you are providing something of value that will genuinely help them with their problem, and you are using this call to action in an ethical way with integrity.

List 5 **CURIOSITY** call to action ideas you can use in your marketing strategy:

1. _____

2. _____

3. _____

4. _____

5. _____

As a rule of thumb with any call to action, we advise that you don't ever use manipulative language just to make a sale and stay completely congruent to your message. Don't make promises that you cannot deliver on, as this will damage your reputation irreparably.

People may never remember something you said or did, but they will always remember how you made them feel.

Always ensure that whatever you do, your message leaves your prospect feeling supported, valued and satisfied. Oh and remember to make sure there is an obvious button or link that takes them to whatever it is you have promised in your call to action.

Congratulations! You have completed all ten steps and are now ready to start attracting your ideal customers.

We felt it appropriate to end this book by suggesting that you live each day as if it were your last day on earth. We don't suggest this as a prescription to go out and be reckless with your life or business. We suggest it purely to remind you of how precious your life really is behind your business and to ensure you are living the life you dream of, supported by the people you really want to spend your time with, and the customers who will pay for you to enjoy it.

We hope this book has been, and continues to be, helpful to you. Revisit the exercises in this book every six months to stay on track and consistently move you toward your personal and business goals.

Accelerate your results and income even further by joining us on our B.R.A.N.D. Accelerator Programme. Receive one of our brochures about the programme by emailing advice@howtobuildabrand.org. We shall hopefully meet you in person on the course!

Your goals will become bigger as your business grows and as you grow personally. You will face challenges both large and small as you grow, but no doubt you will overcome them gracefully, as long as you face them from the space in your heart rather than your head.

Please remember the most important strategy of all and that is to be the brand you want to see in the world. When you become THE brand and people can visibly see how success is working for you, other people will be attracted to you and your life will change as you change the lives of others.

We wish you all the health, wealth, growth and happiness in the world and hope we get to meet you in person very soon.

To your great and continued success!

Sammy & Miles

"Sammy and Miles really are the expert 'go to' team on branding! Their Facebook page at www.facebook.com/BrandExpertTips and YouTube channel, www.YouTube.com/HowToBuildABrand are amazing resources with videos explaining so many facets of marketing. I love the simple, easily understood explanations that even a novice like me can implement. And, better still, Sammy and Miles are friendly, approachable and genuinely focused on helping others build their marketing strategy and business success. You should definitely consider working with them"

Janet Swift, #1 International Best Selling Author

"Sammy and Miles have the expertise, knowhow and passion to help you discover your true genuine brand by uncovering the passion, mission and values of your business, ultimately leading to optimum results. This is all done through a genuine care and invested interest for your business. They work on your brand as if it was their own!!!"

Deenita Pattni, World-Class Recruitment Trainer & Professional Speaking Coach

"During the B.R.A.N.D Accelerator, each section unlocked another piece of the puzzle that helped to bring the brand of BodyUK to light. The programme gave us systems on how to spread our brand message and once I'd completed my strategy day with the team, I had the start of a blueprint in place to streamline exactly where BodyUK is heading over the next 3 years. The existing brand and website have been revamped to attract our ideal customers and we now have a huge arsenal of tools at our disposal. I can say that this programme has massively helped us take things at least 100 steps forwards in just a few months. We now also have a dream team of experts around us from the programme that continue to help us grow and most of this would never have happened without this programme. I suggest you contact Sammy and Miles and speak with them about what you need. Although this programme is called B.R.A.N.D Accelerator, it becomes very clear that your brand is much bigger than just the look and colour of your logo. Your brand strategy really does determine your long term success."

Jem Scragg, Fitness & Health Expert at BodyUK

Made in the USA
Charleston, SC
06 June 2016